Teaching
Science
by Inquiry

Teaching Science by Inquiry

In the Secondary School

Robert B. Sund
Leslie W. Trowbridge

Colorado State College

CHARLES E. MERRILL BOOKS, INC., Columbus, Ohio

Preface

Science education today is in a state of dynamic change. Numerous national projects, starting with the Physical Science Study Committee have devised new and exciting materials stressing inquiry as an approach to science instruction. The inquiry, or discovery, method stresses student-centered rather than teacher-centered class instruction.

In this book we have emphasized the discovery approach to science teaching. Discussion of inquiry-based techniques appears throughout the book, especially in the chapters on psychological foundations of education, the laboratory, demonstrations, discussion, and evaluation.

The text helps teachers to be aware of all the national curriculum developments in the sciences. Many references are made to the work of the Physical Science Study Committee and to the Chemical Bond Approach, the Chemical Education Materials Study, the Biological Sciences Curriculum Study, the Earth Science Curriculum Project, the School Science Curriculum Project, the Princeton University Physical Science Project, Educational Services Incorporated, the Introductory Physical Science course, and the Harvard Project in Physics. In each case, the new and creative ideas of these varied projects are discussed in relation to current trends in science teaching. We endeavor to show the purposes and directions of these projects and their influence on modern science instruction.

This book emphasizes the higher levels of learning, stresses questions which require critical thinking, and provides practical suggestions for the practice teacher. Because beginning teachers often have asked the authors for suggestions in maintaining discipline, a chapter on discipline in science classes, with tested suggestions and hints for classroom control, is included.

The chapter on facilities departs from standard coverage of this topic by suggesting flexibility of facilities and planning for the future rather than repeating traditional design. Practical suggestions on how to use teaching machines, write a program for a machine, construct an invitation to inquiry, make problem tests and self-tests, and design an open-ended experiment are included.

The chapter on creativity stresses the role of the teacher as a stimulator rather than a depressor of creative student activity. It outlines research find-ings and provides suggestions to help teachers become more creative in-structors.

The authors have attempted to write a clear, practical book giving students sufficient philosophical and theoretical background to teach any of the courses in the modern science curriculum, provided they have had the necessary subject-matter preparation. Most of the chapters in the book have been tested on teacher candidates in methods classes. Valuable suggestions were received from the class members; and where the text material failed to achieve its instructional objectives, it was eliminated or revised and strengthened.

The authors, both of whom have had extensive teaching experience in the public schools, have translated this experience into a highly usable textbook and reference source for the beginning teacher as well as the experienced teacher of science.

Contents

One of the great achievements of science is to have developed a method which works almost independently of the people whom it is operated on.
Aldous Huxley

1

What Is Science?

George Gelman walked into the classroom ready to meet his students on his first science teaching job. The teenagers soon filed in laughing and joking with one another. After the bell rang, Mr. Gelman proceeded in a halting manner to call the name of each student and several students helped him by repeating the correct pronunciations of their own names.

He then reviewed a few class procedures and began his first lesson, which involved a discussion of science and its contributions to modern society. The discussion moved rather slowly. The students were not eager on the first day in class to participate because they didn't know how the instructor would respond to their remarks. One girl raised her hand and asked, "Mr. Gelman, what is science anyway?"

What answer would you have given to such a question? A moment's reflection should indicate that this is not an easy question to answer. Try answering it before you read the rest of this chapter; when you finish reading the chapter, close the book and try to answer the question again.

What is science? *Science is both a body of knowledge and a process.* When a student says he is going to study science, we know he is going to study a particular type of knowledge. He is not going to study music, art, or religion but rather such subjects as physics, chemistry, biology, or astronomy.

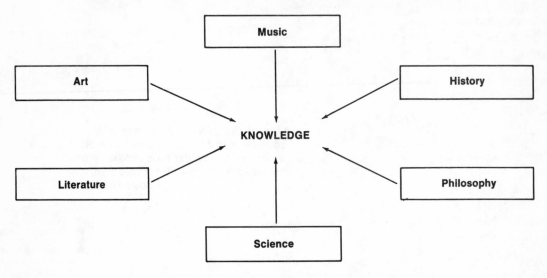

Figure 1

In the scientific subject areas knowledge is organized within various schemes or systems such as the theory of evolution, atomic theory, biochemistry, or radiation biology. The key to knowing whether a certain piece of knowledge is in the realm of science is to determine whether it was obtained by use of scientific processes such as observation, measurement, experimentation, and other operations that the scientific method implies. Science as a process is a means of coming to know about natural phenomena. When he questions, explores, and experiments, a scientist demonstrates the inquiring nature of science. Unfortunately, a student can learn science as a body of knowledge without understanding it *as a process* and without knowing what inquiry involves. The recorded knowledge of science is *history* produced by men using scientific processes. Teachers have traditionally emphasized this product of science but have often failed to give students an understanding of the means of solving problems, one of the most valuable educative objectives for science instruction.

A SCIENCE DEVELOPS THROUGH SUCCESSIVE STEPS

The Observation Phase

One of the first sciences was astronomy. It developed early because its objects—stars, planets, and the moon— could easily be seen. Bacteriology, on the other hand, could hardly unfold until man's senses were extended through such instruments as the optic and electron microscopes. The first phase of any new science is observational. It has to be, since something must be seen before it can be studied and understood.

The Classification Phase

After a period of extensive observation, a science progresses to the second phase of its development—the classification phase. During the period of extensive Western exploration of the world, large numbers of new plants and animals were discovered, and many were brought back to Europe for further study. These had to be classified. In many cases, new categories were needed, and the need produced an improved system of classification. Whether working with rocks, trees, atomic particles, or stars, eventually scientists devise a classification system. This is done to facilitate storing knowledge in our minds or in books and other records. A classification system can be a tremendous intellectual instrument. For example, if you were asked to name ten characteristics of the mammal, gnu, you would have no difficulty even though you may never have seen a gnu. All you have to know are the characteristics of mammals. You would say a gnu has hair, has mammary glands, nurses its young, has a four-chambered heart, has a dorsal aorta, breathes with lungs, has a dorsal nerve cord, is warm blooded, bears its young alive and does not lay eggs, and so on. If there are 30,000 mammals and you know these characteristics are true for each mammal, then you know 30,000 times 10 or 300,000 facts. Knowing details of certain conventional classifications is also extremely important for purposes of precise communication. The use of a scientific classificational system insures accuracy because one name is given to each discreet item within the province of the system; no other object has the same name. Much more is involved in classification than is discussed here, but the point to remember is that all sciences involve intricate problems concerning classification.

Students actively engaged in learning the processes of science.

Photo courtesy of Bob Waters, Colorado State College

The Experimental Phase

The last stage of any scientific discipline to evolve is its experimental phase; this is not to say that classification or observation ceases. Astronomy clearly has shown in its history the development of these three phases. During the periods of the ancient Egyptian, Babylonian, and Greek civilizations, many of the heavenly bodies were observed and recorded. This was the main observational phase of the science. The early astronomers soon discovered that planets, stars, and the moon differed from one another. They placed these in four groups: stars, the moon, planets, and sun. This was the classification stage of astronomy.

Finally, in the 1600's and 1700's discoveries were made about optics, light, and heat; and these eventually led to the laboratory experiments revealing that the color of a radiated body correlates with the amount of heat liberated. This knowledge, gained through research in the laboratory, was then applied to astronomy. Experimentation with and study of the phenomena of light and radiation and of lenses and their applications to astronomy began the experimental phase of the science.

Today sciences develop with greater rapidity. As a consequence, in newly developing sciences these three phases of growth occur almost simultaneously. Almost all sciences that have existed for any length of time are now experiencing development in all three areas—observation, classification, and experimentation. Nevertheless, some sciences are still thought of as mainly observational or classificational, and others are thought of as mainly experimental.

THE PHILOSOPHY OF SCIENCE

Philosophy has been defined as a study of truths underlying all knowledge. Dr. Robert S. Cohen defines it as a "persistent attempt to grapple with foundations."[1] Scientific philosophy concerns itself with how we come to know what we know about natural phenomena; it examines the processes and values by which science determines its truths. The philosophical foundations of science differ from other philosophical views.

Philosophical Views

Dr. Royce[2] has outlined in Figure 2 the ways in which man looks at reality. Study the chart and note the four philosophical approaches represented.

Figure 2 indicates that science basically determines its knowledge by empirical means. Empirical data are obtained by a scientist's feeling, touching, tasting, or using other senses to collect information. Thus, the key to the empirical approach is that it is based on *observation*, either directly or indirectly through the use of apparatus; much of the effort of the scientist is actually devoted to observing and measuring phenomena more accurately so as to obtain better empirical data. Logic and reason are naturally involved in any experimental effort, but science does not accept truths solely on the basis of logic unless they can be verified by some empirical means.

---

[1] "Individuality and Common Purpose, the Philosophy of Science," *Science Teacher*, May, 1964, p. 27.
[2] Joseph R. Royce, "The Search For Meaning," *American Scientist*, XLVII (1959), 4.

Figure 2 shows that theology, on the other hand, bases its views upon faith and logic. No one would think of trying to prove the existence of God by performing an experiment. There is considerable confusion today because of a lack of understanding of the various philosophical means by which man attempts to know his place in the universe. No man is purely empirical in his daily life. An individual consists of components of all of these approaches to knowledge since he thinks, feels, senses, believes, and accepts some things on faith. If you understand this, you are likely to comprehend why science and religion fundamentally are not in conflict. A scientist doing scientific research must base his work upon empirical data, but as a man living outside his laboratory he may often manifest other philosophical views.

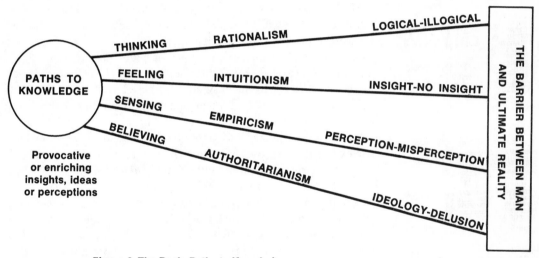

Figure 2–The Basic Paths to Knowledge

SCIENCE IS MECHANISTIC, NOT VITALISTIC

The empirical approach of science is based upon the assumptions that: the universe is intelligible; man can study nature and discover natural laws; there is reality to space, time, and matter; and all natural phenomena can be explained in terms of physical and chemical states. Describing nature in this manner is said to be a mechanistic as opposed to a vitalistic approach. Vitalists do not believe that man can discover all the basic forces of nature and life; they think there is a secret vital entity man will never be able to discover.

CAUSE AND EFFECT

Scientists generally believe that for every change or effect there is a cause; this view is held consistently in science except for some special cases in physics. Much of scientific research is involved with determining causes: What causes cancer? What causes metals to expand? What causes leaves to fall? Science is also interested in effects: What energy is released when the atom is split? What are the effects of smoking? What is the effect of taking too many aspirins? Scientists do not believe that changes occur because of some mysterious magic. They believe that all physical and biological changes can be understood, the causes of change determined, and the effects of change predicted.

SCIENCE DOES NOT EXPLAIN PHENOMENA IN TELEOLOGICAL TERMS

Often students describing the reasons for change do so in teleological terms. Teleology is defined as the doctrine of final causes; the word *telos* in Greek means *end*.

Gary, a tenth-grade student, placed a plant near a window. He noticed that after several days it bent toward the window. When the teacher asked why, he answered, "It bent because it wanted to!" This is a teleological type of explanation. It implies that a plant has an end in mind: to bend toward the light. Where is the "want" part of a plant? If Gary had understood the meaning of a mechanistic explanation as used in science, he would have replied instead, "The plant bent toward the light because there is something stimulating the plant causing the plant to modify its growth in that direction." The reason scientists do not explain things in teleological terms is that this type of description does not contribute to better understanding of what occurred. On the other hand, a mechanistic explanation is more likely to suggest paths for further research. Teleological explanations, because of their vagueness, fail in this respect.

Students involved in the experimental aspects of science.

Photo courtesy of Bob Waters, Colorado State College.

SCIENTISTS ASK "WHAT" AND "HOW" QUESTIONS

Scientists in performing research are mainly interested in answering "what" and "how" questions: What kind of life is found in the Arctic? What wave lengths are first absorbed in water? What particles are there in an atom? "What" questions require mainly descriptive answers: What animals live in a pond? An answer: "Frogs, turtles, and fish." "How" questions often involve the study of some process. How is energy conducted? Answer: "Atoms when heated increase their kinetic energy and produce greater vibration. They interact with adjoining atoms which in turn vibrate other atoms. Energy is transferred from atom to atom in a conductor." Man also asks "why" questions. These are likely to involve theological answers; for example: Why is there life? Why is there sin? Why is there evil? These questions are not answerable by scientific means. They don't lend themselves to empirical proof based upon observational evidence.

SCIENCE FRACTIONATES

In doing scientific research, the scientist works with isolated factors. He does not start on a problem involving the entire universe but rather studies the sun or attempts a less involved study such as an analysis of the wave lengths of light coming from the sun. In order to understand a complex entity, the scientist breaks it down into parts and researches these. With the information gathered from his studies he may then generalize. For example, in studying the nature of the universe the scientist studies the sun, then generalizes from information gathered about it to other stars. Essentially, the scientist divides the whole into bits for study and then puts these bits together to understand the whole. In studying man, the scientist studies the anatomy and physiology of several men. From his research data on these men he may generalize about the characteristics of all men. This approach presents certain problems, since the whole may not be simply the sum of all the parts; but the approach does allow a formidable problem to be reduced so scientists can answer fundamental questions about it.

THE GOALS OF SCIENCE

One purpose of science is to produce principles and theories. A principle is a rule or law about natural phenomena—for example: "Metals expand when heated." "Cells arise only from the division of other cells." "Light is refracted toward the normal when it passes from less dense to more dense media."

A theory is more inclusive than a principle. A theory is defined as a more or less verified explanation accounting for facts or phenomena and specifying relationships between groups of empirical data. A theory has explanatory, predictive, and organizational value. For example, if you have obtained several skeletons from various strata in the earth, you will have to memorize from which level each skeleton came; but if you know the theory of evolution, you can order these skeletons (assuming they are related) and know which skeleton was obtained from the lowest stratum and the sequence of the rest of the skeletons. Knowing a theory of evolution aids you in understanding the relationship of the skeletons and explains their association. Knowledge of evolution helps us organize our information and makes it possible for us to make predictions.

Knowing the theory of evolution enables the scientist to predict the kind of skeleton that might be found at a lower stratal depth. Atomic theory, cell theory, germ theory, and theory of evolution are but a few of the theories devised by man. A moment's reflection on their value certainly indicates why science endeavors to create these orderly explanations.

Theories are based on facts which are derived from observation and experimentation. As our experimentation progresses and reveals new information, theories often have to be modified. Scientists search for theories and principles which are true and unchanging, but the history of science has shown that there is no certainty in science but only probability. Because theories evolve and are modified as our knowledge of nature increases, the goals of science in formulating broad, encompassing ideas of knowledge—theories— never ends. There is always an assignment for the next generation.

With this realization, a scientist is humble about what he knows and thinks he knows. At first thought, it seems that the futile search for certainty would be frustrating; but there is joy in the discovery that knowledge is unending. There is always more to do and learn and more problems to solve. Life itself is a process of solving problems, and a scientist enriches his life by being involved in problems of value to all men.

Junior high school students using the climatarium to work on a science project.

Photo courtesy of Newark School District

RESEARCH

Students often confuse science with research—not all science is research, as was previously indicated in this chapter; but true research involves the use of the processes of science. Research may be defined as an attempt to collect unbiased information about a phenomenon. Research implies active involvement in the solving of a problem not previously answered by man. A student may follow scientific procedures in solving a problem, the answer to which he does not know; however, if the answer has been determined previously by a scientist, the student is scientific but he is not doing research. Since man is often biased, the scientific processes have been devised to insure that man is objective in his decision making and in his approaches to a problem. It should be easy then for a novice to do research, but the untrained mind seldom has learned the techniques by which to guard against unbiased decisions. Training in the processes and techniques of solving problems intelligently requires a long period of education but one having value beyond calculation.

METHODS OF REPORTING SCIENTIFIC INFORMATION

Often teachers have had their students memorize a list, reproduced below, of the steps in the so-called scientific method, with the aim in mind that once the students have memorized these six steps they will be "scientific":

Scientific Method
1. Statement of the problem
2. Formulation of hypotheses
3. Experiment
4. Observation
5. Collection of data
6. Drawing conclusions

IMPORTANT

Nothing can be farther from the truth. These six steps actually are the way scientific information is reported. A scientist when solving a problem will perform all of these steps but not necessarily in the order given. He may have to define and redefine the problem several times and make several hypotheses (good, critical guesses) as to the solution to the problem.

Memorization of the list in no way helps an individual make hypotheses, sort problems, collect data, and draw conclusions. How does one collect data? What is the research design? What kind of variables must be considered? All of these questions and more are involved in doing research. Simple memorization of the six steps is of little help in understanding the processes of science. The only way to learn football is to play it, and so it is with science. The only way a student learns to be scientific is to be placed in situations where he is actively involved in using scientific methods. Try to explain football to a foreign student, and you will soon see how futile it is. You can explain certain fundamentals, and knowledge of these is helpful; but the way really to understand the game is to become a player on a team. By analogy, the science student must be a player on the scientific team.

IMPLICATIONS OF SCIENTIFIC PHILOSOPHY FOR TEACHING SCIENCE

Prospective teachers seldom have had research experience in science. Their college courses traditionally have offered little opportunity for them to devise an experiment or solve problems other than those of a cook-book type. Their science instruction usually has emphasized the products rather than the process of scientific research. As a result, they have generally prepared for their science classes by memorizing material. Memorization tends to emphasize the learning of words, a skill which many can acquire without learning to be scientific. Because prospective teachers have been trained in this manner, they often mistake learning scientific words for an understanding of science. After being employed as teachers, they have emphasized memorization of terms, assuming that if a student knows scientific terms he will have more understanding of science. Teachers have falsely assumed that learning the products of science will enable a student to use the processes of science. Many scientists and science educators have become concerned with this outlook and have made efforts to produce courses and curricula which will give greater attention to the understanding of science as a process. Teachers, as a consequence, have had to become more aware of the inquiring nature of science and have had to communicate this awareness to their students.

Teaching the inquiring aspects of science requires greater understanding of scientific philosophy and considerable skill to implement it in the classroom. It is easy to pour out the facts of science —the product—but it is difficult to teach students to solve problems scientifically. A teacher who understands the philosophical bases of science and incorporates this understanding in his instruction is more likely to lead his students to modify their behavior to face problems in a scientific manner, not only in the laboratory but in life situations as well.

SUMMARY

Science is both a body of knowledge and a process; the body of knowledge is the product of solving problems scientifically. A new science develops through successive stages. These are observation, classification, and experimentation. Some sciences are, however, mainly observational, while others may be classificational or experimental.

The philosophical basis of science is distinguished by its approach to the discovery of knowledge. Science bases its truths upon empirical (observational) data derived from observations of natural phenomena. Science is mechanistic, since it describes causes and effects in physical and chemical terms; teleological explanations are discouraged in science because they are vague and give little direction for further research.

Scientists are concerned with "what" and "how" questions; "what" questions require descriptive answers, and "how" questions usually involve process answers. Theologians, on the other hand, try to answer "why" questions. Since science and religion don't ask the same questions, they are generally not in conflict.

A scientist studying a complex problem often breaks it down into parts. He fractionates the problem in order to study it and then generalizes, from these parts, about the whole. He does research to discover scientific principles to formulate theories about nature. The scientist accepts a specified way in which to report scientific research. The method of reporting research, however, is not necessarily the way the research was actually done.

Teachers have traditionally emphasized the product rather than the process of science. This has been done because teachers have not had a good understanding of the philosophical bases and processes of science.

Further Investigation and Study

1. How would you explain to tenth-grade students the meaning of science? Can they derive much understanding from an explanation?
2. What are the various ways man discovers knowledge? Why aren't they necessarily in conflict?
3. How does empirical data differ from other information?
4. A student says he thinks it is going to rain; another student asks him if he has empirical evidence for that statement. If the first student says yes, what evidence do you think he has?
5. Plato thought that the ultimate reality was in the mind. For example, a perfect circle was an idea in the mind of man. How does scientific philosophy differ from the Platonic view?
6. How would you explain scientifically the blooming of a flower? How would you do it teleologically? Show how the scientific explanation helps you to suggest an experiment related to blooming.
7. What is meant by the statement, "Science fractionates"? What dangers are involved in breaking problems into small parts and then from the research on these parts generalizing about the whole?
8. How has the reading of this chapter modified the way you will teach?
9. Why should a science teacher read about the philosophy of science?
10. A teacher had her students memorize this list of the six steps of the scientific method:
    1. Defining a problem
    2. Making an hypothesis
    3. Devising an experiment
    4. Making observations
    5. Collecting data
    6. Drawing conclusions

    After several weeks, the teacher gave the class a problem. She was amazed to find out that they didn't know how to solve it. What explanation can you give for the students' behavior? How would you have taught to insure better problem-solving competence among the students?
11. Refer to the quotation by Aldous Huxley at the beginning of this chapter. What does this statement mean?

*In the conditions of modern life, the
rule is absolute, the race that
does not value trained intelligence
is doomed.[1]*

Alfred North Whitehead

2

Why Study and Teach Science?

Why should every student going through the public schools take science courses? Why should a future housewife have some knowledge of science? What good is science to a musician or artist? If a girl is going to be a secretary, why should she have to study science? These questions constantly face science teachers and curriculum directors. They are not easily answered. What students are really asking is "What can science do for me that some other subject can't do better?"

Educators generally agree that secondary education should be general in scope. It is their belief that a general education best prepares students to adapt to the multiple changes forced upon them in a society of rapid technical change. Any general education must include science so that future citizens can understand their society.

SCIENTIFIC DEVELOPMENT IN THE AMERICAN SOCIETY

The American society is a dynamically evolving industrial society. Industrial growth derives its energy from technological developments, and technology is based upon discoveries made in pure science. A fundamental basis of our society

---

[1] Alfred North Whitehead, *The Aims of Education* (New York: Mentor Books, The New American Library, 1949).

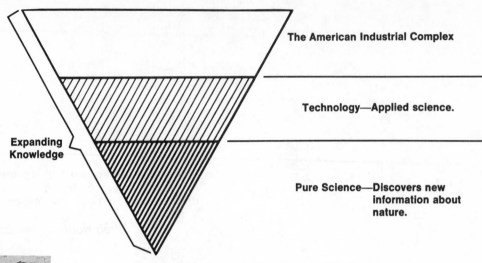

The American Industrial Complex

Technology—Applied science.

Expanding
Knowledge

Pure Science—Discovers new
information about
nature.

Figure 3–The Relationship of Science to Industry

James V. DeRose, Morris H. Shamos, and Rose Lammel, chairman of the Program Committee for the planning of the National Science Teachers Association Convention. Dr. Lammel is an example of a woman leader in the science teaching profession.

Photo courtesy of Science Teacher, *(Vol. 32, No. 5, May, 1965, Ch. 2)*

Helen E. Hale, President of NSTA, presents an award. Ex-president Hale demonstrates a leadership in science education played by women.

Photo courtesy of Science Teacher, *(Vol. 32, No. 5, May, 1965, p. 5)*

is its scientific discoveries and the application of these to our industrial complex. Figure 3 shows schematically the relationships of science to industry.

Refer to Figure 3. Notice how discoveries in science affect technology. This diagram shows that an increase in pure science results in a widening of the entire triangle. It further shows that an increase in scientific information requires more scientists and engineers to apply the knowledge resulting in greater industrial expansion.

SCIENTIFIC AND TECHNICAL PROFESSIONS OFFER GREAT OPPORTUNITIES

American industry sells brainpower and creative ingenuity; it does not compete with the rest of the world on a labor basis, because American labor is too costly. As a result of our need for brainpower, the demand for scientific and technical manpower in the United States has doubled about every ten years, whereas the population over the last fifty years has doubled only once. Figure 4 shows how the population has changed.

The rate of population growth seems to be changing slightly. For example, in 1960, there were 1.4 million scientists and engineers in this country, but the National Science Foundation estimates that by 1970 we will have to have a minimum of 2.5 million. This is not quite a doubling of the scientific-technical population; however, the demands for doctoral graduates in science and engineering will more than double by 1970.[2]

---

[2] National Science Foundation *Investing in Scientific Progress, 1961-1970* (Washington, D. C.: U. S. Government Printing Office, 1961), p. 14.

The National Science Foundation's projected labor requirements for technical manpower are indicated in Figures 5 and 6
and Table 1.

Furthermore, expenditures for research and development increased from 3.5 billion in 1950 to 16 billion in 1964. Figure 7
indicates this trend.

Who does this research? It requires highly trained manpower.
One only has to read the want-ad section of any metropolitan
newspaper to realize how much in demand are scientists and
engineers throughout the world. But a curious fact is that in spite
of this demand enrollments in undergraduate engineering have
not significantly increased. The National Science Foundation reports:

> Engineering enrollments for advanced degrees reached new
> heights in the fall of 1961, while the four-year downward
> trend in undergraduate enrollments for engineers showed
> signs of leveling off. Enrollments for advanced engineering
> degrees were 32,800 at the master's level, up 5 per cent, and
> 7,870 for doctorates, up 22 per cent, for an overall increase
> of more than 8 per cent. Undergraduate engineering enroll-
> ments totaled 232,100, down 1 per cent for the smallest de-
> crease recorded since fall, 1957.[3]

The opportunities for employment in science and engineering
are increasing, and they are likely to accelerate far into the future.
A science major has no fear of unemployment. An indication of
the projected 1960-1970 growth requirements for the various occupations is shown in Figure 8.

Minimal Racial and Religious Bias among Scientists

Recently an international meeting of scientists was held in the
United Nations headquarters in New York. Russian sat next to
American, Japanese next to Frenchmen, and German next to Israeli.
Scientists from many diverse nationalities representing all the
colors and most of the main religions of the world were present.
All the delegates to the meeting, regardless of their backgrounds,
were valued as human beings and as scientists leading the battle
against ignorance and toward enlightened scientific knowledge.

Because the scientific enterprise does not tolerate bias within
its own framework and respects truth regardless of its source, its
workers—scientists—are undoubtedly one of the least biased professional groups. For this reason, an individual belonging to a
religious or racial minority has opportunities in the scientific and
technical fields not offered to him by many other professions.

---

[3] "Highlights of 1961," *Scientific Manpower, 1961* (National Science Foundation 62-22), p. 3.

Figure 4

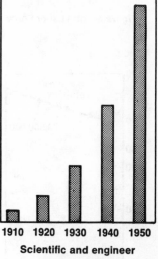

1910 1920 1930 1940 1950

**Scientific and engineer
population doubles
every ten years.**

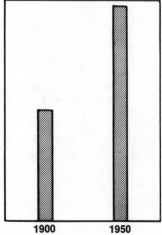

1900   1950

**U.S. population
doubles every fifty years.**

Table 1—Scientists, Engineers, and Technicians by Occupation, 1960 Employment and Projected 1970 Requirements

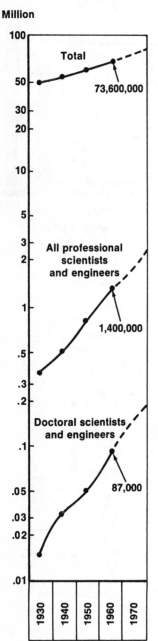

Figure 5–Total Labor Force

Million

Total

73,600,000

All professional scientists and engineers

1,400,000

Doctoral scientists and engineers

87,000

Occupation	1960 Employment	Projected 1970 Requirements	Percent Increase, 1960-70
Scientists and engineers........	1,157,300	1,954,300	69
Engineers	822,000	1,374,700	67
Scientists	335,300	579,600	73
Chemists	103,500	169,500	64
Physicists	29,900	59,300	98
Metallurgists	14,500	24,400	68
Geologists and geophysicists....	23,200	29,100	25
Mathematicians	31,400	65,100	107
Medical scientists.............	31,400	59,700	90
Agricultural scientists..........	39,500	66,100	67
Biological scientists	40,700	76,600	88
Other scientists..............	21,000	29,900	42
Technicians	775,100	1,296,700	67

Source: National Science Foundation, *Scientists, Engineers, and Technicians in the 1960's* (NSF 63-34).

More Women Are Needed in the Science Professions

Although the proportion of women employed in scientific and technical occupations is increasing each year, American society has been wasteful by not using effectively one of its greatest resources—women. National concern has recently been generated in the United States by the realization that Russia employs a far greater proportion of its women in science and engineering than does this country. In 1961, 37 per cent of the Russian engineering students were women, whereas in the United States less than 7 per cent of the students in this field were women. In other fields of science and technology, the Russians have a far greater number of women employed than does the United States.

The Western world's sex bias has robbed our country of a tremendous reservoir of brainpower. Efforts are now under way to give more scholarships and fellowships without regard to sex, to encourage women to enter the scientific professions. Recently a national symposium was held at M.I.T. in which 800 women scientists and engineers considered the problem of increasing the number of women in the ranks of our scientific profession.[4]

---

[4] *Saturday Review*, December 5, 1964, p. 75.

Dr. Maria Goeppert Mayer, Professor of Physics, University of California, San Diego.

Photo courtesy of University of California Public Relations Department.

Dr. Dorothy Crowfoot Hodgkin, Nobel Prize Laureate in Science.

Photo courtesy of Oxford University, Headington, Oxford, England.

Anna Roe has suggested that we should try to change the idea that some professions are masculine and others are feminine. Our culture starts early in the development of the child to mold this attitude. Witness parents' attitudes toward children's toys. A father will buy a baseball bat for a baby boy who can barely hold a spoon. Mechanical toys and science kits are thought to be masculine, and girls are not supposed to be interested in these. What an absurd idea. It is the responsibility of teachers to change this pattern so that those girls with ability may manifest their intellec-

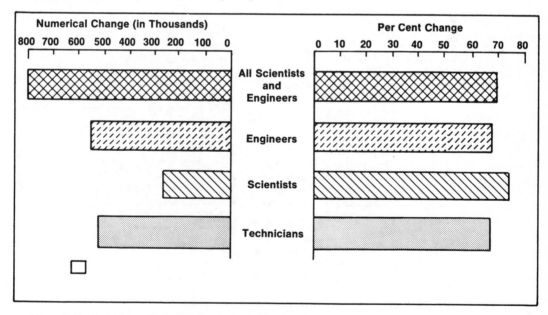

Figure 6–Projected Growth in Requirements for Scientists, Engineers, and Technicians, 1960–70

Source: National Science Foundation, *Scientists, Engineers, and Technicians in the 1960's.*

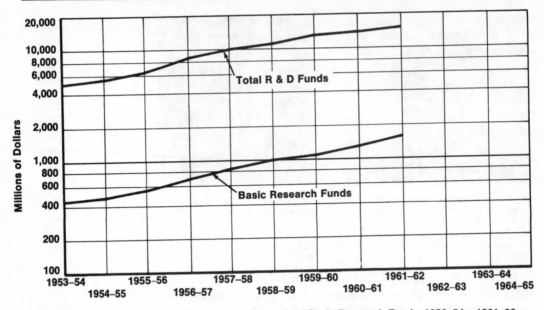

Figure 7–Trends in Research and Development Funds and Basic Research Funds, 1953–54—1961–62.

Source: National Science Foundation, *Thirteenth Annual Report,* 1963
(NSF 64-1).

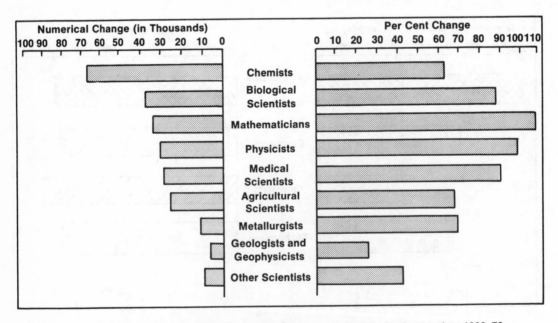

Figure 8–Projected Growth in Requirements for Scientists, by Occupation, 1960–70

Source: National Science Foundation, *Scientists, Engineers, and Technicians in the 1960's, Requirements and Supply* (NSF 63-34).

tual potential, so valuable to our country's survival. We cannot afford to waste any of our valuable resources—most of all the intellectual power of our women.

Science as a profession offers a girl tremendous advantages. In her professional training, she will associate with many men who would make very desirable mates. She might well marry one. After marriage she can easily find employment, and the part-time opportunities in the sciences are manifold. After raising a family, when many women feel "that life has passed by," her profession and the compensation it offers are there to keep her a dynamic and zestful person. Madame Curie certainly presented a desirable model of the dynamic woman—a wife, a mother, and a scientist who richly savored the fruits of living.

THE NEED FOR SCIENTIFIC LITERACY

It is the responsibility of the schools to produce an intelligent citizenry. The ability of our citizens to understand national and international problems is dependent in part upon their scientific literacy. The layman is surrounded by scientific developments and is bombarded with a wealth of scientific information. Koelsche and Morgan in a study of scientific literacy report:

> Six-month subscriptions were taken to 22 newspapers having the largest circulation in their geographical region of the United States and to nine of the most widely-read magazines published in this country. The subscription period was from November 1, 1962, to May 1, 1963. There were 2,999 science-oriented news items clipped from the 31 publications during this interim.[5]

They further report that a layman reading these papers would have to know and understand 175 principles and 693 scientific words.

A literate individual must have some understanding and appreciation of science in order to make valid judgments as a citizen. Remember, national and state legislators often make decisions involving expenditures of funds for science and scientific facilities. If they were not scientifically literate, they could not make intelligent decisions. They could even be easily duped by a body of unscrupulous individuals. The significance of a lay person's making an influential decision involving science was evidenced by the experience of President Roosevelt in World War II. A group of scientists came to him with the suggestion that the United States divert some of its badly needed resources to a project to produce an atomic bomb. This project eventually involved over $2 billion in

---

[5] C. L. Koelsche and A. G. Morgan, *Scientific Literacy in the Sixties* (Athens, Ga.: Printing Department, University of Georgia, 1964), p. 12.

expenditures. The sum of money itself was not as significant as what it stood for in those days when raw materials were badly needed for the production of arms. What decision would President Roosevelt have made if he had had no training in science and did not understand what was being asked of him? How would the destiny of America have been changed?

All questions having to do with the expenditure of funds are relative. It is paramount that our citizens and their representatives understand the purpose and value of science, that they vote proper support for its growth, and that they make decisions based upon sound and literate understanding of science. It is our schools' responsibility to prepare the citizen for this task.

SCIENCE PROVIDES OPPORTUNITIES FOR LEISURE PURSUITS

One benefit of industrialization is that it relieves man from menial tasks so that he can have more leisure. Leisure to the Greeks was the time when they fulfilled their civic responsibilities and family obligations, improved their minds, recreated their souls, and spent some small time in play. Leisure was scarce, however; and most of their time was devoted to work. The amount of leisure time available in America would amaze even the richest of Greeks. Leisure can be a blessing or a curse, depending upon how it is used. Many of our citizens use their leisure not only wastefully but in destructive pursuits; witness the number of alcoholics and neurotics we have in the United States. Science, because of its investigatory character, offers many opportunities for pursuing enriching activities throughout life.

OBJECTIVES OF SCIENCE TEACHING

Thus far we have discussed some of the general reasons for teaching science: manpower opportunities, the literacy of our citizens, and the use of leisure. The *Forty-sixth Yearbook of the National Society for the Study of Education* has listed several other reasons. These are called the objectives or goals of science teaching. A good teacher knows what he is going to teach, how he is going to teach it, and why he is teaching it. In other words, he has objectives he hopes students will reach under his instruction. Leaders in science education have outlined in the *Forty-sixth Yearbook* some of the objectives they feel are the most important to teach in science. They are:

Types of Objectives for Science Teaching

A. Functional information or facts about such matter as:
   1. Our universe—earth, sun, moon, stars, weather, and
      climate.

2. Living things—plants and animals.

3. The human body—structure, function, and care.

4. The nature of matter—elements, compounds, mixtures, chemical change, physical change, solids, liquids, gases.

5. Energy—sources, types of energy, machines.

6. Contributions of science to the life of our times—radio, telephone, telegraph, electric lights, motion pictures, household appliances, airplanes, and guided missiles.

B. Functional concepts, such as understanding of principles (operational thinking):

1. Space is vast.

2. The earth is very old.

3. All life has evolved from simpler forms.

4. All matter is probably electrical in structure.

C. Functional understanding of principles such as:

1. All living things reproduce their kind.

2. Changes in the seasons and differences in weather and climate depend largely upon the relation of the earth to the sun.

3. Energy can be changed from one form to another.

4. All matter is composed of a single element or combinations of elements.

5. Living things in a given environment or locality are mutually interdependent.

D. Instrumental skills, such as ability to:

1. Read science content with understanding and satisfaction.

2. Perform fundamental operations with reasonable accuracy.

3. Perform simple manipulatory activities with science equipment.

4. Read maps, graphs, charts, and tables and to interpret them.

5. Make accurate measurements, readings, interpretations, etc.

E. Problem-solving skills, such as ability to:

1. Sense a problem.

2. Define the problem.

3. Study the situation for all facts and clues bearing upon the problem.

4. Make the best tentative explanations of hypotheses.

5. Select the most likely hypothesis.

6. Test the hypothesis by experimental or other means.

7. Accept tentatively, or reject the hypothesis and test other hypotheses.

8. Draw conclusions.

F. Attitudes, such as:

1. Open mindedness—willingness to consider new facts.

2. Intellectual honesty—scientific integrity, unwillingness to compromise with truth as known.

3. Suspended judgment—scientific control, withholding conclusions until all available facts are in, not generalizing from insufficient data.

G. Appreciations, such as:

1. Appreciation of the contributions of scientists.
2. Appreciation of basic cause-and-effect relationships.
3. Sensitivity to possible uses and applications of science in personal relationships and disposition to use scientific knowledge and abilities in such relationship (attitude).

H. Interests, such as:

1. Interests in some phase of science as a recreational activity or hobby.
2. Interest in science as a field for a vocation.

I. Limitation of scientific method.[6]

Science teachers too often teach what is in the text without realizing what they are really trying to do. Science is not just a list of facts to be pounded into the heads of students. It is, as indicated in the *Forty-sixth Yearbook,* functional understanding of concepts, principles, skills, a set of attitudes, appreciations, and interests. It is teaching students to be alive, dynamic, and thinking human beings.

The Educational Policies Commission has stressed this very point. They have said:

> The purpose which runs through and strengthens all other educational purposes—the common thread of education—is the development of the ability to think. This is the central purpose to which the school must be oriented if it is to accomplish either its traditional tasks or those newly accentuated by recent changes in the world.[7]

Refer once again to the objectives of the *Forty-sixth Yearbook.* Note the categories of objectives and note, too, that facts are only a small part of those objectives. Science teachers and science educators have over the last few years modified their courses so that they can better achieve these objectives. All of modern science curriculum developments stress teaching science as inquiry. One of the paramount reasons for using the inquiry approach is that it gives students more opportunities to think and learn how to think critically. As inquirers, students learn to be independent, to compare, to analyze, to synthesize knowledge, and to develop their mental and creative faculties.

---

[6] *Forty-Sixth Yearbook of the National Society for the Study of Education* (Chicago: University of Chicago Press, 1947), pp. 28-29.

[7] *The Central Purpose of American Education* (Washington, D.C.: National Education Association, 1961), p. 12.

TEACHING GUIDES

Most school systems or state departments of education publish guides for teachers to use. One of these is the General Science Guide of the Public Schools of Chicago; a representative portion of this guide is quoted below.

The guides usually have a section on objectives that is divided into two parts—general and subject-matter objectives. The general objectives are such things as learning how to think and solve problems. These are the long-term objectives teachers hope to stress throughout the entire year of instruction. The subject-matter objectives have to do with the student's mastering science concepts, principles, and laws.

> OBJECTIVES OF THE K-12 SCIENCE PROGRAM OF THE
> CHICAGO PUBLIC SCHOOLS
>
> A coordinated, integrated, sequential science program for the elementary school presupposes certain basic objectives for each grade level which are reinforced and expanded at each succeeding grade level. These objectives are: the development of scientific concepts useful in understanding our natural environment, the development of skills of problem solving, and the development of the habit of scientific thinking.
>
> In the primary grades learning experiences are provided: (1) to develop an understanding of science concepts that will enable the child to describe the natural occurrences persisting about him, (2) to give the child practice in solving problems by different methods and to sensitize him to an awareness that an orderly system is always involved, (3) to develop the understanding that scientific thinking is based upon observable facts.
>
> In the intermediate grades learning experiences are provided: (1) to develop an understanding of science concepts that will enable the child to describe and to discover the cause and effect relationships in the natural occurrences persisting about him, (2) to give the child practice in planning and using previously learned facts and principles as tools in solving problems, and (3) to develop the understanding that in scientific thinking all related evidence is applied without prejudice.
>
> In the upper grades learning experiences are provided: (1) to develop an understanding of science concepts that will enable the child to predict and evaluate the orderly occurrences persisting in nature, (2) to give practice in solving challenging problems which bring previously unrelated but known facts and principles into a new association, and (3) to develop the understanding that scientific thinking utilizes solutions to specific problems to generalize about natural forces, and to recognize the distinction between facts, principles, and laws.
>
> The sciences taught in the secondary school are a continu-

ation of the science program begun and developed at the elementary level of the Chicago public school system. Therefore, the general objectives of high school science teaching are the same as those stated in the opening paragraph above.

In the General Science course learning experiences are provided: (1) to reinforce science concepts for students who have encountered them but who have not fully comprehended them in the elementary grades, (2) to afford the freshman student extended opportunity for developing skill in sensing the precise science problem involved in a problematic situation and in devising a logical procedure for solving the problem, and (3) to advance the student toward deeper insight into the scientific approach and to instill in him attitudes and appreciations specific to scientific thinking.[8]

The subject-matter objectives involve the concepts and scientific principles the teacher wishes to impart in teaching his subject. Scientists and science educators have determined the scientific principles they have thought the most valuable to teach. A list of these for each major subject is available from the U.S. Office of Education in Washington, D.C. A few of the principles taken from the Office of Education list of *Major Principles of Physics, Chemistry, and Geology of Importance for General Education* are quoted below:

1. Energy is often transmitted in the form of waves.
2. Waves travel in straight lines while passing through a homogeneous or uniform medium.
3. When waves strike an object, they may either be absorbed, transmitted, or reflected.
4. Whenever an opaque object intercepts radiant energy traveling in a particular direction, a shadow is cast behind the object.
5. Light travels in straight lines in a medium of uniform optical density.
6. The speed of light in any given substance bears a constant ratio to the speed of light in air.
7. The intensity of illumination decreases as the square of the distance from a point source.
8. When light rays are absorbed, some of the light energy is transformed into heat energy.
9. The darker the color of a surface, the better it absorbs light.
10. If a beam of light falls upon an irregular surface, the rays of light are scattered in all directions.[9]

---

[8] Chicago, Board of Education, *Supplement to the Teaching Guide for Science, General Science, Secondary Schools* (Chicago: the Board, 1961), p. ix.
[9] H. E. Wise, *The Major Principles of Physics, Chemistry, and Geology of Importance for General Education* (U. S. Government publication OE-29025-A [Washington, D. C., 1962]), section on light.

A teacher is always faced with the problem of determining what knowledge is of the most worth. Many of the facts of science will change in the future, but the principles of science will remain relatively unscathed. Knowledge of scientific principles enables an individual to operate more effectively in life. For example, if an individual knows the principle "Metals expand when heated" and he has difficulty in getting a tight lid off a bottle, he merely places the jar under a hot-water tap. The hot water causes the metal to expand, and he takes the lid off with ease. There are many other applications of this principle. The more a student learns scientific principles and has opportunities to apply them, the greater will be the transfer of learning and the better prepared will the student be for effective living.

A teacher should list each day in his lesson plan the concepts and principles he will teach, direct the teaching toward the learning of these, and use them as a basis for devising test questions.

Refer once again to the list of teaching objectives from the *Forty-sixth Yearbook* of the NSSE. Parts *A, B,* and *C* of that list are mainly concerned with subject-matter objectives, whereas parts *D* through *F* are really long-term general objectives of science instruction.

A teacher must know what he hopes to achieve in his instruction and must devote all of his energy and enthusiasm toward these goals if he is to be secure and effective in the classroom. There is a world of difference between an instructor who thinks he will walk into class and talk off the top of his head and the one who has direction and purpose, and knows what he wants to accomplish during a class period and over the school year. Be an efficient and effective teacher—know what, how, and why you teach!

WHY BE A SCIENCE TEACHER?

In addition to the opportunity to contribute to the goals already mentioned in this chapter, there are many reasons for becoming a science teacher. Above all, teaching science is fun. A science teacher has a tremendous advantage over other teachers because a science laboratory is a thrilling place in which to work and students are fascinated with science, especially if it is activity-centered. Furthermore, there is a personal satisfaction in watching students discover the principles and methods of science.

Non-science majors receive instruction in physical science as part of their general education requirement in college.

Photo courtesy of Bob Waters, Colorado State College.

A science teacher's position is also important to the society and to the national defense. We need a continuous supply of intelligent, well-prepared scientists molded in our public schools to keep our defensive efforts above reproach. The science teacher molds future innovators and designers, thereby producing the manpower needed to keep our technical defensive efforts strong.

Few other teachers gain as much prestige or have as high a status in a community as the science teacher. This is due to the recognition by citizens of the value of science and to the fact that science teachers are generally better prepared and educated than other groups of teachers. Even teachers in other fields often hold their science colleagues in high esteem.

Because of the manpower demands in the scientific and professional fields, some trained science teachers never teach but go into business or industry. Their backgrounds, however, in college have been such that they are wanted by these employers. That they are successful in their pursuits is proof of the value of their training. A science teacher also has numerous opportunities to obtain fellowships for further study. This study may lead to an advanced degree enabling the teacher to obtain employment as an instructor in a college or university. The fact that science teaching is fun, valuable to our society, has high status, and offers manifold opportunities for advancement all contribute to the satisfaction of being a science teacher.

SUMMARY

The American industrial society is based upon scientific discoveries. Because of the rapid growth of science and its applications in industry, there have been increasing demands for scientific and technical manpower. There also has been a continually increasing financial support for research in our country. Since research is performed by scientists and technicians, these increased research funds have amplified the demands for scientific and technical manpower.

The scientific professions offer opportunities for racial and religious minorities. The number of women employed in scientific activities has increased, but a greater use of women in the scientific professions is to be encouraged.

Some knowledge of science is valuable to the American citizen because he encounters a large scientific vocabulary in the press; to comprehend what he reads about important developments in science he must understand a considerable number of technical terms. Science because of its breadth and investigational character offers a wealth of leisure pursuits.

Science educators, who believe science instruction can contribute to the education of the American citizen, have outlined certain teaching objectives. These objectives including imparting to students an understanding of basic concepts and principles; instrumental skills; problem-solving skills; and scientific attitudes, appreciations and interests.

The teaching of science offers many rewards beyond monetary ones. The profession is enjoyable and is valuable to our society; its members are accorded high status in the community; and it offers plentiful opportunities for advancement.

Further Investigation and Study

1. How are science, technology, and industry interrelated?
2. What are the scientific and engineering manpower trends through the 1970's and what are the implications for science teaching?
3. How have research expenditures varied over the last ten years? What are the reasons for these changes?
4. In what occupations will there be the greatest demands in 1970?
5. In what types of activities are scientists mainly employed? What relationship exists between the degree held and activity performed?
6. Why is science especially appealing to individuals from minority groups?
7. How does the employment of women in this country contrast with the Soviet Union's employment of women?
8. Give some reasons for the fact that there are fewer women, relatively speaking, in science in this country than in Russia?
9. Why should our citizens be scientifically literate? What did Dr. Koelsche and Dr. Morgan find in their study on scientific literacy?
10. What are the leisural aspects of science?
11. What are teaching objectives? Why have them? What are the nine objective categories outlined by the *Forty-sixth Yearbook* of the NSSE?
12. What is the purpose of a teaching guide?
13. What is the difference between long and short-term objectives?
14. What knowledge is of the greatest worth in science?
15. Why should you know what scientific principles you are going to teach each day?
16. Upon what should you base many of your questions on a test?
17. What are the advantages of being a science teacher?
18. A science teacher is the best counselor for those students who might be interested in becoming scientists or technicians. How would you as a science teacher counsel students?

*If learning actually took place as teachers
believe it does, we could master almost
anything overnight.—William Burton[1]*

*The ultimate goal of the educational system
is to shift to the individual the burden of
pursuing his own education. This will not be a
widely shared pursuit until we get over our
odd conviction that education is what goes on
in school buildings and nowhere else. Not
only does education continue when schooling
ends, but it is not confined to what may be
studied in adult education courses. The world
is an incomparable classroom, and life is a
memorable teacher for those who aren't
afraid of her.—J. W. Gardner[2]*

3

Psychological Foundations of Education

The teaching profession is fundamentally concerned with the attainment of maximum beneficial learning by the individual. A teacher's role is to insure that learning is efficient and effective so students can discover their educational potential. Efficiency and effectiveness in instruction is involved in every educational decision. A good teacher asks: "How efficiently have I organized the activities for my class? How have I allowed for the involvement of students in planning class

[1] William Burton, *The Guidance of Learning Activities* (New York: Appleton-Century & Appleton-Century-Crofts, 1962).

[2] J. W. Gardner, "Self-Development," *Science*, Vol. 143 (February 14, 1964), p. 641. (Copyright 1964 by the American Association for the Advancement of Science).

activities? How effective is this lesson, demonstration, film, text, or program?" In answering these questions he relies on his training in subject matter and educational psychology. The problem of how to stimulate thirty students so that they are thrilled with learning and gain a zest for education which will continue for life is no small task. Perhaps the greatest fringe benefit for a teacher is that there is so much to know and learn about his subject and about how to become an efficient and effective teacher that his work is never done. Routine causes boredom, but in teaching there is little room for routine. Boredom is not the curse of a good science teacher.

Pure science discovers principles and devises theories about natural phenomena. Psychology and sociology are the sciences that study human behavior. Education applies the principles revealed by these sciences to the field of learning. An effective teacher is aware of the knowledge of these disciplines. Science teachers have taken courses in educational psychology to learn principles of human behavior and theories of learning, but this knowledge is of value only if it can be translated into action in the classroom. It is then that the prospective teacher is truly evaluated, not by his professors but by his students.

The following sections discuss both principles of learning and principles of teaching which have great implications for science teaching. As you read about these, think of how you would use them as guidelines in your teaching. Imagine your own class, your teaching, your students, class episodes, and how you would operate as an effective teacher. To memorize a psychological principle takes little intelligence, but a principle can be well applied only by a truly intelligent and gifted person. From the day you start teaching to the day you retire you will be trying to apply principles of learning successfully in your instruction.

In the sections below no attempt has been made to present an exhaustive catalogue of principles but only a helpful list for the prospective teacher.

PRINCIPLES OF LEARNING

1. Students learn best by being actively involved. If they can do an experiment themselves rather than read about it, they will learn better.

2. Positive, or reward, reinforcement is more likely to result in students' learning than negative reinforcement. A teacher who compliments and encourages students is more likely to obtain higher achievement than one who tells them their work is poor or derides them for poor achievement. Threat or punishment may cause avoidance tendencies in the student, preventing learning. Some failure can best be tolerated by providing a backlog of successful experiences.

Students learn best by being actively involved.

Photo courtesy of Harold Pratt, Science Supervisor, Jefferson County, Colorado.

A situation which offers fresh and stimulating experience is a kind of reward and enhances learning.

Photo courtesy of Harold Pratt, Science Supervisor, Jefferson County, Colorado.

3. A situation which offers fresh and stimulating experience is a kind of reward that enhances learning.

4. Learning is transferred to the extent the learner sees possibilities for transfer and has opportunities to apply his knowledge.

5. Meaningful material is easiest learned and best retained.

6. Learning is enhanced by a wide variety of experiences which are organized around purposes accepted by the students. Teach in depth. Don't try to cover the book; cover what you do well, giving opportunities for students to have many experiences with the subject.

7. The learner is always learning other things than what a teacher thinks he is teaching. A teacher may have a student heat a chemical solution to get a precipitate. The teacher is teaching a chemical process; but the student is also learning laboratory skills and how to organize the equipment, be efficient in the laboratory, and work with others. None of these is likely to be tested in an examination.

8. Learning is increased when provided in a rich and varied environment. The richer the classroom, laboratory, and school surroundings in offering opportunities for learning, the greater the level of achievement. A bare, uninteresting room offers little stimulation for learning.

9. Detail must be placed into a structured pattern or it is rapidly forgotten.

10. Learning from reading is increased if time is spent on recalling what has been read rather than on rereading.

TEACHING PRINCIPLES

Pupils learn from each other. Working in groups in laboratory work can enhance learning.

Photo courtesy of Harold Pratt, Science Supervisor, Jefferson County, Colorado.

1. Planned teaching results in more learning.

2. Students tend to achieve in ways they are tested. If you test only for facts, they tend only to memorize facts.

3. Students learn more effectively if they know the objectives and are shown how to gain these ends. Science teachers should spend time discussing the purposes of doing experiments by inquiry and the processes used in solving problems.

4. The teacher's function in the learning process is one of guidance, guiding individuals to reach an objective.

5. Pupils learn from one another. Working in groups in the laboratory can enhance learning.

6. When the understanding of a detail of any theory or apparatus is determined by the whole, then the comprehension of that part must wait until the whole is understood. A teacher doesn't teach about the histology of the body until a student knows about the body's general anatomy.

CONCEPT FORMATION

Teachers are essentially involved in teaching concepts, yet few teachers understand concept formation and its place in mental growth.

We learn all knowledge from our senses. The starting of knowledge then must be a perception of a phenomenon in nature. A child feels, touches, tastes, and smells. He is enraptured with the information his senses send to him. Out of these he then passes from perceptual awareness to conceptual understanding. This is no easy mental jump. Older children too have to go through the same stages of mental activity before they begin to understand and gain meaning.

What is a percept and how are percepts related to concepts? A table you see is a percept; you perceive it. If you are asked to draw a table, this is quite a different story. What you have to do in order to draw a table is to know what makes tableness. Think for a moment of a child trying to learn the word *table*. Better yet, ask several students to draw a table on a piece of paper. They will draw all kinds of variations. Their tables may have one, two, three, four, or six legs. They may be round, oblong, hexagonal, square, or triangular; or some students may even draw a mathematical table. What makes a table a table? How does a child ever get to know the essential qualities of a table? He must have many perceptions of many tables before he abstracts out of these the essential qualities of tableness. After doing this he has formed a mental abstract called a concept; he has a mental picture of a table in his mind.

Percepts Make Concepts

A person's conceptual view never ceases to grow. It expands with knowledge and experience. Think again of the child who develops the concept of *table*. As he goes through life he will see an infinite number of variations of tables, and his understanding of tableness will evolve and increase.

Now think of a complex biological concept such as *cell*. How would you start a lesson to develop an understanding of the cell theory? What concepts are involved? Obviously you would have to teach what a cell is, but how would you start? If learning commences by perception, then there should be several opportunities for students to see cells. The more types of cells they see, the better will be their concept. The traditional statement, "A cell is a basic unit of life containing a nucleus," is a far cry from what a cell is. A teacher who has students just read about or see a film about cells is building a low level of concept formation; but a teacher who has students actually see and experience cells is building not only better conceptual understanding but more lasting learning. There is no end to developing the meaning of *cell*. Compare a tenth-grade biology student's conceptual view of a cell with that of a biochemist or a cytologist. The tenth-grader sees a cell as a flat, round, or oblong small object. The biochemist sees it as a dynamic biochemical complex, constantly changing, using and storing energy. As we live we discover new concepts and increase the horizons of our old ones. Figure 9 depicts mental growth. Notice that as a child grows into adulthood his conceptual growth starts with concrete perceptions and spirals to successive levels of broadened conceptual abstraction.

A teacher, however, must be aware that there are two main types of concepts, those involving abstractions derived from concrete objects—such as *cel'*—and those involving process—such as the kinetic theory of matter, induction, or photosynthesis. Process abstractions are generally harder to teach. They require far more preparation by the teacher. The student must have many experiences before he truly gains insight into their operation. Never assume that because a student can memorize a process and parrot this back to you that he understands it or has much meaningful insight into its operation. Cronbach says, "The depth of understanding, the range of application of a concept, and the precision with which it is used can grow for years after definition is learned."[3] As an individual grows older he reconstructs his previous conceptions on even higher levels of abstraction and thereby increases his wisdom.

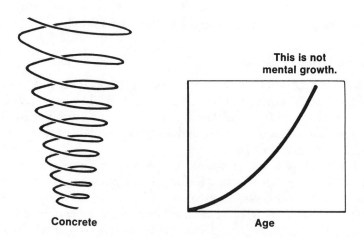

This is not
mental growth.

Concrete   Age

Figure 9–Broad Abstract Conceptions

Note (Figure 9) that mental growth does not occur in a pattern one might represent by a straight line graph. There are stages in the life of an individual when he must build a wealth of experi-

---

[3] L. J. Cronbach, *Educational Psychology* (New York: Harcourt, Brace & World, Inc., 1963), p. 356.

ence and must mature before he ascends into the next level of mental development and becomes capable of forming complex conceptualizations. Figure 10 shows how a concept of a cell may advance through successive stages—and some of the possible misconceptions students may develop.

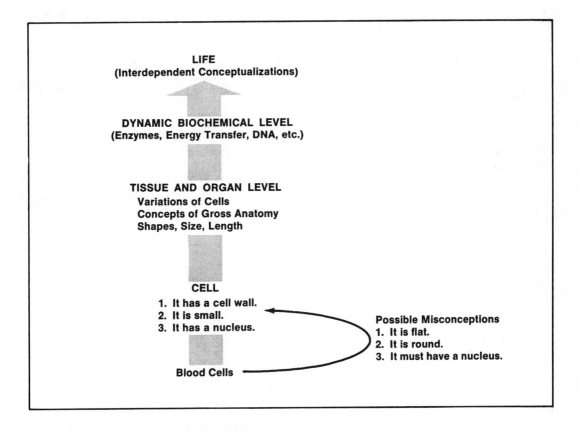

Figure 10–Where Does a Concept Begin And Where Does It End?

Science teachers are interested in teaching the principles of science because these prepare an individual to operate effectively in his environment. Bruner says, "An understanding of fundamental principles and ideas appears to be the main road to adequate 'transfer of training.' You learn a model for understanding other things." He further states:

> We remember a formula, a vivid detail that carries the meaning of an event, an average that stands for a range of events, a caricature or picture that preserves an essence—all of them techniques of condensation and representation. What learning general or fundamental principles does is to ensure that memory loss will not mean total loss, that what remains will permit us to reconstruct the details when needed. A good

theory is the vehicle not only for understanding a phenomenon now but also remembering it tomorrow.[4]

WHAT ARE SCIENTIFIC PRINCIPLES, AND HOW CAN WE TEACH FOR THEM?

Figure 11 indicates that through percepts, concepts are learned; and concepts make principles.

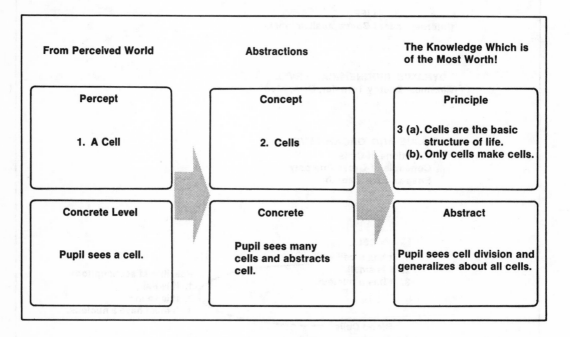

Figure 11–Concept Formation

A science teacher tries to have students learn the principles and theories of science. In order to accomplish this end, the teacher must constantly give students perceptual experiences, building concepts that are necessary to understand principles. There is no end to understanding and learning how, when, and where to apply principles. This is a life-long activity. All science instruction should if possible start with a percept, something a student can see, taste, touch, or smell. At least at this point students are with the instructor in the learning process. At no other place in your teaching can you be sure of where students are in their conceptual understanding.

If a tenth-grade biology teacher wants to teach the principle "The basis of all life is the cell," how should he start to teach for

---

[4] J. Bruner, *The Process of Education* (Cambridge, Mass.: Harvard University Press, 1960), p. 25.

real understanding of this principle? The conceptual frameworks *life* and *cell* are necessary before the meaning of the above statement can be realized. Consider another principle: "Metals when heated expand." To comprehend this, a student has to know the meanings of *metal, heat,* and *expansion.* These are difficult concepts to teach, but they involve thrilling teaching challenges. When a teacher looks at the design of his lesson plans through the percepts-concepts-principle organization, he has better direction and is more assured of his effectiveness as a teacher.

LEVELS OF LEARNING

Some science teachers have operated in the classroom as though there were only one level of learning, the memorization level. They have students memorize vocabulary, scientific names, symbols, categories, and charts and then assume that their students know science. Memorization, simply repeating what has been learned, is the lowest level of learning. A teacher who teaches only for this level of learning is hardly any teacher at all. The eminent scientist Albert Szent-Györgyi says:

> It is widely spread opinion that memorizing will not hurt, that knowledge does no harm. I am afraid it may. Dead knowledge dulls the spirit, fills the stomach without nourishing the body. The mind is not a bottomless pit, and if we put in one thing we might have to leave another out. By a more live teaching we can fill the soul and reserve the mind for the really important things. We may even spare time we need for expanding subjects.[5]

It is necessary for science teachers to realize there are levels of learning and modify their teaching so that there is greater emphasis on the higher levels. Krathwhol, Bloom, and Masia in their *Taxonomy of Education* have placed the levels in six categories, each category having several parts. The main divisions are as follows:

1. Knowledge
2. Comprehension
3. Application
4. Analysis
5. Synthesis
6. Evaluation[6]

[5] A. Szent-Györgyi, "Teaching and the Expanding Knowledge," *Science,* Vol. 146, December 4, 1964, pp. 1278-79. Copyright 1964 by the American Association for the Advancement of Science.

[6] D. R. Krathwhol, B. Bloom, and B. B. Masia, *Taxonomy of Educational Objectives: The Classification of Educational Goals* (New York: David McKay Co., Inc., 1964).

Bradfield and Moredock have classified five levels of understanding. They are:

Level	Performance
I.	Imitating, duplicating, repeating.

    This is the level of initial contact. Student can repeat or duplicate what has just been said, done, or read. Indicates that student is at least conscious or aware of contact with a particular concept or process.

II.   Level I, plus recognizing, identifying, remembering, recalling, classifying.

    To perform on this level, the student must be able to recognize or identify the concept or process when encountered later, or to remember or recall the essential features of the concept or process.

III.   Levels I and II, plus comparing, relating, discriminating, reformulating, illustrating.

    Here the student can compare and relate this concept or process with other concepts or processes and make discriminations. He can formulate in his own words a definition, and he can illustrate or give example.

IV.   Levels I, II, and III, plus explaining, justifying, predicting, estimating, interpreting, making critical judgments, drawing inferences.

    On the basis of his understanding of a concept or process, he can make explanations, give reasons, make predictions and critical judgments, interpret or estimate. This performance represents a high level of understanding.

V.   Levels I, II, III, and IV, plus creating, discovering, reorganizing, formulating new hypotheses, new questions and problems.

    This is the level of original and productive thinking. The student's understanding has developed to such a point that he can make discoveries that are new to him and can restructure and reorganize his knowledge on the basis of his new discoveries and new insights.[7]

Look at Levels III, IV, and V again. How would you design lessons to make students compare, predict, or create? A moment's reflection indicates why teachers have stressed the lower levels of learning. It's much easier to teach students to memorize; it hardly takes any ingenuity on the part of the teacher. But to teach students to think or create requires talent. A teacher must be creative to get others to create. Study these levels and strive in your instruction to encompass all levels of understanding, continually reaching for the highest level. Once you look at teaching in this light, you are faced with a great challenge, a challenge that gives real excitement to teaching and erases forever the common, the mundane, and the plague of many occupations—boredom.

---

[7] James M. Bradfield and H. Stewart Moredock, *Measurement and Evaluation in Education* (New York: The Macmillan Company, 1957), p. 204.

SCIENCE IS INQUIRY

Today the new curriculum developments in science emphasize the teaching of science as inquiry. Traditionally science has been taught as a body of knowledge to be crammed into the heads of the students. The inquiry approach does not stress the accumulation of authoritative information. It is more concerned with students' discovering how scientists come to know what they know. Inquiry is defined as a search for knowledge or truth. The emphasis is on the *search* rather than the product. R. J. Suchman, director of Studies in Inquiry Training, University of Illinois, says:

Science is inquiry.

Photo courtesy of Clark Science Center, Loomis School, Windsor, Conn.

> Inquiry Training is designed to supplement the ordinary science classroom activities. It gives the child a plan of operation that will help him to discover causal factors of physical change through his own initiative and control and not to depend on the explanations and interpretations of teachers or other knowledgeable adults. He learns to formulate hypotheses, to test them through a verbal form of controlled experimentation, and to interpret the results. In a nutshell, the program is aimed at making pupils more independent, systematic, empirical, and inductive in their approach to problems of science.[8]

Dr. Suchman's objectives of inquiry training with elementary children are echoed in the higher levels of education as well. Dr. Schwab, who has been concerned with improving secondary science instruction, has depicted the traditional science course as follows:

> The traditional course has been, on the whole, a literal treatment of science and a rhetoric of conclusions. It has tended to treat only the outcomes, the conclusions of inquiry, divorced from the data which support them and from the conceptual frames which define—and limit—their validity.
>
> The result has been to convey a false image of science as knowledge that is literally true, permanent, even complete. This misleading image is reinforced by the neatness with which our courses are usually organized and expounded. We tend to provide a structure which admits of no loose ends. We minimize doubts and qualification. We strive for exposition characterized by an almost artistic beginning, middle, and end.
>
> The result of these habits has been to create a climate of opinion inimical to science.
>
> From ignorance of the limited scope and validity of scientific conceptions, students are led to expect certain kinds of behavior in commonplace objects, behavior which simply does not occur.

[8] "Rebuilding the Science Program, Inquiry Training in the Elementary School," *Science Teacher*, November, 1960, pp. 42-47.

> This breeds cynicism about science and its value, a cynicism summed up for many of our students by a walling-off, a total alienation of the ideas of theory and practice, science and common sense.
>
> Through failure to discriminate between datum and conception and to understand the role of each in science, the student is led to treat conclusions as unalterable truths. When, five or ten years later, this conviction proves false, he retreats from clarity to confusion and from confusion to generalized suspicion of scientific competence and authority.[9]

Such instruction does not give a realistic view of science. In science we are seldom sure of the results of our experiments. There is always an element of doubt in our knowledge. Science operates on a basis of probability, not certainty; yet teachers generally teach science as a fixed body of knowledge of absolute truths, accumulated and dead. They do not give the student an understanding of the tentative and doubtful components of science, nor do they enlighten the student about the types of evidence used in making tentative conclusions. Schwab says further of the student:

> He needs to see the scientist try to subjugate the complexities of nature to the limitations of available methods of research. He needs to see the readiness with which the inquirer moves to challenge the soundness of his own work and to start afresh.
>
> Most of all, he needs to understand the conditional truth of scientific knowledge. Wherever possible, he needs to know the specific, concrete conditions which limit the truth and the application of the bodies of knowledge he is taught.
>
> A teacher whose own education has been dogmatic and doctrinaire will be unprepared to teach science as inquiry.
>
> First, self-instruction is the only practicable solution to the problem of "coverage." The problem of finding enough classroom time and enough teacher time to "cover" subject matter in the conventional way will remain unsolved until we dispose of the assumption that all "coverage" must be accomplished in the classroom.
>
> I now suggest that a substantial part of "coverage" be done by the student on his own.
>
> If students are outraged and recalcitrant when first faced with the necessity to read and study for themselves (as I am sure many of them will be), it is our own fault and spells out the problem of moral re-education which we face.
>
> Second, self-instruction skill is of great post-school value. Self-instruction must become pervasive if it is to be effectively developed. If science classes alone demand it while others do not, the students will view it as a special and unreasonable imposition. If all departments demand it, it becomes a regu-

---

[9] J. L. Schwab, "Science as Inquiry—An Answer to the Dilemma of Today's Teacher," *Teacher Topics,* (New York: Harcourt, Brace & World, Inc., Science Materials Center), Spring, 1962, p. 3.

lar part of the school experience and students will soon cease to be intimidated by it.

As a few teachers introduce an inquiring curriculum, more and more students will enter college who have been well conditioned to the process. They will move at a faster and more effective pace through teacher training and go out to accelerate the rate at which inquiry permeates the schools and returns its dividends to the college.[10]

Teaching science as inquiry emphasizes the investigative processes of science so that students learn science as a process and understand the empirical basis of scientific evidence. The purpose of the inquiry approach is to involve the student in how a scientist really operates in discovering new knowledge. The objective is to have the student live, for a time, the life of a scientist. It is for this reason that the inquiry approach has also been called the discovery approach. Teaching by inquiry involves instruction that emphasizes activities of identifying problems, observing, measuring, classifying, inferring, predicting or making hypotheses, discovering meaningful patterns, designing experiments, interpreting and analyzing data, and verifying.

The psychological foundation for teaching science as inquiry rests upon the following principles of psychology:

1. Active involvement is superior to passive reception in learning.
2. Learning occurs best when the situation stimulates without coercing and provides for success rather than failure.
3. The way to teach a person to think and be creative is to give him opportunities requiring thinking and creativeness.

In all of the national modern science curriculum developments you will read about later, the emphasis has been placed upon actively involving students in exciting, diverse laboratory activities. These courses have been readily accepted by teachers; and the general response of students, administrators, and parents has been favorable.

Method of Teaching Science as Inquiry

Teaching science as inquiry places the emphasis upon the student doing the learning. It encourages what John Dewey many years ago stressed—learning by doing and becoming actively involved in experiencing. The student is made an inquirer and no longer is allowed to be a passive observer. The emphasis has switched from the traditional teacher-centered class organization to student-centered organization. The inquiry approach requires the learner to be an active participant in the quest for knowledge. In so doing the student discovers his ability to learn *how to learn*

A student actively involved in performing an experiment from the Introductory Physical Science Course. He demonstrates learning through inquiry on an individual basis.

Photo courtesy of Harold Pratt, Science Supervisor, Jefferson County, Colorado.

---

[10] *Ibid.*, p. 3.

by using his own mind to solve problems. The ability to solve problems has great value in the post-school years. Perhaps the most important thing a teacher can do is teach a student *how to learn* and instill confidence so the student can learn on his own. Oppenheimer has said, "Research is action . . . and the question is . . . how to communicate this sense of action to our fellowmen who are not destined to devote their lives to the professional pursuit of new knowledge."[11] There is no way for a student to know the action a scientist experiences except by becoming actively involved in the methods of science. The teacher's role is one of organizing and contriving situations which will set the stage requiring a student to act out the role of a scientist in his activities. It is for this reason that the new curriculum developments devote a considerable amount of time to laboratory and field experiences. In the new courses it is not uncommon for the teacher to use four periods a week for laboratory work. Lecture, because it usually is solely informational in character, has practically no place in the instruction in these courses; however, some time is spent in discussion. The teacher asks questions, the answers to which help integrate the laboratory and text material and give general structure to the course work. In teaching by inquiry, the teacher does not act as a reservoir of stored knowledge. He seldom gives answers to questions but asks a series of questions which help the students to discover for themselves. The emphasis in instruction is on questioning, not answering—more will be said of this later in our book.

The second way a teacher gets students involved in inquiry is to give them examples of actual scientific inquiring situations. These may be patterned after some scientist's work in solving a problem. The teacher presents background information about the problem and then involves the class in a discussion of how the problem could be solved. In the process, students follow the path a scientist used in solving it. Another way teachers instill a sense of inquiry is by becoming inquirers themselves. A teacher may not know the answer to a problem, but he may with his students study and resolve it. Students don't expect a teacher to know everything. They enjoy having their teacher involved in discovering with them some new fact or principle of science. Bruner says in this respect:

> It seems unlikely that a student would develop or have confidence in his intuitive methods of thinking if he never saw them used effectively by his elders. The teacher who is willing to guess at answers to questions asked by the class and then subject his guesses to a critical analysis may be more apt to build those habits into his students than would a teacher who analyzes everything for the class in advance.[12]

---

[11] J. Robert Oppenheimer, *The Open Mind* (New York: Simon and Schuster, Inc., 1955), p. 129.
[12] *Op. cit.*, p. 62.

By being an inquirer, a teacher encourages healthy skepticism of authority. By continually asking for empirical evidence, not just opinion, in discussing problems, he teaches inquiry by example.

Inductive and Deductive Reasoning

Rational thinking is divided by philosophers into two main categories: induction and deduction. In inductive reasoning, one reasons from specifics to the general; and in deductive reasoning, from the general to the specific. This pattern of thought has also been expressed in teaching method. In the inductive approach to teaching, a teacher may move from specifics to generalizations. For example, if a teacher wants students to discover what magnetism does, he gives them magnets to experiment with in various situations. After some time the students discover that the magnets pull only certain substances toward them. The teacher then gives the class other magnets of different shapes and various substances. The students once again experiment and draw the same conclusion. In each specific case the magnets pulled iron-bearing metallic substances toward them. The class then concludes—makes a generalization—that magnets have the ability to pull iron-bearing substances toward them. They have formulated a generalization based upon several specific situations. In so doing they have moved from the specific to the general. They have evolved a generalization inductively. This approach closely follows the way in which many scientific discoveries have been made; it was by the inductive method that scientific principles were first formulated.

Contrast the inductive approach with that of a teacher who teaches deductively. He might tell the class, "Magnets have the ability to pull iron-bearing substances toward them." He then passes out some magnets and magnetic materials to the class. He lets the class see that iron-bearing materials are pulled toward the magnet. The class notes that the magnets attract these substances, and they know from the generalization given by their teacher that these substances are iron-bearing. They have verified the teacher's generalization by placing iron materials near a magnet; they have moved from a generalization about magnets to a specific case, the iron material in front of them; and they have verified what they have been told by the teacher. But what has the teacher done? He has deprived the students of the thrill of discovering for themselves a property of magnetism. Furthermore, what opportunities has the teacher given to the students to develop their capabilities as inquirers? The inductive approach, by contrast, is an inquiring approach which follows the same processes scientists use in solving problems. Its role then in teaching-learning can not be overstressed. Not all learning, just as not all thinking, can be inductive in character; however, a large segment of class activities must be inductive if individuals are to be adequately prepared to think critically and to understand science as a process.

Hurd and Rowe report in the *Review of Educational Research,* "Inductive discovery methods of science instruction failed to produce more effective learning than traditional deductive verification methods."[13] There is, however, some evidence to show that an inductive inquiring approach is superior to the traditional deductive method. Boeck compared an experimental chemistry class at the University of Minnesota High School with eight control classes, one at the University High School and seven throughout Minnesota. With the aid of the instructor the students in the experimental group decided which experiments to do and planned the experimental procedures. The generalizations of the experiments were applied to related problems in the next class period. This procedure was called the inductive-deductive method. The experimental group did as well or better in achievement but was significantly superior in learning the methods of science and the scientific attitudes.[14]

Sister Ernestine Marie O'Connell in thirty-two selected schools involving fifty-six classes and forty teachers found that inductive laboratory learning resulted in higher achievement on the Anderson Chemistry Test and Cooperative Chemistry Test. She further found that the inductively taught groups had higher achievement in chemical-equation balancing.[15] Studies in other areas of science and mathematics have supported the superiority of the inductive method. This, on first thought, may seem curious, because with the inductive method students obviously require far more time to learn information than with the deductive approach. A teacher can, in a few minutes, tell a class that a magnet attracts iron-bearing metallic substances, whereas students' experimenting to determine this fact may require ten or twenty minutes. The superiority of the inductive method is due to its offering active involvement in learning and more meaningful experiences. In inductive teaching the students study less but learn more. The inductive emphasis in instruction requires more class time, but the results are worth it.

Science educators have criticized some school programs for trying to cover too much in too short a time. Dr. J. Darrell Barnard, professor of science education and chairman of the Department of Science and Mathematics Education at New York University, has declared:

---

[13] P. DeHart Hurd and M. B. Rowe, "Science in the Secondary School," *Review of Educational Research,* June, 1964, p. 289.

[14] Clarence H. Boeck, "The Inductive-Deductive Compared to the Deductive-Descriptive Approach to Laboratory Instruction in High School Chemistry," *Journal of Experimental Education,* XIX (March, 1951), pp. 247-53.

[15] "The Comparison of Inductive and Deductive Methods of Teaching High School Chemistry" (Doctoral dissertation, Boston University, 1958).

The majority of school science programs do not permit enough time for teachers or pupils to think their way through to the broad generalizations of science.

It has been assumed that brief exposure by discussion or reading about science results in learning its basic ideas, and that verbalizing about these ideas is evidence of understanding.

In fact, only the exceptional pupil learns science in such a setting, and he probably learns it in spite of the setting.[16]

To have meaningful experiences requires time to think, outline a plan of attack for a problem, gather and check evidence, and make valid interpretations. The development of these skills can not be rushed; but once taught well, the skills are retained.

Teachers teach for retention. "Greater understanding of what is taught produces more rapid learning, better retention, and better adaptation to new conditions."[17] What good is instruction if what is learned today is forgotten tomorrow? Nevertheless, many science teachers are fact-oriented in their instruction; their emphasis is upon memorization of information and not upon understanding. The forgetting curve for factual information is shown in Figure 12. This curve has a steep initial drop and eventually levels off to a low plateau of retention. For example, Steneth and Davis report that only 19 per cent of high school chemistry can be recalled four years later.[18] Many studies in education have substantiated this finding. Other studies in educational psychology have shown that details in learning may be lost rapidly, whereas general ideas and central themes are well retained.

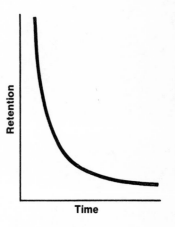

Figure 12

Teaching by inquiry—because of its emphasis upon the processes of science, discovery, and understanding of the principles and main themes of science—insures better learning and retention of knowledge. A teacher who truly understands this approach has a great psychological advantage, enabling him to be a more efficient and above all effective developer of our most valued resources—our children's minds.

SUMMARY

An efficient and effective teacher must be able to apply the principles of psychology. These show that students learn best if they are actively involved, if they receive encouragement and reinforcement, study meaningful material, have a wide variety of experiences in a rich and varied environment, and learn detail in a

[16] J. Darrell Barnard, "Urges 'Too Much, Too Fast' Approach be Eliminated from Science Teaching," *Teacher Topics*, Spring, 1962, p. 3.

[17] Cronbach, *op. cit.*, p. 350.

[18] M. D. Steneth and R. A. Davis, "The Permanence of School Learning," *Educational Administration and Supervision*, XL (1954), pp. 449-60.

structured pattern. Students also achieve better if the teaching is planned, if they know the objectives, and if they have opportunities to learn from one another. They tend to study the kinds of things for which they are tested; if they are tested for memorized facts they will tend simply to memorize.

Science teachers teach scientific concepts and principles. To understand a concept, a student must have had many relevant percepts. Science teaching should proceed from percepts to concepts to principles to theories.

Six levels of learning can be identified; they are: knowledge, comprehension, application, analysis, synthesis, and evaluation. Teaching science as inquiry helps to develop higher learning, since it involves students more in the processes of science and enables them to be creative.

A teacher who teaches inductively is more likely to involve students in inquiry, thereby giving them a better conception of science as a process. Factual information without understanding results in little retention. Detailed information is lost rapidly, but general ideas and themes may be retained well.

Further Investigation and Study

1. Define what is meant by principles of learning. Why should a science teacher know them?
2. Suppose that you were going to teach a unit on genetics in one class and one on chemical bonding in another class. How would you start the units and why? State your answers in terms of psychological principles.
3. Suppose you wanted to teach about diffusion. How would you do this?
4. What are percepts, concepts, principles, and theories? How are they related?
5. Look over the list of psychological principles in this chapter. Which three do you think would be the most helpful in your teaching and why?
6. Suppose you wanted to teach what a molecule is. How would you teach this, and what is the justification for your approach?
7. Why should science teachers stress the learning of concepts and principles?
8. What are the levels of learning? What would you do in your teaching to facilitate attainment of the higher levels?
9. What do you think of Szent-Györgyi's comments on memorization?
10. How are inquiry and inductive teaching related?
11. Describe how you would teach some scientific principle inductively and how you would teach it deductively.
12. How does the inquiry approach differ from the way you have been taught in several classes?
13. What are the psychological bases for using inquiry as an approach to teaching?
14. Why shouldn't a teacher try to "cover the book" in his course?

4

Secondary Science Curriculums under Change

John Currey, engineer at Rocketdyne Corporation, was invited to speak at Warren High School on Wednesday morning. His topic was "Recent Advances in the Space Sciences." Because it was years since he had visited a high school, Mr. Currey decided to spend the day visiting classes after his talk. A physics class met at 10:00 following the morning assembly. Mr. Currey decided to visit it because the teacher, Mrs. Starks, had mentioned that the class was studying circular motion and centripetal force, topics closely related to Mr. Currey's talk of the morning.

The class assembled quickly and immediately began to work before Mrs. Starks came into the physics laboratory. Materials were ready on the demonstration desk, and students helped themselves to the small kits labeled "Centripetal Force."

Groups of two proceeded to assemble the materials. In a few minutes, trials were being taken and data gathered. A small rubber stopper attached to a string which went through a small glass tube and was fastened to several metal washers was swung in a circle about the head. Revolutions were counted, and several variations of the experiment were tried.

Mr. Currey was impressed. It was obvious the students had prepared before coming to class. They appeared to know how to proceed. Theirs was an interesting way to learn about centripetal force. A simple apparatus was used.

Students performing astronomical studies in the Earth Science Curriculum Project.

Photo courtesy of Bob Waters, Colorado State College

Measurements were taken, and data were recorded. The trials were repeated. Several variations were tried; groups were not all using the same procedures. A glance at a laboratory guide revealed only a few guiding questions and hints.

Mr. Currey reflected on how different this laboratory approach was from that of his high school days. There were no blanks to fill in the laboratory manual. The class was not preceded by a discussion of what the students were supposed to find out. There didn't seem to be a rigid procedure. The students seemed honestly interested in finding out the relationships between radius of swing and mass of the washers used in the experiment. There was no evidence of boredom.

A visit to an earth science class for ninth grade brought a few additional surprises. Here a junior high school class was actually experimenting. Its purpose was to measure the diameter of the sun! This was being done by a few measurements of the diameter of a small bright spot on a piece of paper formed by rays of sunlight coming through a pinhole. Solution of a simple proportion gave students the answer. On checking with a few groups, Mr. Currey found that the calculated results varied somewhat, but the students were not especially disturbed. They seemed excited about their accomplishment!

When Mr. Currey left the school at the end of the day he reminisced about his own high school classes. They hadn't seemed nearly this exciting.

What has brought about the change Mr. Currey observed? The date most often referred to as marking the beginning of a serious re-evaluation of our science teaching is October 4, 1957. This was the launching date of the first man-made satellite to orbit the earth. It is interesting to speculate what the reaction would have been if the first satellite had been put aloft by the United States. As it was, the Russian scientists beat our own by a mere four months; and the reverberations set off in education by the rumblings of the first Russian satellite booster are still being felt. Each year brings increasing evidence of the massive reorganization of science curriculums as well as other subjects in our educational system. It is likely that active changes and modernizations will go on for many decades.

It is an exciting time to be entering the science teaching field. Challenging assignments are on every hand; unlimited opportunities for improving existing courses are available in every school system; large-scale curriculum projects are multiplying each year; and innumerable varieties of new teaching techniques and materials are waiting to be tested. There is no limit of valuable work to be done.

THE NEED FOR CHANGE

Science teaching in the secondary school has traditionally been concerned mainly with the products of science. Textbooks in high school physics, chemistry, biology, physical science, and general science have been written predominantly by high school teachers of these subjects. These authors have been concerned with the accurate communication of scientific knowledge to the high school student. In the nature of their positions, they were rarely involved in actual scientific research extracting new knowledge from nature; consequently, the methods of scientific research were given lip service, but students were not given practice in putting these methods to use.

As scientific advances were compounded with increasing rapidity in the first half of the twentieth century, textbooks became larger in order to include the newer advances and applications. The science discipline took on the appearance to the high school student of a compendium of knowledge to be memorized or in some way digested. Little attention was paid to the logic of thought development and to the basic cohesiveness of the discipline.

Recognition of the burgeoning knowledge in each of the sciences led curriculum planners to try new arrangements in sequence. The real problems caused by excessive attention to applications of science knowledge and an encyclopedia approach to the subject were not solved, however.

Forces Which Bring about Change

It has been said that scientific knowledge is increasing at an exponential rate. In the past ten years, it is believed, the total quantity of knowledge in any given science field has more than doubled. The prospects for the future are even more profound. The sheer mass of information accumulated year by year in advancing science fields is a powerful force for change. School curriculum planners are forced to make choices about which information is to be taught and which is not. It is virtually impossible to teach it all.

The advent of Sputnik I was another powerful force. When a rival nation launched a satellite before the U.S. did, it was decided that our educational system needed a severe overhauling; and the secondary science curriculums received the first impact of this view. Results of the revision efforts will be discussed in detail later in this chapter.

A gradual shift in education emphasis from the products to the processes of science is still in progress. The inquiry approach in laboratory work is replacing the verification approach. Less emphasis is being put on memorizing the results of scientific experiments and more upon scientific methods and attitudes of the experimenter.

Recent years have seen numerous innovations in the teaching field, largely spurred by technological advancements. Television teaching, teaching machines, programmed instruction, team teaching, and telelectures have come into use. Problems which were insurmountable a few years ago now are yielding to new audio-visual techniques. Many curriculum changes have come about because of the force of these advancements.

TRADITIONAL SCIENCE COURSES

In order to understand the reasons for the present revitalization of science courses in junior and senior high schools, it is necessary to look briefly at the historical development of the science curriculum.

Secondary science courses have been relatively stable over the years. New courses entered the curriculum from time to time, but only after the character of the school population changed or national emergencies made their existence necessary. Courses which came into being usually found permanent status. Changes were gradual and reflected changing conditions such as industrial advancements, compulsory school laws, or national defense needs.

Each of the traditional courses—physics, chemistry, biology, and general science—will be discussed briefly. The newcomers, physical science and earth science, and the modern versions of all the science courses will then be given consideration.

Physics

Physics first was known as "natural philosophy" and appeared in the academies of the early 1800's. Content was organized into topics similar to those of our traditional courses today. Mechanics, fluids, heat, light, sound, magnetism, and electricty were the topics taught, mainly by recitation. The Civil War and the advent of land-grant colleges in the 1860's placed emphasis on military and vocational aspects of science, and the course became known as physics. Laboratory instruction was emphasized. A list of standard experiments, called *The Descriptive List*, was circulated by Harvard in 1886 for use by the high schools. Candidates for admission to Harvard who offered physics as a prerequisite were then tested by use of these experiments.

The content of high school physics remained nearly constant for more than sixty years except for the addition of technological information as new advancements occurred. This information was inserted in or appended to the standard course and the textbooks grew thicker. Little was ever removed, but attempts were made to improve the practical nature of the course.

An important part of physics is gathering data and quantitative measurement.
Photo courtesy of Harold Pratt, Science Supervisor, Jefferson County, Colorado.

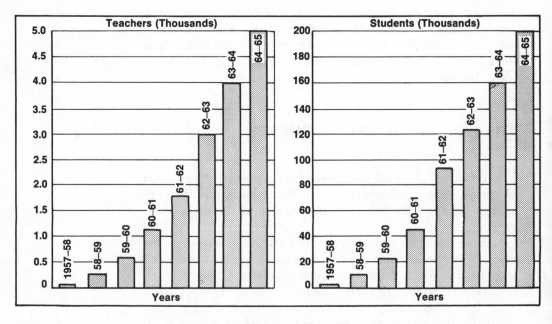

Figure 13

Source: Letter to PSSC teachers from Educational Services, Incorporated, 164 Main S Watertown, Mass., February, 1965, p. 2.

Laboratory work was guided largely by laboratory workbooks and consisted almost entirely of exercises in verification of physical constants, such as coefficients of expansion, heats of fusion and vaporization, and acceleration of gravity. True experimentation was almost entirely absent from high school physics courses.

In 1956, a group of university physicists at Cambridge, Massachusetts, took a serious look at the secondary school physics curriculum and found it did not represent the content or spirit of modern physics. From this group, the Physical Science Study Committee was formed with the objective of producing a modern course for the high school.

In the four years following, this group developed a textbook, laboratory guide, teacher's guide, set of apparatus, monographs, and films. All of these aids were correlated closely with one another in order to produce an effective teaching package. In addition, there was a large number of summer institutes for upgrading teachers in modern physics and in the philosophy of the new course. The success of this approach to high school physics is still being evaluated. Figure 13 shows the increase in the number of teachers and in student enrollments in years immediately following the advent of the course.

Some of the important differences between the PSSC course and traditional high school physics are:

1. Fewer topics covered at greater depth
2. Greater emphasis on laboratory work
3. More emphasis on basic physics
4. Less attention to technological applications
5. Developmental approach showing origins of basic ideas of physics
6. Increased difficulty and rigor of the course

New PSSC Physics course shows greater emphasis on laboratory work.

Photo courtesy of Bob Waters, Colorado State College.

Teachers and administrators have conflicting opinions about the merits of the PSSC course. There is general agreement that it is a definite improvement over traditional courses, especially for better-than-average students. For average or below-average physics students, its greater merit is questionable.

A project is now under way to develop a course more suitable for the average student. The Harvard Project in Physics attempts to treat physics as a lively and fundamental science, closely related to achievements both in science and outside science itself.[1] It is hoped that in this way the course may catch the interest of a large, untapped group who ordinarily do not enroll in physics.

Other approaches to the teaching of secondary physics have been tried out in recent years. A complete physics course on film was produced by a grant from the Fund for Advancement of Education. These were the Harvey White films, each thirty minutes long, which made up a series of 162 films. About 400 educational

[1] *Newsletter No. 1* of the Harvard Project Physics, Pierce Hall, 29 Oxford Street, Harvard University, Cambridge, Massachusetts.

units involving up to 50,000 students used the films. Several experiments testing the effectiveness of this method of teaching physics were carried out throughout the country. Results indicated that the achievement gains in physics knowledge were about the same as those from conventional instruction; however, definite negative attitudes toward the film course developed among students in the tested schools. Students appear to prefer conventional methods with the major instruction being given by a physics teacher in the classroom.

Chemistry

The teaching of high school chemistry began in the early 1800's in girls' academies. The years of the Civil War gave a stimulus to the course because of the military and industrial applications of the science. Laboratory work was increased during those years, and an effort was made to reproduce many of the classical experiments of early chemists such as Priestley and Lavoisier. As with physics, Harvard in 1886 placed chemistry on the optional list for college entrance but controlled the quality of entering students by publishing a *Pamphlet* of sixty experiments, on which the prospective enrollee was tested in the laboratory. The influence of *The Pamphlet* was profound, and the high school chemistry course became highly standardized. Laboratory workbooks were developed, containing "experiments" that were mainly exercises in observation and manipulation of chemical reactions.

With the influx of larger numbers of students in the 1900's, high school chemistry proliferated into a variety of types in an effort to satisfy the needs of students who were not primarily science-oriented or who were not planning to enter college. Enrollments in chemistry remained at approximately 35 per cent of the eleventh grade, the class in which the course was usually taught.

In 1957, a summer conference of chemistry teachers at Reed College in Portland, Oregon, produced a plan for a new type of chemistry course and initiated the Chemical Bond Approach Project. There followed a series of writing conferences, usage by trial schools, and the production of a commercial textbook in 1963. The major theme of this course is the chemical bond; and particular attention is given to *mental models* (conceptual schemes) of structure, kinetic theory, and energy.

The laboratory program and textbook parallel and reinforce each other. No unusual chemicals or equipment are required, and the cost of conducting the CBA chemistry course is not significantly different from that of conducting conventional courses.

A second course-improvement project in chemistry was initiated at Harvey Mudd College in Claremont, California, in 1959. Called

The Chem Study Course emphasizes inquiry in the laboratory before discussion.

Photo courtesy of Bob Waters, Colorado State College.

the Chemical Education Materials Study, the project developed a course that is strongly based on experiment, with the text and laboratory work thoroughly integrated. In addition to the text and laboratory manual, a teacher's guide, a score of excellent films, and a series of wall charts were prepared.

Both of these chemistry programs received grants from the National Science Foundation, which supported numerous inservice and summer institutes for teachers. The enrollments in CBA and CHEM chemistry are increasing.

Biology

This course had its beginnings in botany, physiology, and zoology and was patterned after college courses in these subjects in the nineteenth century. A course of study in biology appeared in New York in 1905, and the College Entrance Examination Board prepared an examination for the course in 1913. Biology was placed in the ninth grade in schools of the six-three-three type of organization and in the tenth grade of eight-four schools.

Of all the high school sciences, biology enjoyed the largest enrollment. A combination of factors operated to bring this about. Placement in the ninth or tenth grade where the effect of school dropout is less pronounced, the effect of compulsory education laws, the non-mathematical nature of the course, and the general requirement of a minimum of one science course for graduation from high school combined to keep enrollments increasing over the years. Approximately 68 per cent of tenth-grade students enroll in the biology course.[2]

The biology course changed from one comparable to college courses in botany and zoology and emphasizing systematic study of plant and animal phyla to a descriptive course showing interrelationships between living things and based upon needs and interests of high-school-age young people. Laboratory work was largely based on recognition, identification, and classification of life forms. The absence of plant and animal growing rooms and shortage of equipment resulted in a sterile and textbook-oriented course in many high schools.

To modernize the secondary school biology course, the American Institute of Biological Sciences in 1958 organized the Biological Sciences Curriculum Study (BSCS). Arnold B. Grobman of the University of Colorado was appointed director. In discussing the design of the course developed by the BSCS, he said, "A realistic general biology program must take into account a wider range of student ability, interests, and potential than exists in other high

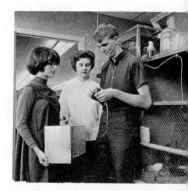

Modern biology requires the maintenance and study of experimental animals.

Photo courtesy of Bob Waters, Colorado State College.

---

2 Kenneth Brown and Ellsworth Obourn, *Offerings and Enrollments in Science and Mathematics in Public High Schools 1958* (Washington, D. C.: U. S. Government Printing Office, 1961).

school science courses. It must be a course that most tenth grade students can handle, and at the same time prove challenging to the above average student. For these reasons the committee thought it undesirable to limit the course to a single design."[3]

Students using a quadrant in studying BSCS Biology.

Photo courtesy of Bob Waters, Colorado State College.

Three separate courses were developed, based upon a molecular approach, a cellular approach, and an ecological approach, respectively. Although the courses are different in emphasis, several common themes run through them:

1. Change of living things through time-evolution
2. Diversity of type and unity of pattern of living things
3. Genetic continuity of life
4. Biological roots of behavior
5. Complementarity of organisms and environment
6. Complementarity of structure and function
7. Regulation and homeostasis: the maintenance of life in the face of change
8. Science as inquiry
9. Intellectual history of biological concepts[4]

BSCS Biology is laboratory-centered, requiring high quality equipment.

Photo courtesy of Bob Waters, Colorado State College.

A complete set of materials is provided for the course. Textbooks, laboratory guides, teacher's guides, supplementary readings, and tests are but a few of these materials. Innovations include the Laboratory Blocks, consisting of a series of interlocking and correlated experiments on a special topic of biology. Eleven dif-

---

[3] Quoted in American Association for the Advancement of Science, *The New School Science: A Report to School Administrators on Regional Orientation Conferences in Science* (Publication No. 63-6 [Washington, D.C., 1963]), p. 27.

[4] *Ibid.*, p. 29.

ferent "blocks" have been developed, including, for example, "Plant Growth and Development," "Microbes: Their Growth and Interaction," and "Interdependence of Structure and Function."

A second-level course has been prepared for advanced biology. Other supplementary materials are excerpts from historical papers, BSCS Invitations to Enquiry, discussion outlines for the laboratory, films on laboratory techniques, the BSCS *Teacher's Handbook,* and the BSCS Pamphlet Series.

The BSCS biology courses are receiving generally favorable response throughout the country. Several versions of the course are available, and it has been found that different versions are chosen in different regions. Several foreign countries also are experimenting with the course.

Junior High School Science

Science in the junior high school has been faced with perplexing problems since its inception. General science was the course offered in the ninth grade of eight-four schools at the time the first junior high schools came into existence. Begun in the decade 1910-20, the course was designed to satisfy the needs and interests of students in early adolescence. The first course was established through research and was designed to fill a current need.

With the rapid development of junior high schools in the 1920's and 1930's, general science was adopted as a suitable course for the seventh and eighth grades as well as the ninth. Some of the factors operating at that time which encouraged the development of the general science course were:

1. Influx of larger numbers of students into the schools at grades seven, eight, and nine because of compulsory-education laws which kept children in school to age sixteen

2. Increasing concern for a type of education which was needs-centered and designed for life itself

3. Recognition of the importance of a continuous sequence of science offerings from grades one to twelve, with planned long-range goals

The difficulties encountered in junior high school science were of the following nature:

1. A shortage of well-trained general science teachers. Many teachers at this level were physics, chemistry, and biology teachers whose primary interest was not with the problems of junior high school science. Also, teachers in other disciplines such as English, mathematics, and physical education were recruited to teach science. For these reasons the quality of science instruction at these levels suffered.

2. A serious degree of repetition in grades seven, eight, and nine. Publishers of textbooks frequently prepared "series" of

general science texts for these grades in an effort to relieve this problem, but the variations in school organization such as six-three-three, eight-two-two and eight-four necessitated a considerable degree of repetition of science topics in order to produce universally salable textbooks.

3. Deficiencies in equipment and facilities for teaching science. Many science classes were taught in ordinary classrooms without water or gas outlets and without adequate facilities for demonstrations and experiments.

4. Lack of clear knowledge of what junior high ;chool science should actually accomplish. Objectives ranged from "preparation for the rigorous science courses in the senior high school" to "general education for good citizenship." Much thought was given to development of attitudes and interests. Some felt general science should be exploratory in nature. Courses designed around this premise became rapid surveys of chemistry, physics, astronomy, meteorology, biology and geology. Others believed students should study the applications of science in the world around them. Courses of this kind dwelt on home appliances, transportation, communication, health problems, and natural resources.

Enrollments in general science grew to about 65 per cent of the ninth-grade classes by 1956, then declined as substitute courses began to permeate the ninth grade and as the seventh and eighth grades took over more of the general science offerings.[5]

NEW SCIENCE COURSES IN THE JUNIOR HIGH SCHOOL

Revision of junior high school science courses through national curriculum studies was delayed while attention centered on the senior high school courses.

Early in 1963, a grant was made to the American Geological Institute to support a curriculum development, called the Earth Science Curriculum Project, for the ninth grade. This is an interdisciplinary course in the areas of geology, meteorology, astronomy, and oceanography. Its emphasis is on laboratory and field study in which students actively participate in the genuine process of scientific inquiry.

Materials of the ESCP include a textbook, a laboratory guide, a teacher's guide, films, laboratory equipment and maps, and a pamphlet series. Trial usage of the materials and a testing program are going on in fifteen test centers around the country. A commercial form of the textbook and laboratory guide are planned for publication in September, 1967.

Topographical maps are used in the Earth Science Curriculum Project course.

Photo courtesy of Bob Waters, Colorado State College.

---

[5] Brown and Obourn, *op. cit.*

A serious problem faced by the ESCP is the preparation of teachers qualified to teach the course. Figure 14 shows the future-

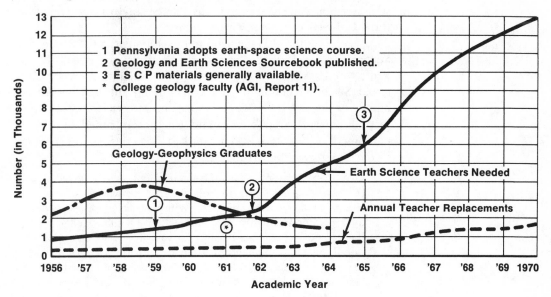

1 Pennsylvania adopts earth-space science course.
2 Geology and Earth Sciences Sourcebook published.
3 E S C P materials generally available.
* College geology faculty (AGI, Report 11).

Geology-Geophysics Graduates

Earth Science Teachers Needed

Annual Teacher Replacements

Figure 14–Estimated Demand for Earth Science Teachers

demand estimates for earth science teachers.[6] By 1970, the estimated annual demand for new replacement teachers alone will be about 1,600 per year.

A large number of present earth science teachers are inadequately trained. In many cases they have been "recruited" from other subjects and must be retrained in the use of ESCP materials if the course is to succeed.

Certification requirements vary widely from state to state.[7]

Earth Science Curriculum Project students observing and studying in a natural setting.

Earth Science Curriculum Project students investigating in the laboratory.
Photo courtesy of Harold Pratt, Science Supervisor, Jefferson County, Colorado.

---

[6] *Newsletter No. 2* of the Earth Science Curriculum Project, Box 1559, Boulder, Colorado (January, 1964).

[7] *Newsletter No. 3* of the Earth Science Curriculum Project (April, 1964).

Twenty states have no requirements for teaching earth science. New York, on the other hand, requires a minimum of fifty-seven semester hours in science and mathematics and the equivalent of three full-year courses in earth science.

A second junior high curriculum development is the Secondary School Science Project directed by Frederick L. Ferris, Jr., of Princeton University.[8] This project, also supported by the National Science Foundation, concentrates on the earth sciences, mainly geology. A unit, "Time, Space, and Matter," was developed in preliminary textbook form and was accompanied by kits of equipment and materials. The aims of this course are expressed in the *Progress Report*, which states:

> Over the past twenty years, the changes that have occurred in the world—particularly the phenomenal growth of science and technology—have created an urgent need for a more dynamic approach to science instruction. Our knowledge of the physical world has become so vast and is changing so rapidly that it is no longer feasible, even if it were desirable, to present science to students as a compendium of all that has been learned through the ages. The study of science today must offer the student not merely an account of what has been discovered, but a systematic and logical method of thinking for himself.[9]

Eight regional centers with fifty-six participating schools throughout the nation tried out the materials of the Secondary School Science Project in 1965. The majority of these, 53 per cent, were eighth grades, and 39 per cent were ninth-grade classes.

A third program developed for the junior high school is that of the Introductory Physical Science Program of Educational Services, Incorporated.[10] This project is directed by Uri Haber-Schaim and is supported by the National Science Foundation. Its purpose is to develop a one-year course in physical science for use in junior high schools. Laboratory work is emphasized, and equipment has been designed in such a way that students can perform the experiments in ordinary classrooms. The Table of Contents of the IPS course includes the following topics:

Chapter I	Introduction
Chapter II	Quantity of Matter: Mass
Chapter III	Characteristic Properties
Chapter IV	Solubility and Solvents
Chapter V	The Separation of Substances
Chapter VI	Compounds and Elements
Chapter VII	Radioactivity

[8] Secondary School Science Project, *Progress Report III* (Princeton, N. J.: Princeton University, Winter, 1965).

[9] *Ibid.*, p. 9.

[10] *Preliminary Edition: Introductory Physical Science Program* (Watertown, Mass.: Educational Services, Incorporated, 164 Main Street, 1964).

The Introductory Physical Science course is being tested in a number of centers throughout the United States, and materials will be made available commercially at the conclusion of the testing period.

A complete listing of the current and recently completed science-course-improvement projects is given at the end of this chapter.

COMMON ELEMENTS OF THE NEW COURSES

Surveying the materials of the several new courses now being developed in secondary school science, one is impressed by their close similarity in types of materials offered and in general objectives. The following common elements are discernible:

1. Their respective brochures and descriptive literature proclaim them to be designed not especially for an elite group but for the students customarily enrolled in a secondary science course.
2. There is less emphasis on applications and technology than in the traditional courses.
3. There is more emphasis on abstractions, theory, and basic science.
4. There is increased emphasis on discovery-type laboratory. Students are given practice in extracting information from nature.
5. There is more rigorous treatment of subject matter.

Ninth grade students studying variation by statistical analysis in the Earth Science Curriculum Project.

Photo courtesy of Bob Waters, Colorado State College.

6. Quantitative techniques are used frequently. Practice is given in data gathering, recording, graphing, and analysis.
7. They present newer concepts in their subject matter.
8. They involve up-grading of teacher competency for successful teaching of the courses. An extensive program of summer institutes and inservice institutes, financed by the National Science Foundation, is an intrinsic part of each of the new curriculum programs.
9. They are accompanied by a large variety of teaching aids, well integrated and designed to supplement the courses.
10. Their construction has embodied good teaching and learning practices. Students are active participants in the learning process and carry more responsibility for their own learning than in traditional courses.
11. They include many clever innovations, most of which are adaptable to traditional courses.
12. They give opportunities for the good student to extend his exploration of the subject.
13. They are flexible enough that average and below-average students can make acceptable progress within the framework of the course.
14. They present science in a favorable light and provide an understanding of what a scientist is and does in our society.

Although these observations are tentative and are based on preliminary materials for some of the more recent courses, further revisions are not expected to involve different aims. The common elements indicate certain aspects of curriculum development in science which are likely to become more prominent the next few years.

IMPLICATIONS FOR THE SCIENCE TEACHER

The science teacher today is faced with enormous responsibilities. In addition to keeping up with his day-to-day teaching, he must remain alert to current changes and improvements. The swing toward "discovery" and "inquiry" methods demands the best possible knowledge of his subject. He must become well informed about new teaching materials and audio-visual devices. He is faced with certain decisions concerning the adoption of new courses. Having decided to try one or the other in his classroom, he must become thoroughly familiar with its content and philosophy.

In return for this excessive load and responsibility, the science teacher today works in a generally favorable climate of cooperation. Parents and school administrators recognize the need for modern and effective science courses in the schools. Support for better classrooms and laboratories is generally forthcoming.

Junior High School Sciences emphasizes all forms of inquiry including the outdoor laboratory experiences.

Photo courtesy of Harold Pratt, Science Supervisor, Jefferson County, Colorado.

In addition, the dedicated science teacher is challenged by new teaching methods and stimulated by new courses. The excitement of participation in a testing program for a new curriculum project or the thrill of creative opportunities provided by teaching a new course is ample payment for the extra responsibilities. A science teacher today works in a lively, growing era of change with unlimited horizons.

SUMMARY

The need for changes in secondary school science became increasingly evident midway through the twentieth century. A number of forces at work brought about conditions which affected the curriculum. The rapid increase in scientific knowledge, the competitive nature of the race for space, technological advancements in teaching tools, and a gradual dissatisfaction with the encyclopedic approach to the teaching of science combined to bring changes about.

The first secondary science course to react to these pressures was physics, followed by chemistry, biology, and junior high science, in that order. New courses for all these subjects appeared, stimulated by massive financial support from the National Science Foundation and a few other agencies. The final effects of these large-scale curriculum revisions are not yet known. Teachers of these subjects have taken up the challenge for the better teaching of science by attending summer institutes and inservice institutes for up-grading their own competencies.

Students of the secondary school sciences are being given opportunities for increased laboratory work and application of inquiry methods for learning. They are directed to better understandings of how scientists work and how knowledge is obtained. More attention is given to the processes of science. New apparatus and facilities promote investigations of natural phenomena, while the teacher becomes more of a director of research than a dispenser of knowledge.

The impact of modern curriculum changes will be felt for many years. It is doubtful whether as stable a pattern of science offerings as that characteristic of the first half of the twentieth century will again be achieved. Science of the future will need to be dynamic and changeable in order to meet the demands of a rapidly accelerating scientific age. As the new modes set by the current curriculum revisions become more widely established, students of science will gain the skills and knowledge needed to handle the problems of this age successfully.

A List of Science Curriculum Projects for the Secondary School

(Projects and original directors)

1. Biological Sciences Curriculum Study, University of Colorado, Boulder, Colorado. Dr. Arnold B. Grobman, director.
2. Chemical Bond Approach Project, Earlham College, Richmond, Indiana. Dr. Laurence E. Strong, director.
3. Chemical Education Materials Study, University of California, Berkeley, California. Dr. George C. Pimental, director.
4. Earth Science Curriculum Project, P. O. Box 1559, Boulder, Colorado. Dr. Robert L. Heller, director.
5. Harvard Project Physics, Pierce Hall, 29 Oxford Street, Harvard University, Cambridge, Massachusetts. Dr. Gerald Holton and Dr. Fletcher Watson, co-directors.
6. Introductory Physical Science Program, Educational Services, Incorporated, 164 Main Street, Watertown, Massachusetts. Dr. Uri Haber-Schaim, director.
7. Physical Science Study Committee, Educational Services, Incorporated, 164 Main Street, Watertown, Massachusetts. Dr. Jerrold R. Zacharias, director.

Further Investigation and Study

1. Write to each of the curriculum projects listed above and request their latest reports. Prepare a brief summary of their aims, materials available, and current status.
2. Obtain from your state department of education information on the numbers of schools using the new courses in your state. Prepare a graph showing the trends over the past five years. What are the prospects for the next five years?
3. After studying the materials of one of the new courses in your field of teaching interest, make a list of the demonstrations or experiments which could be adapted satisfactorily to a traditional science course. Illustrate the modifications that would be necessary.
4. How do the new courses handle problems of individual differences? Cite examples of how this is done.
5. What advantages can you see in the new courses? What disadvantages are there? How might the disadvantages be overcome?
6. Write a prediction of what science teaching will be like ten years from now. What new courses, probable technological improvements for the classroom, trends in teacher needs, revisions in objectives, etc. can you foresee?

The Secondary School Curriculum Projects*

In December, 1962, the American Association for the Advancement of Science established an Information Clearinghouse on New Science and Mathematics Curricula at the University of Maryland Science Teaching Center in College Park. Activities of the Clearinghouse include the collection of data on new and continuing projects, the deposition of such curriculum materials for study and perusal by others, and the dissemination of pertinent information to interested individuals and groups. Material has been furnished to the Clearinghouse from local, state, and national programs in the United States and from several projects in foreign countries. Over 350 individuals, including the directors of the college commissions, have been contacted for K-16 information for the annual reports.

The following chart summarizes information about the activities of major ongoing projects in science curriculum for secondary schools. The excerpts here are from the Third Annual Report of the Information Clearinghouse on New Science and Mathematics Curricula, March 1965. That publication consists mainly of information on the most recent project activities as reported by the project directors themselves.

Brief Summaries of Science Curriculum Projects of Particular Interest to Secondary School Science Teachers

Project Name	Director's Name/ Project Address	Support: Organizational/ Financial	General Purpose	Science Materials Produced	Present or Future Activities
AAAS Commission on Science Education (AAAS K-16)	John R. Mayor and Arthur H. Livermore/AAAS, 1515 Massachusetts Ave., N.W., Washington, D. C. 20005	American Association for the Advancement of Science/National Science Foundation	Broad concerns for science education at all levels including curriculum development for grades K-16 and teacher preparation. Sponsors Information Clearinghouse on new projects	Elementary science materials K–5 from a process approach, teacher's commentary, equipment kits for parts 1–4, kits for testing individual processes, and a project newsletter	During the 1965 summer writing conference at Michigan State University, materials for grade 6 will be developed and additional equipment kits for all grades will be produced. Revision and extension of evaluations, inservice training programs, and the Information Clearinghouse located at University of Maryland
Biological Sciences Curriculum Study (BSCS)	Arnold B. Grobman/ University of Colorado, P.O. Box 930, Boulder, Colorado 80301	American Institute of Biological Sciences (1959–63), now University of Colorado/National Science Foundation	To contribute to the improvement of biological education through the preparation of curriculum materials related to the study of biology	A first course (three versions—10th grade), and BSCS (Second Course), (12th grade), special materials for low-ability students, laboratory blocks, biology teacher's handbook, and numerous supplemental materials for biology teachers and students, BSCS Newsletter	Commercial publication of the BSCS Second Course by June 1965; final revision of the special materials during the summer of 1965; preparation of a guide for teaching disadvantaged students, additional single-topic films, pamphlets and lab blocks, revision of three versions and continued evaluation of materials

* Text and summaries by J. David Lockard (Director, AAAS Information Clearinghouse, University of Maryland, College Park), *The Science Teacher*, May, 1965, pp. 48–49.

Project Name	Director's Name/ Project Address	Support: Organizational/ Financial	General Purpose	Science Materials Produced	Present or Future Activities
Chemical Bond Approach Project (CBA)	Laurence E. Strong/ Earlham College, Richmond, Indiana, 47375	No organizational support/National Science Foundation	Design of introductory course in chemistry which emphasizes chemical bonding and chemistry as a process of investigation	Chemistry text, student laboratory guide, teacher's guide, supplementary readings, chart of electronegativities, four self-instruction programs	Development of additional self-instructional programs in chemistry and revised set of student examinations on the CBA course
Chemical Education Materials Study (CHEM)	George C. Pimental/ Wing B, Gayley Road, University of California, Berkeley, California 94720	University of California and (until 9/63) Harvey Mudd College, Claremont, California/National Science Foundation	To stimulate and prepare high school students for college chemistry and to give other high school chemistry students an understanding of the importance of science	Chemistry text, laboratory manual, teacher's guide, programed instruction pamphlets, achievement tests, films, and CHEM Study Newsletter	Production of additional motion pictures, filmstrips, and film loops
The Earth Sciences Curriculum Project (ESCP)	Robert L. Heller/ Earth Science Curriculum Project, P.O. Box 1559, Boulder, Colorado 80301	American Geological Institute/ National Science Foundation	To develop a text, lab manual, and teacher's guide for use in secondary school earth science courses	Experimental copies of a text, laboratory manual, teacher's guide, Reference Series pamphlets, and ESCP Newsletters	Evaluation and revision of the text, lab manual and teacher's guide; development of additional Reference Series pamphlets, field study guides, and single topic pamphlets; writing conferences in the summers of 1965 and 1966 on items to be published commercially in summer 1967

Project Name	Director's Name/ Project Address	Support: Organizational/ Financial	General Purpose	Science Materials Produced	Present or Future Activities
Harvard Project Physics (HPP)	Gerald Holton and Fletcher G. Watson/ Pierce Hall, 29 Oxford Street, Harvard University, Cambridge, Massachusetts 02138	Harvard University/U.S. Office of Education, The Carnegie Corporation, and The Sloan Foundation	To develop a new kind of physics course for the science oriented and the science-shy, centered on a solid introduction to physics but stressing the humanistic background of the sciences	Thirty chapters of a physics text, twenty laboratory experiments, two filmstrips, and the Harvard Project Physics Newsletter	Development of ten additional chapters of the text, instructional film loops, an introductory 16mm film, fifteen additional laboratory experiments, a book of selected readings, tests, programed instruction, paperback monographs and laboratory equipment
Introductory Physical Science	Uri Haber-Schaim/ Physical Science Study Committee, 164 Main St., Watertown, Massachusetts 02172	Educational Services Incorporated/ National Science Foundation	To develop a one-year course in physical science for use in junior high with an emphasis on student laboratory work	Seven chapters of the basic text, teacher's guide for first five chapters, lab equipment, and apparatus	Completion of text and teacher's guide, and development of additional lab equipment and apparatus
Minnesota Mathematics and Science Teaching (MINNE-MAST)	Paul C. Rosenbloom and James J. Werntz, Jr./2nd Floor, TSCE, University of Minnesota, Minneapolis, Minnesota 55455	University of Minnesota/National Science Foundation	To produce coordinated mathematics and science curricula for grades K–9; and pre-service and in-service mathematics, science and methods courses	Nine units for K–7 science, seven anthology of science units K–7, science methods courses, eight 8mm sound films for science, outline and sample units for college science, and MINNEMAST reports	Development of additional science and mathematics materials and teacher preparation courses, evaluation of materials and courses, and writing conference in summer 1965

Project Name	Director's Name/ Project Address	Support: Organizational/ Financial	General Purpose	Science Materials Produced	Present or Future Activities
Physical Science Study Committee Advanced Topics	Uri Haber-Schaim/ Physical Science Study Committee, 164 Main St., Watertown, Massachusetts 02172	Educational Services Incorporated/ National Science Foundation	Development of advanced topics in physics for use in high school and college physics courses	Five chapters of a text, teacher's guides, laboratory guide, three films, and equipment and apparatus for the laboratory	Development of additional chapters on entropy and changes in atoms and nuclei, quantum physics and statistical physics
Physical Science Study Committee Physics (PSSC)	Jerrold R. Zacharias/ PSSC–ESI, 164 Main St., Watertown, Massachusetts 02172	Educational Services Incorporated/ National Science Foundation	To present physics as a unified but continuing process by which men seek to understand the nature of the physical world	Physics text, laboratory guide, laboratory apparatus, films, Teacher's Resource Book and Guide, Science Study Series, and PSSC tests	Publication in Fall 1965 of a Second Edition of the text, and development of related topics and materials (PSSC Advanced Topics and PSSC Introductory Physical Science described above)
School Science Curriculum Project	Rupert N. Evans, Dean, College of Education, University of Illinois/805 W. Pennsylvania Ave., Urbana, Illinois 61801	University of Illinois/National Science Foundation	To develop improved science materials for elementary and junior high schools	Science and mathematics units in draft form now being tested in schools	Revision of present materials and development of additional topics in a writing conference and a two-week orientation and planning session for fall evaluation, both during summer of 1965
Secondary School Science Project	Frederick L. Ferris, Jr./Secondary School Science Project, J.C. Green Hall, Princeton University, Princeton, New Jersey	Princeton University/National Science Foundation and Princeton University	To develop a program for secondary school grades, centered on geology that will lead students to an understanding of the nature of the earth	Text, student investigation, booklets, science reading series, laboratory kit, student record book, teacher folios, tests and examinations, and film loops	One year's course materials to be ready for commercial distribution late in 1966; periodic conferences regarding improvement of materials and readying of one year's work for commercial release

The artistry of teaching science is dependent on how skillfully the teacher blends several of the methods into a unified teaching lesson. The nature of the lesson, the personality and goals of the teacher, the climate of the class, and the interests and needs of the students will determine the ultimate selection and utilization of appropriate teaching methods in science.[1]

Nathan S. Washton

5

Lesson Planning for Science Teaching

The teacher of science is especially fortunate because of the abundance of things of science which he can use in his teaching. All about him are examples of natural and scientific phenomena. The daily cycle of events, the endless variety of clouds and weather, the growth of plants and animals, the passage of the seasons all contribute to an endless store of materials for scientific discussions. There are rocks and minerals to be collected, flora and fauna in season, and numerous examples of scientific devices to be used as teaching aids in his classes.

An alert and enthusiastic science teacher will not miss the opportunity to use the things of science in his teaching plans. Clever use of appropriate items and examples will inject a degree of interest and spontaneity into his classes which is unmatched by any other method. Students will respond by bringing items for discussion, newspaper clippings, and interesting scientific articles. The spirit of such a classroom will be enthusiastic, exciting, and enjoyable to students and teacher alike. Students will look forward with pleasant anticipation to returning to class the next day. It is probable that learning will be productive and satisfying.

---

[1] Quoted in Ellsworth S. Obourn and John H. Woodburn, *Teaching the Pursuit of Science* (New York: The Macmillan Company, 1965), p. 289.

How does the science teacher put the things of science to use? Are there meaningful ways to plan for effective teaching? Can the teacher maintain sequence and organization and at the same time stimulate interest? Can the objectives of science teaching be realized while permitting the objects of science to dominate the scene? These are questions each teacher must face when planning his yearly and daily work.

The beginning steps in lesson planning should involve much thought before anything is put down on paper. Questions such as "What do I want to accomplish with this lesson?" "What do the students already know about this topic?" "How can I build on what they already know?" "How can I illustrate the main points of the lesson?" must be answered to the teacher's satisfaction before a lesson plan can be prepared.

It is certain that students vary in abilities and interests. Plans must attempt to provide for these variations. Some method of motivating each student must be found. Only by knowing something of the background of each student can the teacher be effective in this task. This presents a strong argument for taking a personal interest in the students in one's classes. The small human contacts in a friendly classroom, an interested question here and there, can achieve this better than any other method.

Circumstances vary, depending on the teacher's purpose; but it is often a good idea to start a lesson with a concrete object or device on which to focus attention. A demonstration or illustration tied in to the main point of the lesson serves as an ideal springboard for discussion and questioning. The stiffness and formality which sometimes accompanies a class period is overcome by this approach, and the class interest is usually high. If the teacher is

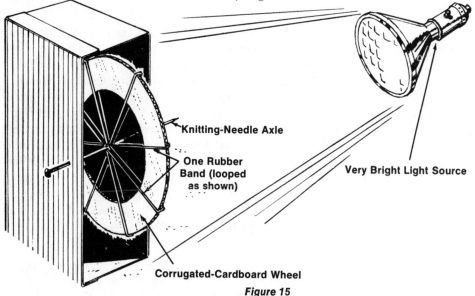

Knitting-Needle Axle

One Rubber Band (looped as shown)

Very Bright Light Source

Corrugated-Cardboard Wheel

Figure 15

careful to avoid giving away all the secrets of the device or object, it can become the basis for a problem-solving or inquiry lesson.

An example is given below of this approach as used in a tenth-grade physical science class which has just finished the study of heat and its effects on expansion and contraction of materials.

The "rubber-band wheel" is set up as shown in Figure 15. A strong light is shone upon one half of the wheel, and the wheel slowly turns. The question "What makes it turn?" becomes an obvious one to ask. Students who have learned that heated objects expand may come to the conclusion that the rubber bands expand under the strong light, thus throwing off the center of gravity, causing the wheel to rotate. Closer analysis, however, shows that the wheel should then turn in the opposite direction. A genuine problem thus presents itself which should stimulate thinking.

After several ideas are suggested, tested, and discarded, the class may come to the realization that rubber bands under tension contract when heated. This would explain the observed rotation. The correctness of this assumption can be tested by suspending a weight on a stretched rubber band. Heating the rubber band with the spotlight shows it definitely to contract, thus explaining the phenomenon.

With this approach, the teacher begins the class in an interesting manner. Students are encouraged to participate, and an inquiring attitude is stimulated. Students are taught that there frequently are important exceptions to general rules and that one must constantly be on the alert for them.

PLANNING A SCIENCE LESSON

Lesson planning is more than just making sure there is something to do for the entire class period. Unless it is the very first lesson of the year, it is probable that assignments have been made and that the nature of the subject matter is understood. Thus, the basis for planning has already been established.

For the sake of conducting an interesting class period, it is important for the teacher to vary the methods from day to day and even within the class period itself. *It is deadly to fall into the same repetitive pattern of teaching day after day.* Even an excellent method can suffer from overuse. With the great variety of methods to choose from and with the potential excitement of inventing a new technique or modification of one, the science teacher is in an excellent position to plan a highly effective lesson.

Mr. Foster looked forward to making his plans for the eighth-grade general science class on Monday morning. As he thought of the students in his class, it seemed that he might involve them in class participation and generate enthusiasm by doing a demonstration-experiment. The topic for consideration was the explanation of the simple Mendelian ratio of 1-2-1 for the offspring in the first generation produced by the crossing of two pure strains. He would use the crossing of pure white and pure black guinea pigs as a sample case to illustrate this phenomenon.

In order to demonstrate the purely statistical nature of the results obtained in this cross and of the effect of dominant over recessive genes, Mr. Foster decided to make a simple arrow spinner that could be attached to the blackboard with a suction cup. Then a circle could be drawn on the blackboard, around the spinner, and labeled as shown in Figure 16. With this device it would be possible to engage the class in a "game of chance," give them practice in keeping a record of the data, and put across the point of the lesson in an interesting manner.

After constructing the spinner, Mr. Foster decided to give it a trial run to see whether it would perform satisfactorily and whether the demonstration could be accommodated in the fifty-minute class period. Out of forty trials, the results he got in his trial run were as follows:

Figure 16

	BB	Bw	wB	ww
Trials:	11	8	11	10

The time required was ten minutes, and the results appeared to Mr. Foster to be sufficiently close to the expected values to illustrate the point. He decided to plan his class period around this demonstration-experiment.

On paper, Mr. Foster's lesson plan looked like this:

General Science 8   *Monday, April 20*

Topic: Simple Mendelian ratio
Purpose: To show the statistical nature of the Mendelian ratio
    10 min. Remarks and questions:
        1. What is meant by *dominant gene?* By *recessive gene?*
        2. Suppose a pure-bred white and a pure-bred black guinea pig *(BB,ww)* were mated. What genes have they for color? What would be the color of their offspring?
        3. What are the possible combinations of dominant and recessive genes for color of coat? *(BB, Bw, wB, ww)*
        4. What might be the proportions of each of these combinations in the offspring? (1-2-1)
        5. How could we *show* this to be the result of statistical probability?
    Activity: Set up the blackboard spinner. Select a volunteer to spin it. Select another volunteer to keep a record on the blackboard under the headings *BB, Bw, wB,* and *ww.* Continue for 10-15 minutes.
    20 min. Discussion:
        1. What are the actual colors of offspring which have each of the possible gene combinations?

2. Why aren't the results in an exact ratio of 1-2-1?
3. Could we improve the results?
4. Student questions (anticipated).
Assignment: A volunteer assignment—two boys or girls might run this experiment for more trials to see what the results would be.
Evaluation:
Time OK? _____ Interest? _____ Understanding? _____

Mr. Foster's lesson plan shows the essential features of a good written plan. The writing of it was preceded by considerable thought regarding purpose and method to be used. The plan itself was concise and brief enough to serve as a working guide. Estimates of the time needed for various activities were made. Leading questions for the discussions were suggested, and some thought was given to the probable questions students might ask. Provision was made for extended work by individuals who might become motivated to pursue it further. Space was left for a note or two regarding the success of the lesson.

It is likely that Mr. Foster will use this idea again at another time. For this reason he will probably file it away for future reference. In modified form it can become a basis for preparing a similar plan for a different class of students at some future date.

Lesson plans should not be re-used in original form year after year. This can only lead to loss of spontaneity and lowered effectiveness. Plans for each year's class should be made anew with an effort toward a creative approach. However, the resources of a past successful lesson can be used for ideas and guidance in planning anew.

A practice teacher implementing his lesson plan.

Photo courtesy of Bob Waters, Colorado State College.

THE DAILY LESSON PLAN

Why Plan?

Planning gives direction. For the beginning teacher it is a necessary step in refinement of the art of effective teaching. It enables the teacher to build self-assurance into his classroom presentations. A teacher girded with a well-prepared plan meets his class with forthrightness and confidence. The effect upon the class is usually beneficial. Incipient discipline problems are frequently discouraged; and, most important of all, classroom goals are established firmly, and a plan of action for achievement of these goals is put into effect.

Preparing the Teaching Plan

Thought planning should precede any written plans. Questions such as "Why teach this?" "What good is it?" "How can it be used?" "How can it be demonstrated?" ought to be answered before committing anything to paper. The teacher should have a firm grasp of goals and purposes at this point and be prepared to give justifications, at least to his own satisfaction. He should hold the image of individual students and class character before him at all times, remembering that learning is an individual matter and that no teaching is done unless learning takes place.

The written plan should be concise and functional. The format may vary with the situation and with the individual teacher, but it should be teachable. There should be provision for a listing of main concepts to be taught or skills to be developed. Questions useful as guides to discussion should be noted. Types of anticipated student questions should be listed. All materials needed for the class period should be checked for suitability. Activities and assignments should be noted in sufficient detail to insure a smooth class hour and effective teaching.

Teaching from the Plan

During the class hour, a teaching plan ought to be as unobtrusive as possible. It may be referred to when needed. Main ideas may be memorized and sequence followed, but usually not at the expense of flexibility. As the teacher gains experience, he will be able to extemporize within the framework of the plan and conduct a class period charged with interest and enthusiasm.

Evaluating the Lesson Plan

The experience gained in teaching should be recorded with brief notations on the written plan. This can be done immediately after class, or during the class period if time permits. Suggestions for timing, organization, student reactions, and improvements of a demonstration or other technique can be noted for future use. The modified plan can form the basis for new lesson planning in the future. It should be labeled and filed for future use.

The Long-Range Lesson Plan: An Illustrative Case

Miss Henderson was a new teacher of tenth-grade physical science at Warren High School. The head of the science department, Mr. Longwell, who had taught the course the previous year, had talked briefly with Miss Henderson concerning the objectives and general nature of the course.

No textbook was being used. Mr. Longwell believed that most physical science textbooks attempted to cover too many topics in a one-year course. In order to permit time for greater depth of study, only five major areas were taught in physical science at Warren High; these were the nature of the atom, the nature of the molecule, nuclear energy, radiant energy, and man's applications of physical science. Materials for the course were provided by Mimeographing and by the purchase of small paperback books on appropriate science topics.

On discussing the objectives of the physical science course, Miss Henderson and Mr. Longwell agreed that it should serve a dual role—to introduce students to the more rigorous specialized chemistry and physics courses in the eleventh and twelfth grades of Warren High School and to function as a terminal science course for those students who were planning to go into non-science areas of study. The attempt was made to approach the chosen topics from an activity and laboratory point of view as much as possible.

With this background of understanding of the course, Miss Henderson decided to outline the year's work. Her first task was to plan the sequence of topics. She decided that the sequence used by Mr. Longwell—atom, molecule, nucleus, radiations, applications—had stood the test of experience and seemed to be a logical sequence; therefore, she would use this sequence the first year and modify it in the future if necessary. With only five areas to study, it seemed feasible to plan about six weeks on each of the first three topics and eight weeks on each of the last two. This would enable the class to finish the third topic at the end of the first semester. Miss Henderson realized that this schedule might have to be modified, but she was prepared to make the necessary adjustments when needed.

Over the next few days, other parts of the long-range plan were put into place. Films were ordered to arrive at the proper times—as nearly as could be estimated so early in the year. Dates of holidays and examination periods were considered.

Some thought was given to a possible excursion or two during the teaching of the final topic, on applications; but the dates were left tentative. The storage room was checked for apparatus and laboratory supplies and seemed adequate, but Miss Henderson knew certain unavailable materials might be needed on short notice. She checked with Mr. Longwell and found that expendable items could be obtained within a week from a laboratory supply house.

Miss Henderson kept a loose-leaf planning notebook for each of her classes. The long-range plan and schedule was placed in the front of this notebook, and space was allotted for notes and modifications.

The Teaching Unit

A beginning teacher can be assisted by a teaching-unit plan which is designed in moderate detail for a period of a month or six weeks. The unit topic is usually a cohesive area of study which fits into the long-range plans and objectives. The teaching unit frequently contains the following sections and characteristics.

1. Objectives	4. Materials
2. Content	5. Evaluation
3. Methods	6. Teaching Sequence

The objectives ought to be brief statements of purpose for the unit. They should serve as constant reminders to the teacher of the things to be accomplished in the time allotted. They should be practicable, timely, and carefully suited to the capabilities of the class. Statements of platitudes, characteristic of some objectives lists, should be avoided. Objectives should be testable.

Content refers to the actual subject material to be taught in the unit. Because this may be voluminous, the teaching-unit plan cannot list all of it in minute detail; however, the plan may list major principles, pertinent facts of major importance, examples and illustrations, and references to specific knowledges in text material deemed important for the unit. An outline form may be used in this part of the unit plan. Because of the chronological nature of the teaching unit, specific content and references to subject matter can be distributed in a sequential manner throughout the unit.

Methods and procedures to be used in teaching should be planned as carefully as possible. Certain parts of the teaching unit may be taught more suitably by one method than by another. For example, an appropriate film may be the most effective teaching agent for a particular subtopic. Another time, individual work in the laboratory may be the best way to achieve the teaching objectives. At still another time, discussion of a problem by small groups within the class may be the best mode of teaching.

A teacher of science must constantly be on the alert for more effective teaching methods and must guard against stereotyping his teaching. Careful planning of the teaching unit can achieve the proper balance and variety for a stimulating class experience. Materials must be planned with care in order to insure their availability at the time they are needed. In some cases, ordering is necessary a few weeks in advance. Apparatus should be checked to see if it is in working order. Development of the teaching unit will undoubtedly involve several hours work in the library, getting ideas for reading materials and activities. Consideration should be given to the needs of slow and rapid learners, and suitable materials should be arranged for these students. If Mimeographed materials are to be used, arrangements must be made for preparing, typing, and duplicating these materials.

Evaluation should be thought of as a continuing process throughout the study of the unit. One of the major functions of evaluation is to keep students informed of their progress and to give them realistic assessments of their own abilities. The use of assigned work, short quizzes, conferences, and unit tests must be planned in the teaching unit. Not all of the evaluative devices and techniques can be planned in detail in advance, but provision for their use can be incorporated. Evaluation should be based upon the objectives of the unit.

The teaching sequence may be outlined for the period of time involved, but flexibility for change must be provided. This can be done by arranging for alternative procedures, omission or addition of certain subject matter, provision for unplanned periods interspersed occasionally to take up slack or give needed time for completion of a topic.

The teaching unit should be thought of as a guide for action rather than a calendar of events. Slavish attention to the pre-planned schedule can result in ineffective rigidity. On the other hand, reasonable attention to the sequence, objectives, and procedures of the teaching unit can promote better learning and feelings of satisfaction and accomplishment when it is finished. A sample format for a teaching unit on the topic of nuclear energy follows:

Teaching Unit on Nuclear Energy

Class: Physical Science 10   Warren High School
Period: December 1-January 24
Objectives:
1. Present current information on structure of the nucleus.
2. Teach methods used in obtaining nuclear energy.
3. Show applications of nuclear energy to peacetime uses.
4. Develop responsible attitudes for control and use of nuclear energy.

Dates		*Materials and*
(Tentative)	*Topic*	*Activities*
	1. Introduction	Resource people
	2. Minor objectives	Films and filmstrips
	3. Science principles	Experiments
	4. Skills to be taught	Demonstrations
	5. Facts and concepts	Projects (student)
	6. Attitudes and	Field trips
	appreciations	Committee work
	7. Generalizations	Assignments
		Tests and quizzes
		Open houses
		Resource books
		Periodicals
		Charts

The Resource Unit

The practicing science teacher finds it necessary to develop resources upon which to draw for materials and ideas in his day-to-day lesson planning. The resource unit fulfills this need admirably.

Although it should not be thought of merely as a loose collection of odds and ends pertaining to a given topic, the resource unit can be more flexible than a teaching unit. No attempt is made to build a time sequence into the unit. This is left to the judgment of the teacher as he formulates his daily teaching plans. Or, in some cases, a brief teaching unit based on the materials and objectives of the resource unit can be prepared as a guide for time and sequence.

The format of the resource unit may be variable, depending on the teacher's preferences and the topic with which the unit deals. A loose-leaf notebook of the eight-and-a-half by eleven-inch size may accommodate the needed materials conveniently. Because of the likelihood of growth and expansion as more material is gathered, a series of manila folders, properly labeled, may prove to be a more convenient method of containing the unit. A card-file system is sometimes used, with a supplementary folder for papers of larger size. With the cards conveniently cross-indexed and provision made for disposal of outdated items, the card-file resource unit can be a useful item to the experienced teacher as well as to the beginning teacher of science.

Sections usually included within a resource unit are as follows:
1. List of aims and purposes
2. Important knowledge objectives
3. List of activities and projects, with brief plans for carrying them out
4. Suitable demonstrations and experiments—ranging from simple to complex
5. References and source books

6. Tests and other evaluative materials
7. Lists of films, filmstrips, slides, transparencies, charts, models, and other visual aids
8. Bibliographies for student reading and teacher reference
9. Miscellaneous teaching aids, study guides, free and inexpensive materials, etc.

Construction of a good resource unit is a task which is never entirely finished but which can lead to improved science teaching year after year. Just as an orchard requires pruning in order to produce good fruit, the resource unit must be treated periodically in the same way in order to keep it effective for lesson planning.

A sample abbreviated resource unit is reproduced below:

Resource Unit on The Nature of the Atom

Class: Physical Science 10   Warren High School

Period: September 15 - November 1   Number of students: <u>24</u>

Major Goals of the Unit:
1. To learn the structure of the atom and historical development of present understandings of the atom
2. To learn the symbols for the elements and the basic information of the periodic chart
3. To learn to write formulas and equations for chemical reactions
4. To perform the basic chemical reactions in the laboratory
5. To learn some applications of chemistry to the work of the world.

Important Knowledge Objectives:
1. Definition of atom
2. Definition of molecule
3. Symbols for thirty of the most commonly used chemical elements
4. Significance of rows and columns of the periodic chart
5. Meaning of valence—common valences
6. Meaning of activity series
7. Rules for naming compounds—acids, bases, and salts
8. Rules for writing equations
9. Four basic chemical reactions
10. Rules for balancing simple equations

Important Skill Objectives (Laboratory):
1. Safety procedures in the laboratory
2. Recognition and handling of basic laboratory equipment —assembling
3. Use of the trip balance—weighings
4. Observation of chemical reactions in a test tube
5. Recording data—keeping laboratory notebook
6. Drawing graphs of data
7. Using *Handbook of Chemistry and Physics*
8. Cleaning glassware and apparatus
9. Techniques of laboratory work
10. Writing a laboratory report

List of Activities and Projects:

1. Learn the sources of the names and symbols for the elements. What revisions in naming the elements have taken place in recent years?
2. Compare the short form and the long form of the periodic chart. What are the advantages and disadvantages of each?
3. Construct models, using suitable objects such as Tinker Toys, rubber stoppers, gumdrops, toothpicks, etc., of several common compounds (e.g., H_2O, CO_2, NaCl, NH_3, etc.)
4. Design a large chart showing the chemical processes involved in smelting of iron, or production of sulfuric acid.
5. Prepare the materials for a bulletin-board display on one of the following topics:
   a. Naming of chemical compounds
   b. Atomic diameters
   c. Types of chemical bonding
   d. Four basic chemical reactions
   e. An industrial process using chemistry

Experiments and Laboratory Exercises:

1. Familiarization with laboratory equipment
   a. Names and identification of:
      1) Ringstand
      2) Bunsen burner
      3) Beaker
      4) Florence flask
      5) Erlenmeyer flask
      6) Test tube and test-tube rack
      7) Igniter
      8) Trip balance
      9) Crucible
      10) Mortar and pestle
      11) Test-tube holder
      12) Burette clamp
      13) Other common items
2. Safety materials and procedures in the laboratory
   a. Laboratory aprons
   b. Laboratory goggles
   c. Heating a liquid in a test tube
   d. Lighting the Bunsen burner
   e. Handling and pouring acids
   f. Pouring acid into water
   g. Use of the trip balance
   h. Labeling reagents
   i. Emergency procedures in events of accidents
   j. Other safety precautions
3. Preparing and assembling glass tubing and glassware
   a. Procedures for working glass tubing
      1) Cutting
      2) Fire polishing
      3) Bending

        4) Drawing a capillary tube
        5) Sealing a glass tube
    b. Assembly of a simple apparatus using glassware;
       e.g., a wash bottle
4. Representative chemical reactions
    a. Composition or synthesis
        1) $Fe + S \rightarrow FeS$
    b. Decomposition
        1) $2KC10_3 \rightarrow 2KCl + 30_2 \uparrow$
    c. Replacement
        1) $Fe + CuSo_4 \rightarrow FeSo_4 + Cu \downarrow$
    d. Ionic
        1) $Ag^+ + Cl^- \rightarrow Ag^+Cl^- \downarrow$
5. Volume determination of a gas by water displacement
    a. Manufacture hydrogen by replacement with zinc in
       hydrochloric acid.
       Capture the gas in an inverted container by water
       displacement.
       Measure the volume of the displaced water.
        1) Under what conditions will this equal the volume
           of the gas manufactured? How can you achieve
           these conditions?
6. A simple qualitative analysis experiment using an unknown compound
   (details to be worked out after students have done the
   preceding experiments)
References and Source Books:
   Teacher
       1. Chemistry textbooks
           a. *Modern Chemistry*, Holt, Rinehart & Winston
           b. *Chemistry: A Modern Course*, Charles E. Merrill
              Books, Inc.
           c. *Chemistry and You*, Lyons & Carnahan.
           d. *Chemistry for Progress,* Prentice-Hall, Inc.
           e. *Chemistry, An Experimental Science*, CHEM
              Study, W. H. Freeman and Company
           f. *Chemical Systems*, CBA, McGraw-Hill Book Com-
              pany
       2. Resource books
           a. *A Sourcebook for the Physical Sciences*, Harcourt,
              Brace & World
           b. *Chemistry Problems*, Holt, Rinehart, & Winston
           c. *Scientific Experiments in Chemistry*, Holt, Rine-
              hart, & Winston
   Student
       1. *How To Do an Experiment*, Harcourt, Brace & World
       2. *The Chemical Elements*, Science Service
       3. *Science Projects Handbook*, Science Service
       4. *Handbook of Chemistry and Physics*, Chemical Rub-
          ber Company
       5. *Welch Vest-Pocket Chart of the Atom*, (classroom sup-
          ply) Welch Scientific Company

Tests and Evaluation Materials:
1. Quizzes
   a. Symbol-identification quiz
   b. Quiz on naming acids, bases, and salts
   c. Quiz on types of chemical reactions
2. Practical quiz on laboratory work
   a. Naming of items of laboratory equipment
   b. Laboratory-procedures quiz: weighing, glass working, use of chemical tables
3. Unit achievement test
   a. Twenty multiple-choice questions. (Any, all, or none of choices may be correct.)
   b. Twenty completion questions.
   c. Twenty modified true-false questions.
   d. Five short-answer essay questions.

Lists of Audio-Visual Materials:
1. Films
   a. *Chemical Families*, Modern Learning Aids, New York, 22 minutes, color
   b. *Chemical Reactions*, Edited Pictures, 20 minutes, black and white
   c. *Molecular Motions*, Modern Learning Aids, 13 minutes, color
2. Models
   a. Student Molecular Models, O. H. Johns Glass Company, Ltd., Toronto, Canada
3. Charts
   a. Periodic Chart of the Elements, Welch Scientific Company
   b. Chart of the metric system

LESSON PLANNING FOR TEACHING BY INQUIRY METHODS

Recent developments of new courses in secondary science have brought new emphasis on inquiry and discovery methods in the classroom. The typical teacher of science may be hesitant about using these methods because of lack of familiarity with them and because his own training may have emphasized other classroom procedures. He may have had little experience working in classrooms in which the responsibility for learning rests primarily with the individual student.

Lesson planning for the "discovery classroom" presents certain unique problems. To assess these problems, it may be helpful to consider a laboratory lesson of the open-ended type and to identify at the outset the characteristics of this type of experimentation.

The Manufacturing Chemists' Association has identified a number of features of the open-ended experiment as follows:

1. The experiment asks a broad question—the design of the method is frequently left up to the student.
2. The student generally does not know the answer to the question before doing the experiment.
3. The student must thoroughly *understand* the problem, the *reason* for the problem, and the possible *methods* to be used to solve the problem.
4. The student makes his own observations and draws his own conclusions.
5. The write-up of the experiment should be a written statement of the purpose of the experiment, the data, and the conclusions drawn.
6. The open-ended experiment requires more thinking on the part of the student to interpret what he observes and determines.
7. The data may be interpreted on many different levels of student ability.
8. The answer to the problem posed in the experiment can lead to new problems, which in turn can act as bases for further experimentation and discussion.
9. The experiment is adaptable to laboratory periods of varying length.
10. The student does not ordinarily know in advance the result to expect.
11. The student may in some experiments contribute his result to a class result, and it can become a matter of pride that his contribution to the group result is accurate and significant.
12. There frequently is no one "right" answer to the experiment. Each student has to find out for himself the right answer for his own apparatus.
13. The experiment may cause students to see that many searching questions can be centered upon a single experiment and that an experiment should be observed and questioned from every viewpoint.
14. The student may investigate some properties and on the basis of these properties may be asked to make an explanation which accounts for the properties.
15. The student may be asked to reach a generalization from data which he has collected and to use this generalization to predict the behavior or experimental result of a related experiment.
16. The experiment may initiate a problem for further investigation at home or after school.[2]

It is apparent that students in the discovery laboratory are given much more responsibility in planning experiments and carrying

[2] *Scientific Experiments in Chemistry* (New York: Holt, Rinehart & Winston, Inc., 1961).

them to completion than has traditionally been the case. Effective handling of this responsibility will depend largely on how well the science teacher can provide experiences that will develop students capable of designing experiments, gathering data, and drawing conclusions from them.

Planning for such experiences should be done with the following points in mind:

1. Students probably have not had many previous opportunities of this type. Some may feel the need for explicit directions because this is what they are used to. The initial progress made by these students may be disappointing and frustrating, both to student and teacher.

2. Acceptance of responsibility for one's own learning is a challenge which some students may tend to resist. Passive learning in which the teacher has been the key person for initiating a course of action has probably been ingrained in the student's background.

3. First attempts should be on a small scale, with opportunities for greater choice and greater responsibility increasing as the student gains experience.

4. Rather than acting as a dispenser of information, the teacher should provide situations in which questions are asked. The student should be encouraged to formulate and ask questions —of himself, of the experiment, of resource persons, and of library resource materials.

5. Experience in analyzing the results of an experiment must be provided. The ability to see relationships, to organize data so that meaningful patterns emerge, to draw inferences, and to visualize ways of improving the experiment is a necessary skill which must be developed for effective learning by the inquiry method.

An example of a laboratory experiment which can lead to training in inquiry and discovery is the monolayer experiment for determining the size of a single molecule. In this experiment the student is given a minimum of instructions and is encouraged to devise techniques to arrive at a satisfactory result. A lesson plan for this experiment might look like this:

Class: Physics 12   Section: 9:00 A.M.
Date: November 12
Topic: Calculating Avogadro's Number-Laboratory Experiment
Aims:
1. To measure the size of a molecule of oleic acid
2. To devise suitable techniques for measuring an extremely small length
3. To recognize the use and limitations of scientific assumptions
4. To calculate Avogadro's number

Procedures:
1. Distribute Mimeographed copies of instructions for the experiment the day before.
2. Allow students to choose partners and work in groups of two.
3. Have students draw the necessary materials from the stockroom. Insist on clean-up and return of all items at end of class period!

Materials:
1. Twelve ripple tank trays
2. Twelve monolayer kits (oleic acid, alcohol, eyedropper, 10 milliliter graduate)
3. Lycopodium powder
4. Twelve large beakers

References:
1. PSSC, *Physics*, D. C. Heath & Company, p. 118
2. Lehrman, *Scientific Experiments in Physics*, Holt, Rinehart, & Winston, p. 54
3. "Molecular Constants," *Handbook of Chemistry and Physics*, Chemical Rubber Company

Evaluation of Lesson Plan:
1. Sufficient time? _____
2. Instructions adequate? _____
3. Results of experiment all right? _____
4. Reports all right? _____

The Mimeographed instruction sheet to be distributed to students to guide them in performing the monolayer experiment might be as follows:

Instruction Sheet

Physics 12   Date: November 12
Name: _____

Experiment No. 6 Calculating Avogadro's Number by Use of the Monolayer

General Instructions:

Your purpose in this experiment is to employ a monolayer of stearic acid or oleic acid to determine the size of a single molecule of an organic acid and from the measurements obtained to calculate Avogadro's Number. There are several basic assumptions you will have to make, and your results may be expected to be quite satisfactory if they are within an order of magnitude of the accepted value. The main point of the experiment is to learn a technique for obtaining a measurement of something very small and to recognize the limitations of the method. A second point is to obtain a clearer understanding of what Avogadro's Number is and how it can be calculated directly.

Materials Needed:

1 ripple tank tray or suitable substitute at least 18 in. by 18 in.

Oleic acid or stearic acid
Methyl alcohol for dilution
1 eyedropper
1 graduate (10 ml. preferably)
1 large beaker
Lycopodium powder or chalk dust

Suggested Procedures:

1. One drop of pure oleic acid or stearic acid will be too concentrated. It will need to be diluted about 1 to 200 or 1 to 400 with methyl alcohol. What effect will the alcohol have on the experiment? (It will assist in spreading the oleic acid on the water surface but will not affect the final results.) What will probably happen to the alcohol when it is placed on the water surface? (Being highly soluble in water and volatile as well, the alcohol will probably dissolve in the water or evaporate quickly.)

2. You will need to know the volume of one drop of the oleic acid-alcohol solution. How can you measure the volume of one drop? Remember greater accuracy can be achieved by getting the volume of many drops and taking an average. (Count the drops required to fill one cubic centimeter in the graduate.)

3. When you put a drop of solution on the water surface, what kind of geometrical figure will it assume? (Cylindrical.) What is the formula for volume of such a figure? (Vol. $= \pi r^2 h$.) To find the height of this figure, what information do you need? (Volume of the drop and radius of the circle.) What assumption may you be making here? Is it a reasonable assumption? (You are assuming that the layer is just one molecule thick.) How could you test the validity of this assumption?

   (Compute the area of the circles formed by one drop, two drops, three drops, etc. You will find the areas approximately double and then triple with the second and third drops. This supports the idea that the oleic acid spreads out to a layer just one molecule thick and does not "pile up" in the center of the circle. The only other conclusion is that oleic acid molecules always come in multiples of one drop—a conclusion not justified by other observations.)

   If the assumption is not valid, what kind of conclusion can you draw from your final result? (The final result will give a value which is too large.)

4. What effect may the lycopodium powder or chalk dust have on the diameter of the circle produced by the drop of oleic or stearic acid? (It may restrict the free spread of the acid on the water surface.) How can this effect be minimized? (By using just a *very* small amount of the powder or dust.)

5. How can you achieve a better result for the area covered by one drop of the acid? (By taking the average radii produced by one, two, or three drops.)

6. What is the molecular weight of oleic acid? (282.) What is its density? (0.895 grams per cubic centimeter.)

7. Knowing the information about oleic acid from the previous question, how can you use the molecular diameter of oleic acid to calculate Avogadro's Number?

   (Divide grams per mole by grams per cubic centimeter to get volume of a mole of oleic acid. Then divide cubic centimeters per mole by cubic centimeters per molecule to get N, the number of molecules per mole, which is Avogadro's Number.)

   What assumption must you make? (You must assume some standard shape for the molecule of acid, such as cubical, spherical, rectangular, or some other shape.)

8. What is your calculated result for Avogadro's Number? (Student answer.) What is the generally accepted value? (Approximately 6×10^{23} molecules per mole.) How might your assumptions máde in Question 7 affect your final result? (If you assume a cubical shape, you may get too small a result. Actually the molecule of oleic acid is believed to be about ten times as long as it is wide, and when lying on the water is oriented vertically with the small end in contact with the water surface. Thus, a better assumption would be that the volume of a single molecule is approximately $h^3 \times 10^{-2}$ cubic centimeters.)

9. Tabulate the data obtained in this experiment, show your calculations and the final result.

10. Your experiment report should describe the problem you are attempting, a brief description of your procedure and materials used, tabulations of your data, and the conclusions reached in the experiment. It should be written clearly enough that an uninformed person could read your report, understand it, and if necessary repeat the experiment on the basis of your report alone.

SUMMARY

The lesson plan is a guide for action, not a rigid blueprint to be followed unswervingly. It should be flexible and modified when needed.

Much thought precedes the writing of a lesson plan. Questions of "What is the purpose of the lesson?" "What major generalizations are to be taught?" "How is the material best presented?" "What kinds of individuals are in the class?" are considered before planning the sequence on paper.

The format of the lesson plan should be functional and comfortable to the teacher. Individual teachers select the format most useful to them. It is important to have it as concise as possible within the limitations of effective teaching. During the actual teaching, the lesson plan should be unobtrusive but available for reference.

At least two of long-range unit lesson plans exist. The teaching unit is planned with a time sequence in mind and usually contains provision for statements of objectives, outlines of content, methods, materials, and evaluation techniques. The resource unit does not usually concern itself with chronology but may be thought of as a reservoir upon which to draw for daily lesson planning. It may contain lists of aims, important knowledge objectives, lists of activities and projects, suitable demonstrations and experiments, references, films, bibliographies, sample tests, assignments, and other teaching aids.

Planning for teaching by an inquiry or discovery method usually requires a somewhat different approach than more traditional methods. The role of the teacher becomes one of guidance and direction, with greater responsibility for learning placed upon the student himself. Plans must provide more time, more questioning, greater variety of materials, and willingness on the part of the teacher to allow individual variations in progress by students.

Thorough lesson planning is a necessary facet of effective science teaching. Good teaching does not happen by accident. It is particularly important that a prospective teacher of science recognize the values and benefits to be derived from careful, inspired planning in the art of science teaching.

Further Investigation and Study

1. Select a specific short-range objective for a science class, such as "to develop skill in use of the microscope" or "to learn how to use the slide rule." Plan a lesson to achieve this objective, incorporating the features of a good lesson plan.
2. Using the lesson plan prepared in Exercise 1, or a similar one, teach your classmates in a hypothetical classroom situation. Invite them to play the role of a secondary science class, with appropriate questions and activities. Solicit their constructive criticisms and comments.

A student does not learn to "learn for himself" merely by being told to do so. Hence the enquiring classroom is one in which the questions asked are not designed primarily to discover whether the student knows the answer but to exemplify to the student the sorts of questions he must ask of the materials he studies and how to find the answers.[1]
Joseph J. Schwab

6

Methods of Science Teaching: Inquiry through Laboratory Work

It has often been said that science is not really science unless it is accompanied by experimentation and laboratory work. In the secondary schools in recent years, there has been a resurgence of interest in the laboratory as the focal point for the study of science. It is worth noting that this is not the first time in the history of science education in the United States that the laboratory has come into prominence. The late 1800's saw the construction of laboratories in secondary schools and colleges with a corresponding change in emphasis in the methods of instruction in the sciences. The recitation method and the catechetical approach to learning of science principles was gradually replaced by "experiments" in laboratories with the expressed purpose of verifying the laws of physics and chemistry. It was believed that students would learn science best by repeating, in an abbreviated fashion, the classical experiments of Newton, Galileo, Hooke, Priestley, Boyle, and many others. Students would see principles of natural science at work and from these observa-

---

[1] Quoted in Ellsworth S. Obourn and John H. Woodburn, *Teaching the Pursuit of Science*, p. 3.

tions would come to understand the underlying science concepts. Laboratories and apparatus were designed to duplicate as nearly as possible the materials and equipment used in the original experiments, with "modern" refinements to insure reasonable accuracy in the hands of science students.

As a stimulation to the laboratory approach, Harvard University in 1886 prepared a *Descriptive List* of several score of experiments in physics, emphasizing the verification approach. High school students anticipating entrance at Harvard were required to do these experiments and were subject to examination in the material upon college entrance. A similar list of chemistry experiments set forth in *The Pamphlet* in 1886 was provided for essentially the same purpose.

The effect of these two documents on the direction and scope of subsequent development of high school laboratories and science curriculums was profound. A survey of high school physics and chemistry laboratory workbooks sixty years later revealed that nearly 50 per cent of the 1886 Harvard experiments were still retained in the courses of study. As a result of this strong influence, several generations of science students in the first half of the twentieth century were conditioned to the type of laboratory experiments in which the major emphasis was verification and demonstration of known science principles. Little time or guidance was provided for true experimentation upon problems of which the solutions were unknown. The methods of science were taught as procedural formulas to be followed more or less by rote, and with the belief that all problems could be solved in a mechanical, albeit systematic, manner. Students rarely had the opportunity, except on individual projects outside the classroom and laboratory, to experience true scientific endeavors in the solution of "new" problems.

It should be noted that there were some exceptions to this pattern at various times during the period. Occasional conscientious teachers of physics, chemistry, and biology attempted to modify their courses to adopt more of an experimental approach and to give emphasis to inquiry methods. These efforts were sporadic, however, and did not result in general acceptance. The problems of large class size, overworked teachers, shortages of suitable equipment and facilities, and the absence of clear-cut goals for teaching "science and its methods" in place of "teaching about science" prevented the rapid modification of high school science courses.

THE INQUIRY APPROACH

Since the late 1950's we have seen a definite shift in emphasis in high school science. Once again the laboratory has become the center of attention at all levels of secondary science, including the junior high school. The particular goals and methods used in the various new curriculum projects of the Physical Science Committee, the Biological Sciences Curriculum Study, the Chemical Education Materials Study, the Chemical Bond Approach Project, the Earth Science Curriculum Project, and others are discussed in detail in Chapter 4. Without exception, these projects emphasize and provide for inquiry methods, in which students themselves are the investigators and opportunities for creativity are abundantly present.

The method of inquiry in the science laboratory can be promoted by a number of fairly simple but important changes. Joseph Schwab, in describing the "inquiring curriculum" has this to say about the methods of inquiry:

> In general, conversion of the laboratory from the dogmatic to the inquiring mode is achieved by making two changes. First, a substantial part of the laboratory work is made to lead rather than lag the classroom phase of science teaching. The reason for this change will be clarified in a moment. Second, the merely demonstrative function of the laboratory (which serves the purpose of the dogmatic curriculum) is subordinated to two other functions.
>
> One of these functions consists in a new service to the classroom phase of instruction. With classroom materials converted from a rhetoric of conclusions to an exhibition of the course of inquiry, conclusions alone will no longer be the major component. Instead we will deal with units which consist of the statement of a scientific problem, a view of the data needed for its solution, an account of the interpretation of these data, and a statement of the conclusions forged by the interpretation. Such units as these will convey the wanted meta-lesson about the nature of inquiry. But they will appear exceedingly easy and simple, conveying little of the real flavor of scientific inquiries, unless the verbal statement of the problem situation and of the difficulties involved in the acquisition of data is given meaning by an exhibition of their real physical referents.
>
> This illustrates the first function of the inquiring laboratory. In brief, it is the replacement of illustrations only of conclusions by illustrations of problem situations.
>
> The second function of the inquiring laboratory is to provide occasions for an invitation to the conduct of miniature but exemplary programs of inquiry. The manual for such a laboratory ceases to be a volume which tells the student what to do and what to expect.
>
> Three different levels of openness and permissiveness are available for such invitations to laboratory inquiry. At the simplest level, the manual can pose problems and describe ways and means by which the student can discover relations he does not already know from his books. At a second level,

problems are posed by the manual but methods as well as answers are left open. At a third level, problem, as well as answer and method, are left open. The student is confronted with the raw phenomenon—let it be even as apparently simple a thing as a pendulum. He pushes and pulls, alters first one and then another of its aspects, begins to discern a problem to be solved, then moves toward its solution.

The inquiring laboratory is characterized by a third general feature: it erases the artificial distinction between classroom and laboratory, between mind and hand.[2]

Richard J. Suchman, in a study with fifth- and sixth-graders regarding inquiry training, made the following observations:

> The program is designed to train fifth and sixth graders in the skills and methods that are necessary to make systematic studies of the physical world. The pupil learns that when he observes a phenomenon which he does not understand, he need not throw up his hands in despair or ask someone to explain it. He learns to gather data, experiment, formulate and test hypotheses; to break down a confusing tangle of objects and events into variables that can be examined in relation to each other. He learns to study the effects of one variable on another while holding the remaining factors constant. He learns to look beyond the events that are readily observable and to isolate important but elusive conditions. In time he develops a *strategy of inquiry:* a general approach to finding out why a given event takes place. He learns that to predict and control events he must first determine the conditions that are necessary (and sufficient) for the events to occur. By manipulating "cause and effect" in this manner, the inquiring child moves beyond the concrete situation to higher levels of abstraction and generalization, using his own skills and powers of perception.[3]

Alfred Novak reports comments by Dr. Warren Weaver, vice-president of the Sloan Foundation, concerning scientific inquiry in the laboratory at the college-freshman level:

> It seems to me absolutely essential students do something more than listen to lectures, look at demonstration experiments, study a textbook, recite a lesson. The students simply must do something on their own, with their own minds and with their own hands. They must have a scientific experience, even if it is so simple as swinging a bunch of keys hanging on a string and timing this pendulum with their pulse.[4]

---

[2] Reprinted by permission of the publishers from Paul F. Brandwein and Joseph J. Schwab, *The Teaching of Science as Enquiry* (Cambridge, Mass.: Harvard University Press, Copyright, 1962, by the President and Fellows of Harvard College), pp. 52-53.

[3] "Inquiry Training: An Approach to Problem Solving," *Laboratories in the Classroom* (New York: Science Materials Center, 1960), pp. 73-76.

[4] Alfred Novak, "Scientific Inquiry in the Laboratory," *The American Biology Teacher*, Vol. 25, No. 5 (May, 1963), pp. 342-46.

Novak recommends "laboratories that can run the spectrum from text-centered to the self-energized laboratory which is completely student-centered and student-activated; i.e., completely unstructured by the teacher." He continues:

> In such an array of laboratory experiments, the student emerges from the laboratory with some understanding of the problems and operations of a scientist. He begins to feel his dependence on a conceptual framework that establishes, designs, and directs experimentation. The student learns the limits of both his thinking ability and his perceptual senses. He feels the need for acquiring a certain amount of basic information. He begins to appreciate the "right" tack in the quest for knowledge. He sees the usefulness of various instruments that help him solve the problem. He sees the pyramiding of the problems when his attack on one problem results in four or fourteen more or where two or three minor problems have to be cleared up before the solution to the major problem can begin to shape up. He becomes aware of the amount of routine in the quest for knowledge. He is exposed to failure frequently, but on occasion he feels the excitement of discovery.[5]

SKILL DEVELOPMENT IN THE LABORATORY

The complaint has frequently been lodged against science teaching that students and teachers alike have difficulty expressing exactly what the goals of science teaching should be.

In taking up this challenge, an attempt has been made to identify the types of skills which science students ought to "be able to do better" after having taken the courses in science in the junior high school and senior high school. We have listed five categories of skills, including the following: acquisitive, organizational, creative, manipulative, and communicative. No attempt is made to rank these categories in order of importance, or even to imply that any one category may be more important than any other. Within each of the categories, however, an effort has been made to list specific skills in order of increasing difficulty. In general, it was felt that those skills which required only the use of one's own unaided senses were simpler than those which require use of instruments, or higher orders of manual and mental dexterity. The categories and the specific skills within them, with some elaboration, are as follows:

Physical Science Study Committee Class demonstrating a well organized laboratory activity with little or no assistance from the instructor.

Photo courtesy of Bob Waters, Colorado State College.

A. Acquisitive Skills

    1. Listening—being attentive, alert, questioning

    2. Observing—being accurate, alert, systematic

---

[5] *Ibid.*, p. 345.

    3. Searching—locating sources, using several sources, being self-reliant, acquiring library skills

    4. Inquiring—asking, interviewing, corresponding

    5. Investigating—reading background information, formulating problems

    6. Gathering data—tabulating, organizing, classifying, recording

    7. Research—locating a problem, learning background, setting up experiments, analyzing data, drawing conclusions

B. Organizational Skills

    1. Recording—tabulating, charting, working systematically, working regularly, recording completely

    2. Comparing—noticing how things are alike, looking for similarities, noticing identical features

    3. Contrasting—noticing how things differ, looking for dissimilarities, noticing unlike features

    4. Classifying—putting things into groups and subgroups, identifying categories, deciding between alternatives

    5. Organizing—putting items in order, establishing a system, filing, labeling, arranging

    6. Outlining—employing major headings and subheadings, using sequential, logical organization

    7. Reviewing—picking out important items, memorizing, associating

    8. Evaluating—recognizing good and poor features, knowing how to improve grade

    9. Analyzing—seeing implications and relationships, picking out causes and effects, locating new problems

C. Creative Skills

    1. Planning ahead—seeing possible results and probable modes of attack, setting up hypotheses

    2. Designing a new problem, a new approach, a new device or system

    3. Inventing—creating a method, device, or technique

    4. Synthesizing—putting familiar things together in a new arrangement, hybridizing, drawing together

D. Manipulative Skills

    1. Using an instrument—knowing instrument's parts, how it works, how to adjust it, its proper use for task, its limitations

    2. Caring for an instrument—knowing how to store it, using proper settings, keeping it clean, handling it properly, knowing rate capacity, transporting instrument safely

    3. Demonstration—setting up apparatus, making it work, describing parts and function, illustrating scientific principles

    4. Experimentation—recognizing a problem, planning a procedure, collecting data, recording data, analyzing data, drawing conclusions

  5. Repair—repairing and maintaining equipment, instruments, etc.
  6. Construction—building needed items of simple equipment for demonstration and experimentation
  7. Calibration—learning the basic information about calibration, calibrating a thermometer, balance, timer, or other instrument

E. Communicative Skills
  1. Asking questions—learning to formulate good questions, to be selective in asking, to resort to own devices for finding answers whenever possible
  2. Discussion—learning to contribute own ideas, listening to ideas of others, keeping on the topic, sharing available time equitably, arriving at conclusions
  3. Explanation—describing to someone else clearly, clarifying major points, exhibiting patience, being willing to repeat
  4. Reporting—orally reporting to a class or teacher in capsule form the significant material on a science topic
  5. Writing—writing a report of an experiment or demonstration—not just filling in a blank but starting with a blank sheet of paper, describing the problem, the method of attack, the data collected, the methods of analysis, the conclusions drawn, and the implications for further work
  6. Criticism—constructively criticizing or evaluating a piece of work, a scientific procedure or conclusion
  7. Graphing—putting in graphical form the results of a study or experiment, being able to interpret the graph to someone else
  8. Teaching—after becoming familiar with a topic or semi-expert in it, teaching the material to one's classmates in such a manner that it will not have to be retaught by the teacher

Mere identification of skills to be taught is of course only a first step in the realization of a science objective. In order to bring about skill development and ultimate mastery of the desired skills, the teacher must devise suitable teaching plans and student activities. It goes without saying that, in this type of learning at least, "learning by doing" is an important maxim. Pupils must be given opportunities to carry out activities which give repeated practice in the skills to be taught. The laboratory becomes an important facility at this point because most of the skills involve procedures which, to a greater or lesser extent, require materials and apparatus.

Two sample lessons oriented toward skill development are given as illustrations:

Lesson I

Grade level: Elementary or junior high

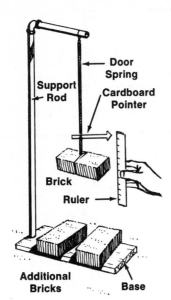

Door Spring
Support Rod
Cardboard Pointer
Brick
Ruler
Additional Bricks
Base

Table I

Weight (Bricks)	Stretch (Inches)
1	1.5
2	3.0
3	4.5
4	6.0

Graph I

Weight (Bricks)

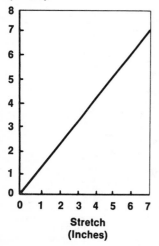

Stretch (Inches)

Objectives: To gain practice in the skills of: (a) measurement, (b) record keeping, (c) graphing

Subject: Forces produced by springs

Problem: How does the length of a spring depend on the force exerted on it?

Procedure: Work in pairs, or do as a student demonstration with all students recording the data and drawing the graph.

Set up the spring and weights as shown in the diagram. Add weights one at a time and check the readings again each time.

Record the results as shown in Table I.
Graph the results as shown in Graph I.

Materials: Door springs, several bricks, ruler, string

Conclusion: The change in length of a spring is directly proportional to the change in the force exerted on it—if the spring is not stretched beyond its elastic limit.

Probable skills developed:

a. Set-up and adjustment of apparatus (manipulative)
b. Observation of initial conditions and changes due to experimental factors (acquisitive)
c. Recording of data (organizational)
d. Graphing and analysis of data (organizational and communicative)
e. Drawing conclusions (organizational)

Evaluation: Can the student—

a. Set up the apparatus for use?
b. Devise a plan of procedure?
c. Read a scale to the limits of its accuracy?
d. Record data in a tabular form?
e. Plot a graph?
f. Interpret a graph?
g. Draw conclusions from the experiment?
h. Recognize sources of error?
i. Report his results in lucid fashion?

Lesson II

Grade level: Senior high

Objective: To gain practice in the skills of: (a) measurement, (b) recording, (c) graphing

Subject: Magnetism

Problem: How does the strength of magnetic force change with distance?

Procedure: Work in pairs. (Also could be done as a student demonstration with all students recording the data and drawing the graph.)

Set up a magnet as shown in the diagram:

Materials: Compass, bar magnet, ruler, protractor

Conclusion: The strength of a magnetic field decreases inversely with the square of the distance from the magnetic pole.

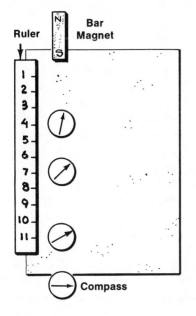

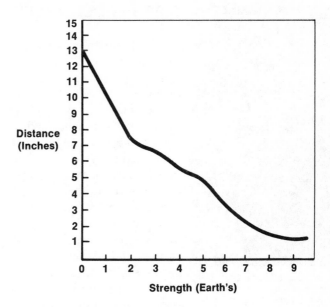

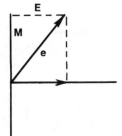

$$\tan \Theta = \frac{E}{M}$$

$$M = \frac{E}{\tan \Theta} = \frac{1}{1/\sqrt{3}}$$

Data:

Distance	Angle	Strength
13″	90°	0
10″	45°	1 Earth
6″	30°	1.732 Earths
3″	3°	5 Earths

Skills developed:
  a. Reading angles from a protractor or circular scale; reading distances on a (1) linear scale (2) logarithmic scale
  b. Plotting graphs
  c. Analyzing graphs
  d. Using trigonometry
  e. Writing a report of an experiment
Evaluation: Can the student—
  a. Set up the apparatus for use?
  b. Gather the necessary materials unaided?
  c. Find a N-S direction?
  d. Obtain several points of data?
  e. Record the data systematically?
  f. Calculate the tangent of an angle and compute the strength of magnetic field?
  g. Graph the data?
  h. Analyze the meaning of the graph?
  i. Explain the result to a teacher or other student?
  j. Write a suitable report of the experiment?

OPEN-ENDED EXPERIMENTS

Use of Incubator for Drosophila culture providing several possibilities for open-ended experiments.

Photo courtesy of the Biology Dept., Oak Park and River Forest High School, Illinois.

The trend toward inquiry and discovery as modes of experimentation in modern secondary school laboratories has been accompanied by replacement and modification of the traditional laboratory workbooks and manuals. Whereas earlier objectives of laboratory work emphasized demonstration, reproduction of classical experiments and verification of known scientific principles, the modern experiment is more nearly deserving of the label "experimentation." Laboratory guides have been produced in which problems are proposed for study in the laboratory, with a minimum of explicit instructions. Procedures are frequently suggested in general terms, and recommended materials are listed; alternative methods are encouraged. The student is expected to observe his experiment carefully and to report his observations without the restriction of having to arrive at some "correct conclusion" established beforehand. In an elementary sense, the student becomes a true experimenter, employing suitable scientific techniques for the problem at hand. The adjective *open-ended* has been applied to experiments of this type, and this label derives from an effort by the Manufacturing Chemists' Association in 1958 to improve the quality of high school chemistry experiments.[6]

The unique characteristics of the open-ended experiments are listed in Chapter 5. Chemistry experiments prepared by the MCA are designed to exploit these characteristics to the fullest extent. New courses in physics, biology, chemistry, earth science, and elementary science in recent years tend to emphasize similar goals in their laboratory work. For example, a typical experiment in the laboratory guide of the Physical Science Study Committee physics course is one dealing with refraction of waves of water in a ripple tank.[7] After carrying out some investigations in answer to guide questions in the experiment, the student is given the following information and questions: "To establish the quantitative relation between the angles of incidence and refraction requires considerable care. Keeping the frequency constant, you can measure the angle of refraction for four or five different angles of incidence. Over what range should you choose the angles of incidence? What do you conclude from your results?" It is apparent here that the student will be required to extend himself beyond the normal laboratory work in order to secure answers to the questions asked of him. Also, he is encouraged to continue study in greater depth in order to refine his results.

Another example of the open-ended experiment—in the laboratory manual of the text, *Investigating the Earth*, by the Earth Sciences Curriculum Project—is an investigation into reflection,

---

[6] *Ibid.*, chap. 5, p. 20.
[7] *Laboratory Guide for Physics* (Boston: D. C. Heath & Company, 1960).

absorption, and penetration of radiation that is carried out by a variety of activities. In a section called "Subsequent Activities," the following statements and questions are included:

1. Place flat objects of different materials in the sun. (Include a mirror.) Feel them after a few minutes. Compare their temperatures.
2. Consider that the amount of energy absorbed by a layer of material is proportional to the amount of energy incident on it. Imagine that a medium, say water, is divided into layers. What can you say about the penetration of the incident energy? Will the amount of energy absorbed be the same in each layer?[8]

Here again we see the attempt made to extend the students' investigations in greater depth and perhaps beyond school time in order to secure answers to the questions asked.

A third example of the efforts to make the laboratory an inquiring type of experience and of the open-endedness of experiments is an experiment suggestion from the Chemical Bond Approach course. In this experiment, a title, "The Decomposition of Potassium Chlorate (V)" is given. A problem is stated: Devise a series of experimental procedures to study the decomposition of potassium chlorate (V).[9] This is all the help provided. The student is expected to analyze the problem, design a procedure, prepare apparatus, gather data, analyze the data, draw conclusions, and check the conclusions on his own. Needless to say, a student successful at this type of laboratory procedure will learn much about the ways of a scientist and of the problems of extracting scientific information from nature.

ORGANIZING LABORATORY WORK

Effectiveness of the laboratory experience is directly related to the amount of individual participation by students. *Individual participation* here means active involvement in the experiment with definite responsibilities for its progress and success. In theory, the ideal arrangement would be to have each student wholly responsible for carrying out the experiment from start to finish. In this way, the preliminary planning, the gathering of materials, preparation of apparatus, design of the method, collection of data, analysis of results, and drawing of conclusions is unmistakably the work of the individual student, and the accompanying learning is at a maximum.

Biological Sciences Curriculum Study class studying genetics.

Photo courtesy of Bob Waters, Colorado State College.

---

8 *Investigating the Earth—Laboratory Manual* (Boulder, Colo.: Johnson Publishing Company, 1964).

9 Chemical Bond Approach Project, *Investigating Chemical Systems* (New York: Webster Division, McGraw-Hill Book Company, 1963).

In reality, the maximum learning may be achieved, for certain students, by working in pairs or very small groups. With good cooperation and sharing of duties, the stimulation of pair or small-group activity may be beneficial. In group work, a shy student may be stimulated into action and thought processes of which he may be entirely incapable by himself. An extroverted student may assume directive and leadership qualities not developed in individual work. The science teacher must be aware of these possibilities and plan the execution of laboratory work accordingly. There ought to be opportunities in the laboratory to provide experiences using both arrangements. Avoidance of stereotyped and inflexible arrangements should be of concern to the teacher of laboratory sciences.

Complexity of experiments will vary greatly. Even in a typical laboratory science, such as chemistry, "experiments" may be no more than carrying out a preplanned exercise of observation and data gathering, or they may be as extensive and demanding as research on a problem whose solution is totally unknown. Arrangements for laboratory work must accommodate these extremes. A student of general science in the junior high school may need more of the "exercise" type of experiment in order to gain the skills needed for complex experiments. On the other hand, he should likewise be afforded opportunities to work on true experiments in order to sense the joy of discovery in the manner of a practicing scientist.

ORIENTING STUDENTS FOR LABORATORY WORK

In general, students of the sciences look forward to a laboratory class with pleasant anticipation. Being pragmatic by nature, they sense that this is "truly science" and that an exciting experience awaits them. This attitude, most prevalent in the junior high school, must be carefully nurtured and guided as the student progresses to more rigorous sciences. If laboratory work becomes a bore because of excessively rigid formality, unexciting exercises, "cookbook" techniques, or whatever reason, the student effectively will have been lost as a potential science participant. An atmosphere of excitement, curiosity, interest, and enthusiasm for science should be encouraged in the laboratory. This must be tempered by care and restraint in use of apparatus and diligence in the tasks assigned. Obviously a hands-off policy regarding equipment cannot be adopted, nor can a complete laissez-faire attitude be condoned. Respect for the problem, the materials, and the probable results of experimentation must be developed. The laboratory experience is but one vehicle by which the objectives of science teaching are developed. Suitably carried out, it can be one of the most effective methods of teaching and learning.

Orientation for laboratory work may involve creating a suitable frame of mind for the investigation of a problem. The problem must appear real to the student and worthy of study. He must have some knowledge of possible methods of attack. He should know what equipment or apparatus is needed and be familiar with its use. Time for work on the problem must be available to the student. In a given situation, the science teacher may need to give attention to one or more of these factors in order to begin students on their laboratory investigations.

THE PLACE OF DISCUSSION IN LABORATORY WORK

In recent years, there has been a trend toward placement of laboratory work at the very beginning of a new unit of study. The laboratory guide book or manual is designed to identify problems requiring observation and solution. The student performs the assigned tasks or devises procedures of his own to arrive at a solution to the problem. In the course of doing this, he discovers the need for further information in order to explain his observations. He is motivated to read a textbook, search for information in a sourcebook or handbook, read supplementary material, or consult his teacher.

Laboratory work is followed by class discussions, short lectures, or question periods. During these activities, student questions are answered, clarifications of observed phenomena are made, and certain misconceptions may be discussed. Other activities such as problem assignments, projects, extra reading, reports, tests, and demonstrations may follow in their proper context as part of the teaching and learning process.

In this method, it is likely that more than half of the total class time is spent in laboratory activities. The follow-up sessions described above become extremely important. The need for the teacher to ascertain the accuracy of the learned concepts, to correct misconceptions, and to promote maximum learning is usually greater than in a conventional course. At the same time, the student is more directly involved in the task and may be more highly motivated than he would otherwise be.

LABORATORY WORK IN THE JUNIOR HIGH SCHOOL

Extension of laboratory practices to the junior high school is occurring with greater frequency. Facilities for effective laboratory work are being built into modern junior high schools, and youth of this age level are beginning to experience laboratory work on a regular, planned basis. Examples of this trend are the course

Junior high school students are enthusiastic participants in laboratory method of teaching. Laboratory instruction may be on an individual or team basis.

Photo courtesy of Harold Pratt, Science Supervisor, Jefferson County, Colorado.

developed by the Earth Sciences Curriculum Project[10] and the Introductory Physical Science Course of Educational Services, Incorporated.[11]

Junior high school students are enthusiastic participants in the laboratory method of teaching. Curiosity and a buoyant approach to learning make this group responsive to the laboratory approach, and proper guidance by the teacher can make this method a fruitful one for junior high school students. Because junior high school science leads to more rigorous and laboratory-oriented sciences in the senior high school, it is worthwhile to consider what its contributions are to more effective learning when the student reaches biology, chemistry, or physics. It is reasonable to assume that certain attitudes, knowledges, and skills learned well in the junior high school can contribute to better and perhaps more rapid learning in the senior high school.

The following is a suggested list of knowledges and skills which might be developed in seventh-, eighth-, and ninth-grade science and which are considered desirable prerequisites for senior high science:

1. To understand the purposes of the laboratory in the study of science
2. To understand and be familiar with the simple tools of the laboratory
3. To understand and use the metric system in simple measurement and computation
4. To attain the understanding necessary for the proper reporting of observations of an experiment
5. To keep neat and accurate records of laboratory experiments
6. To understand the operation of simple ratios and proportions
7. To be able to understand the construction and reading of simple graphs
8. To understand and use the simpler forms of exponential notation
9. To understand the proper use and operation of the Bunsen burner
10. To use the slide rule for simple operations
11. To be able to understand and demonstrate the use of a trip balance
12. To work with glass tubing in performing laboratory experiments

[10] See *Investigating the Earth—Laboratory Manual.*
[11] See *Introductory Physical Science Project* (Watertown, Mass.: Educational Services, Incorporated, 164 Main St., 1964).

13. To keep glassware and equipment clean
14. To put together simple equipment in performing laboratory experiments
15. To measure accurately in linear, cubic, and weight units

Laboratory work in the junior high school can be broadened to include such features as out-of-doors observations, excursions, and certain types of project activities, as well as conventional experimentation in laboratory surroundings. Systematic night-time observations of planets, constellations, meteors, the moon, and other astronomical objects may properly be considered laboratory work. Similarly, meteorological observations and experiments involving record keeping and correlations of data are included under this heading. Excursions for collecting purposes, observations of topographical features, studies of pond life, and ecological investigations are true laboratory work. The narrow connotation of *laboratory work* as something which takes place only in a specially designed room called a laboratory must be avoided in the junior high school sciences.

EVALUATION OF LABORATORY WORK

Broad concepts of evaluation include giving attention to all of the activities which students are engaged in during their secondary school years. With increasing time and emphasis devoted to laboratory work, it becomes necessary to devise suitable methods of evaluating this activity. As with all evaluation, identification of the goals of the activity or teaching method must precede determination of the actual procedures to be used in the evaluations. For laboratory work, a suggested list of goals is as follows:

1. To develop skills in problem solving through identification of problems, collection and interpretation of data, and drawing conclusions

Outdoor laboratory area showing a greenhouse and an ecological area.

Photo courtesy of Bob Waters, Colorado State College.

2. To develop skills of manipulation of laboratory apparatus
3. To establish systematic habits of record keeping
4. To develop scientific attitudes
5. To learn scientific methods in the solution of problems
6. To develop self-reliance and dependability
7. To discover unexplored avenues of interest and investigation
8. To promote enthusiasm for the subject of science

Specific activities in which students are usually involved in laboratory work include the following:

1. Planning an experiment and forming hypotheses
2. Planning an excursion for collecting purposes
3. Setting up apparatus
4. Constructing materials and apparatus
5. Observing natural phenomena
6. Observing a process in an indoor laboratory
7. Searching for authoritative documentary information on the topic
8. Gathering data and recording it
9. Collecting specimens
10. Classifying and organizing materials
11. Making modifications of equipment
12. Reading instruments
13. Calibrating apparatus
14. Drawing charts and graphs
15. Analyzing data
16. Drawing conclusions from the data
17. Writing a report of the experiment
18. Describing and explaining an experiment to someone else
19. Identifying further problems for study
20. Dismantling, cleaning, storing, and repairing apparatus

Evaluation of these activities and of the general outcomes of laboratory work may be done in a variety of ways. Among these ways are practical tests, use of unknowns, achievement tests, direct observation of laboratory techniques, written reports, individual conferences, and group conferences.

In a practical test, a student may be directed to perform a certain laboratory task. Direct observation of the techniques used, the correctness of procedures, and the results obtained may be made by the teacher. Procedures such as identification of unknown chemicals, a common practice in qualitative analysis in chemistry, might be extended to earth sciences, biology, and physics. Achievement tests, designed to assess understandings of course content, are an important evaluative technique for laboratory work because of the concern that correct knowledge be obtained through the methods of the laboratory. Pure recognition and recall tests are not usually suitable forms for achievement tests of laboratory experience. Tests which depend upon accurate observation, recognition of pertinent data, and ability to reason logically are more suitable for measuring outcomes of laboratory work.

Writing a Laboratory Report

The written report, a frequently used method of evaluating progress and understandings in the laboratory, needs to be scrutinized. Too often, the written report becomes a stereotyped form which loses its value as an instrument of evaluation. Each student is required to present his information in a standard form that leaves little opportunity for creativity and flexibility.

The following characteristics of a good experiment report point out the essential items required yet leave room for initiative and creativity on the part of the student. In this type of report, the student begins his report with a blank sheet of paper. As he writes, he keeps the following criteria in mind:

1. The reader can tell exactly what the student is trying to find out.
2. The reader can see the procedure the student is using to arrive at an answer to the problem. The description is clear, concise, and complete.
3. The data collected are organized in good form for ease of understanding.
4. All measurements have their proper units attached to them.
5. Diagrams, if used, are sufficiently large for clarity and are carefully labeled. Diagrams are useful only for making more clear to the reader what the experiment is about.
6. Graphs, if used, are titled, labeled, and neatly drawn. The purpose of a graph is to show relationships between data obtained, for the purpose of drawing conclusions about the experiment.
7. Conclusions should give some answer to the problem, based on the data obtained in the experiment.
8. This report should serve the student in the future, as he is reviewing the work of the course, to recall exactly what the experiment was about and what conclusions he reached.
9. The main criterion for evaluation of this experiment report is: Is this report written clearly enough that an uninformed person could read it, know exactly what was being attempted, how it was done, and what conclusions were reached; and, if necessary, could he duplicate the experiment himself, using this report alone as a guide?

The range and variety of activities performed by students in the laboratory make it necessary to employ a variety of evaluation methods. A teacher of science must be aware of these and alert to new possibilities as well. Increasing emphasis on laboratory methods is almost certain to broaden, rather than narrow, the range of individual differences among students. Suitable means for evaluating the progress and achievement of these students in their laboratory experiences must be devised.

SAFETY PRECAUTIONS IN THE LABORATORY

An inevitable result of greater student participation in laboratory work is increased exposure to potentially dangerous apparatus and materials. Instead of viewing this fact as a deterrent to the laboratory method of teaching, the alert and dedicated science teacher will approach the problem realistically and will take the proper precautions to avoid accidents among students in the laboratory.

Accidents and injuries in the laboratory frequently occur because of students' lack of knowledge of the proper techniques and procedures. These techniques can be taught in advance if the teacher plans properly. Certain minimum standards of acceptable procedures may be demanded of students before allowing them to work in the laboratory. The motivation to engage in laboratory work is usually strong enough to overcome the student's reluctance to develop the requisite skills, particularly if he is convinced of the inherent dangers and the need for proper safety techniques.

Some general laboratory skills which will prepare the student to work safely are these:

1. Ability to handle glass tubing—cutting, bending, fire-polishing, drawing tubing into capillaries, inserting tubing into rubber stoppers, and removing tubing from rubber stoppers
2. Ability to heat test tubes of chemicals—knowledge of proper rate of heating, direction, use of test tube racks, etc.
3. Ability to handle acids—pouring, proper use of stopper to avoid contamination, dilution in water, return of acid bottles to designated shelves, etc.
4. Ability to test for presence of noxious gases safely
5. Ability to treat acid spillage or burns from caustic solutions
6. Ability to operate fire extinguishers
7. Ability to set up gas generators properly
8. Ability to use standard carpenter tools
9. Ability to use dissecting equipment, scalpels, etc.

In a survey of accidents in high school chemistry laboratories in California, reported by McComber, it was found generally that poor laboratory techniques were responsible for accidents. There were more serious accidents in large classes, and accidents were more frequent when horseplay was involved. Forty per cent of the accidents occurred among students who were above average in scientific inquisitiveness. The types of accidents which most frequently had serious results were explosions and burns from phosphorus; the easy availability of dangerous chemicals used occasionally in the normal chemistry course seemed to contribute to accidents as well.[12]

The following safety precautions to be observed in the chemistry laboratory may be put into effect in a school by discussing them with the students, supplying copies for the students' notebooks, and posting them in a prominent place in the laboratory:

A List of Safety Precautions in the
Chemistry Laboratory

The work you do in the chemistry laboratory is a very important part of your chemistry course. Here you will learn to make observations of experiments and draw your own conclusions about what you observe. The following is a list of safety rules to follow in making your laboratory work as safe and efficient as possible:

1. Observe all instructions given by the teacher. Ask for help when you need it.
2. In case of an accident, report to your teacher immediately.
3. Be careful in using flames. Keep clothing away from the flame and do not use flames near inflammable liquids.
4. Follow the directions carefully for the handling of all chemicals.
5. If acids or bases are spilled, wash immediately with quantities of water. Be sure you know where the neutralizing solution is located in the laboratory. Ask your teacher how to use it.
6. Read the labels on all reagents very carefully. Make a habit of reading each label twice on any reagent used in an experiment.
7. Dispose of waste materials in the proper receptacles. Solid materials should be placed in special crocks provided for the purpose.
8. Be sure you know the location and proper usage of the fire extinguishers and fire blankets provided in the laboratory.
9. Consider the laboratory a place for serious work. There is no excuse for horseplay or practical jokes in a science laboratory.

SUMMARY

Laboratory work in the junior and senior high school is undergoing rapid change. From the emphasis on "verification" experiments in the traditional mode, the student is now invited to "inquire into" or "investigate" a problem. Laboratory experience

---

[12] Robert McComber, "Chemistry Accidents in High School," *Journal of Chemical Education*, July, 1961, p. 367-68.

becomes the initial experience with a new topic of subject matter. This is followed by discussion, reading, and further experimentation. The experiment may lead to new problems which warrant investigation, thus earning the label "open-ended." In reporting the results of his experiment, the student concentrates on reporting his observations, his collection of data, his analysis, and conclusions based on the experiment alone. A "right answer" for student *A* may be different from a "right answer" for student *B*. In the new mode of laboratory work, the student learns more accurately what science it. He finds that the process of science may be equal to or more important than the products of science.

The junior high school is becoming increasingly oriented toward a laboratory approach. Not only does this approach give students an early start in learning the methods of science, but certain skills are introduced and practiced which will have value in later sciences taken in the senior high school.

With more of the responsibility for learning in the laboratory being allocated to the student himself, the matter of safety becomes even more important. Care must be taken by the teacher of science to train students adequately in the use of laboratory apparatus and materials. This training may precede actual work in the laboratory or be an intrinsic part of the laboratory work early in the students' experience.

The promise of science for the future has never been greater. A breakthrough has been achieved in which students at last have become participants in the search for knowledge, not mere recipients of facts and generalizations dispensed by authoritative teachers and textbooks. The laboratory is the key instrument in the new mode of science teaching.

Further Investigation and Study

1. Design an experiment which students can do in the classroom or laboratory and which gives practice in the skills of science as discussed on pages 93-95. Choose a particular grade level and select suitable apparatus and materials to achieve the "skill-development" objectives.
2. Suggest a suitable format for a laboratory report in a high school science. Keep in mind that this is not to be a rigorous form but one that is kept flexible and open to student initiative.
3. Study the laboratory guides of several of the following curriculum projects: PSSC, BSCS, CHEM Study, CBAC, ESCP, IPS, and others. What similarities do you find? How do these laboratory guides differ from traditional laboratory manuals? Be prepared to discuss these differences in class.

*Reality is not a datum, not something
given or imposed, but a
construction which man makes
out of the given material.*
José Ortega y Gasset

7

Methods of Science Teaching: Inquiry through Demonstrations

In the first-period general science class, Mr. O'Brien took a candle out of a box and placed it on the demonstration desk. He told the class he would show them the difference between a physical and a chemical change. He struck a match and placed the candle over the flame until the wick burned. Soon, some of the wax was melting, dripping, and then solidifying. He said, "This is an example of a physical change. The candle is partially burning and the wax is changed in the process of burning to carbon dioxide and water. This is a chemical change." The students watched the demonstration, and some wrote notes in their notebooks.

Across the hall, Mr. Jackson was teaching the same unit. He also wanted to have students learn about physical and chemical changes. Mr. Jackson was not certain how he was going to do this. He asked Mr. O'Brien if he knew a good demonstration to show these changes. Mr. O'Brien suggested he burn a candle. Mr. Jackson, however, went about teaching these concepts in a different manner. After the bell rang and the students were seated, Mr. Jackson took a candle and a match box out of his demonstration desk and placed them on top of the desk.

He asked, "Does anyone know what I am going to do with the candle and match?"

Art answered, "You are going to light it."

Mr. Jackson replied, "That's right, but what will happen to the match and candle when I light them? Will they be the same? What will happen to the candle when it burns? Will it drip?"

Several students raised their hands and suggested answers to his questions. He lit the candle and it started to drip. He asked, "Why does the candle drip? Will the dripped material burn? Where did the dripped material come from, and how did it change while the candle was burning?"

George explained that the material only melted and then recooled. Mr. Jackson asked the rest of the class what they thought of George's explanation: "What evidence was there for his suggestion?"

Several members of the class discussed the matter and agreed that this material had only changed form in the process of melting and resolidifying.

Mr. Jackson asked, "Does anyone know what we call this type of change?"

Two students raised their hands and suggested that it might be a physical change.

Mr. Jackson then proceeded in a similar manner to ask about what was happening to the candle as it burned. Why did it get shorter, and why would it eventually have to be replaced? The class discussed this matter and eventually discovered that the candle was changing chemically.

Which of the above teaching methods do you think would be the more effective way to demonstrate physical and chemical changes and why? What did students learn from Mr. Jackson's approach that they might not have learned from Mr. O'Brien's? Which of the above methods stressed the inquiry approach and why? Which method do you think took instructors more time to prepare? Which would be more inductive in its approach? Why do you think teachers have traditionally emphasized the deductive method in giving demonstrations? These questions and others are discussed in this chapter.

A demonstration has been defined as showing something to another person or group. Clearly, there are several ways things can be shown. You can hold up an object such as a piece of sulfur and say, "This is sulfur"; or you can state, "Sulfur burns," light some sulfur, and show that it burns. Showing in this way mainly involves observation or verification. Mr. O'Brien's use of a demonstration was of this type.

A demonstration can also be given inductively by the instructor's asking several questions but seldom giving any answers. An inductive demonstration has the advantage of stressing inquiry. This encourages students to analyze and make hypotheses based upon their knowledge. Their motivation is high because they like being confronted with riddles, and in an inductive demonstration they are constantly confronted with riddles. The strength of this motivation becomes apparent when one considers the popularity of TV quiz programs over the last twenty years. Inviting students to inquire why something occurs taxes their minds and requires them to think. Thinking is an active mental process. The only way students learn to think is by having opportunities to think. An inductive demonstration provides this opportunity because the answers the students give to the instructor's questions act as "feedback." The teacher has a better understanding of the students' comprehension of the demonstration. The feedback acts as a guide for further questioning by him until the students discover the concepts and principles involved in the demonstration and the teacher is sure they know its meaning and purpose.

Demonstrations, in addition to serving as simple observations of material and verification of a process, may also be experimental in nature. A demonstration is an experiment if it involves a problem the solution to which is not immediately apparent to the class. Students particularly like experimental demonstrations because they usually have more action. Students enjoy action, not words! They love to watch something happening before their eyes.

TECHNIQUES OF PLANNING AND GIVING A DEMONSTRATION

To plan an efficient and effective demonstration requires extensive organization and consideration of the following points:

1. The first step is to list the concepts and principles you wish to teach. Direct the design of the entire demonstration to the attainment of these.

2. If the principle you wish to teach is complex, break it down into concepts and give several examples for each concept. For example: Photosynthesis involves understanding concepts of radiant energy, chlorophyll, carbon dioxide, glucose, water, temperature, a chemical change, and gases. A student's memorizing that green plants can make sugar in light with water results in little understanding if he does not know the meaning of the concepts listed above.

3. Choose an activity that will show the concepts you wish to teach. Consult the following sources for possible suggestions for activities:

Heller, R. *Geology and Earth Sciences Sourcebook for Elementary and Secondary Schools.* (Prepared under guidance of the American Geological Institute.) New York: Holt, Rinehart & Winston, Inc., 1962.

Hone, E.; Joseph, A.; *et al. A Sourcebook for Elementary Science.* New York: Harcourt, Brace & World, Inc., 1962.

Joseph, A.; Brandwein, P.; *et al. A Sourcebook for the Physical Sciences.* New York: Harcourt, Brace & World, Inc., 1961.

A Chemical Education Materials Study Demonstration. Note that it is easily visible. It provides for the inductive method of teaching.

Photo courtesy of Bob Waters, Colorado State College.

Morholt, E.; Brandwein, P.; and Joseph, A. *A Sourcebook for the Biological Sciences*. New York: Harcourt, Brace & World, Inc., 1966.

Special general science sourcebooks:

Bureau of Secondary Curriculum Development, New York State Education Department. *The General Science Handbooks, Part I, II, and III*. Albany, 1961.

United Nations Educational, Scientific and Cultural Organization. *UNESCO Sourcebook for Science Teaching*. Paris, 1956.

Other sourcebooks in biology:

Feldman, S. *Techniques and Investigations in the Life Sciences*. New York: Holt, Rinehart & Winston, Inc., 1962.

Lawson, C., and Paulson, R. E. *Laboratory and Field Studies in Biology, A Sourcebook for Secondary Schools*. New York: Holt, Rinehart & Winston, Inc., 1960.

Miller, David, and Blaydes, Glenn. *Methods and Materials for Teaching the Biological Sciences*. New York: McGraw-Hill Book Company, 1962.

4. Gather and assemble the necessary equipment.

5. Go through the demonstration at least once before class begins.

6. Outline the questions you will ask during the demonstration. This is especially important in doing an inductive or discovery demonstration.

7. Consider how you will use visual aids, especially the overhead projector, to supplement the purpose of the demonstration.

8. Decide on the evaluation technique to use.

    A. Written techniques

        1. Essay—a. Have students take notes and record data during the demonstration.

            b. Have them write a summary of the demonstration.

        2. Quiz—Have students write answers to questions to see whether they really understood the purpose of the demonstration. Stress application of principles.

    B. Verbal techniques

        1. Ask students to summarize the purpose of the demonstration.

        2. Ask for applications of the principles they have learned by giving them problems in which they will have to aply these principles.

9. When you plan a demonstration, do it well, with the intention that you will probably use it for several years. This helps to lessen your preparation in future years. Evaluate a demonstration immediately after giving it to determine the weaknesses and strengths of the presentation. Add any questions which will contribute to

inductive presentation when you use the demonstration again. The next time you give it, it will require only a few moments preparation.

10. Consider the time a demonstration will take. Try to move it rapidly enough to keep students attentive. Prolonged or complicated demonstrations are generally undesirable because they don't hold the students' interest.

11. Reproduced below is a plan for an inquiry demonstration lesson. Notice the application of the above suggested format in constructing the lesson. It consists of four sections:

    A. List of concepts and principles
    B. Activities to discover these
    C. Suggested questions to ask to help students discover the concepts and principles
    D. Evaluation

A Teacher-Student Demonstration
Blood-Circulatory System

Concepts and Principles:
    The heart beats and pumps blood through the body.
    Invertebrate animals may have hearts.
    Blood moves rapidly through the blood vessels.
    Blood vessels are not all the same size.
    Blood circulates.
    All animals have individual variation; some animals are warm-blooded, and some are cold-blooded.
    Students gain an understanding of the relationships between structure and function.

Procedure:
    Step 1. Obtain several live earthworms. Place them on a paper towel so that every two or three students will have a worm to watch.
    Step 2. Have them look carefully at the worm and see whether they can find a blood vessel. There will be one that is easily seen on the back of the worm. Have them watch this vessel closely to determine how it changes in color.
    Ask: Have you found the blood vessel on the worm?
      Where is this vessel located?

      Does the vessel seem to have the same color all the time?

      Why doesn't it have the same color all the time?

      What is going through the blood vessel to give it that color?

      Do you think the earthworm has a heart?

      See if you can count how many times the heart beats a minute.
    Step 3. Record on the board how many times the heart beats as stated by several students. Determine the average in order to get the average beat.

Ask: Why do we average these numbers in order to get the number of times the heart beats for a worm? (Answer: Because each worm is a little different from the next worm. Also, the individuals who watched the heart might have made a mistake. An error due to faulty observation or procedures is called experimental error. Averaging their results when collecting data to help lessen the effects of experimental error in their results is the practice of scientists.)

What is a warm-blooded animal? (Answer: One whose body temperature remains nearly the same regardless of the temperature of the environment.)

Is man a warm-blooded animal?

Do you think the worm is a warm-blooded animal? Suggest an experiment we might do to determine this.

How could we tell whether a worm is a warm-blooded animal?

Step 4. Place some worms in ice water for a few minutes. Now count the number of times the hearts seem to beat.

Ask: Does the heart of the worm beat faster or slower after taken out of cold water? (The hearts will not beat as fast because the entire body activities are slowed down by cold temperatures.)

Show a dissected worm and a chart of the circulatory system of the worm for the class to study. Discuss the structure and function of the worm's circulatory system.

Student Activities

1. How would you determine whether a frog is warm-blooded?
2. In the worm, how does blood seem to move in the blood vessels? How is the circulatory system constructed to serve this function?
3. From exterior observation, what evidence is there that the worm has a heart? Is this an assumption you made about the worm, or is it a fact?
4. John noticed his pet turtle was very inactive after Christmas vacation. He thought his turtle was sick. Can you suggest another hypothesis, and how would you prove your hypothesis?
5. What advantage has a warm-blooded animal over a cold-blooded animal?
6. Why don't you see blood vessels over all the worm's body?
7. Why were several students' reports used in determining how many times the hearts beat in a worm?
8. Why is this method more scientific?
9. What is experimental error?

10. Why did you place the worms in cold water?
11. Why don't trout, high in the Rockies, bite well after the temperature drops below freezing levels over an extended period?

AWARENESS IN GIVING A DEMONSTRATION

The following points should be considered when one gives a demonstration:

1. Is it easily visible? If you are working with small things, can you use a projector to make them more visible?

2. Are you audible? Do you speak loudly enough and fluctuate the tone and volume of your voice to avoid monotonous delivery? When a student responds do you ask him to speak up so other students can hear? Do you repeat questions and answers of students for emphasis and audibility?

3. Do you display zest in giving the demonstration? Are you excited with the demonstration? Do you make it come alive? A good demonstrator is rather a "ham." He uses dramatic techniques to excite and involve his students. The way in which a teacher makes a demonstration come alive is as much an art as is reading Shakespeare well to an enraptured audience.

4. How do you stage the demonstration? How do you start it to involve everyone immediately? One suggestion is to place unique objects on a demonstration desk. For example, a transfusion bottle or a Van de Graff generator placed on a desk does much to motivate students' inquisitive minds. Before you even begin, you have the students with you, wondering what you are going to do.

   a. Teach inductively. Start your demonstration with a question. If you have interesting equipment, ask your students what they think you are going to do with the equipment. Spend some time just questioning about the apparatus. In the construction of a transfusion bottle, for example, there are several scientific principles involved, such as: partial vacuum, air pressure, sterile conditions, food for the cells placed in the bottle, and anticoagulants to prevent clotting of the blood.

   b. Ask questions constantly about what you are going to do, what's happening, why they think it is happening, and what the demonstration is proving or illustrating.

   c. Know the purpose of what you are demonstrating. Use the questions you devised only as a guide. The questions you have anticipated may be excellent, but also be ready to pick up suggestions from the questions students ask during the time they are observing the demonstration.

   d. Give positive reinforcement. Always recognize a reply: "Say, I think you have something there." "Good, you're thinking." "What do the rest of you think of John's remarks?" When a student gives a good explanation, compliment him. Try never to act negatively to a student's answer. Don't say, "That's wrong." Rather say, "It's good you're thinking, but your answer is not quite what I wanted."

5. Use the blackboard to describe the purpose of the demonstration. Verbal explanations are seldom enough. Any picture or diagram you make on the board immediately attracts the students' attention. Remember that your students have lived in a TV-centered environment; as soon as they see a visual representation on the board they are drawn to it. A beginning teacher often fails to realize or even consider how the blackboard can complement the learning activity.

6. At the conclusion of the demonstration have a student summarize what has occurred in the demonstration and its purpose. This helps to fix the purpose of the demonstration in the minds of the students.

7. Evaluate your lesson—orally or in a written summary.

WAYS TO PRESENT A DEMONSTRATION

There are several ways in which a demonstration can be given. A teacher-centered demonstration is seldom the best way because it does not involve students enough. When students participate actively in giving a demonstration they are more interested and consequently learn more. There are five ways in which a demonstration can be presented. They are:

1. Teacher demonstration. The teacher prepares and gives the demonstration by himself. This approach has the advantage usually of better organization and more sophisticated presentation.

2. Teacher-student demonstration. This is a team approach in which the student assists the teacher. This gives recognition to the student. The class may be more attentive because they like to watch one of their peers perform.

3. Student group demonstration. This can be used on occasion; it has the advantage of more actively involving students in the presentation.

The group approach can be used to advantage if students are allowed to select the individuals in their group. The teacher should evaluate the group as a whole and assign the group a grade which is the same for each of its members. The groups will form at first along friendship lines. If, however, some of the members of the group are not productive they will be rejected the next time groups are selected. The peer pressure to produce and become actively involved in the activity replaces the necessity for a teacher to encourage students to work. This group arrangement may also be effective in organizing laboratory work. The only problem is that the teacher initially has to be patient until the group pressures are brought to bear upon the non-productive students in the class.

4. Individual student demonstration. This can be a very effective demonstration, especially if the student giving the demonstration has high status among his peers. An effective way to have individual student demonstrations is to have upperclassmen come in from advanced science classes and present demonstrations to the lowerclassmen. A freshman general science class may become enthralled when a physics or chemistry senior comes into their class to give a demonstration. An upperclass student excited about giving a demonstration helps to convey that excitement to the students in the class.

5. Guest demonstration. Guest demonstrators can do much to relieve a boring pattern of routine class activities. Other science teachers in the school may be called in to present a demonstration or activity in which they have some special competence. Professional scientists are often willing to give special demonstrations. In certain parts of our country, scientific societies and industries have established groups which present exciting science demonstrations to schools. The Southern California Industry-Education Council and the Greater Washington Council are but two of these groups.

Dr. Obourn of the U.S. Office of Education has recently stressed the importance and desirability of the silent demonstration. In the passage below he compares the teacher-talking demonstrations with silent demonstrations:

The Silent Demonstration

The usual kind of demonstration by which science teachers give their students visual or auditory experiences is the teacher-talking demonstration. In this performance the teacher is actor and commentator. The pupils, who are supposed to be learning from the new experience how to attack a difficulty or develop a concept, are spectators. But they do not necessarily learn scientific facts or principles from a demonstration in which everything is done for them. Pupils really learn when they observe and react to what is presented.

There is a kind of demonstration that is likely to ensure, on the part of the student, careful observation, accurate recording of data, and practical application, later, of the ideas gained from the experience. This procedure is the *silent demonstration*. The following comparison of the two kinds of demonstrations shows how they differ.

Teacher-Talking Demonstrations	*Silent Demonstration*
Teacher states purposes of the demonstration.	Pupil must discover purpose as the demonstration progresses.
Teacher names pieces of apparatus and describes arrangement.	Teacher uses apparatus. Pupils observe equipment and arrangement.
Teacher is manipulator and technician, tells what is being done, points out and usually explains results.	Teacher performs experiment. Pupils observe what is being done and then describe results.
Teacher often points out the things which should have happened and accounts for unexpected results.	Pupils record results as observed. Teacher checks for accuracy and honesty in reporting. Teacher repeats the experiment if necessary.
Teacher summarizes the results and states the conclusions to be drawn. Pupils usually copy the conclusions as stated.	Pupils summarize data and draw their own conclusions based on what they observed. Teacher checks conclusions and repeats experiment if necessary.
Teacher explains the importance of the experiment and tells how it is applied in everyday life.	Pupils attempt to answer application questions related to the demonstration.

The silent demonstration, since it cannot be supplemented or strengthened by explanation, requires more careful planning than does the teacher-talking demonstration. In preparing the silent demonstration, the teacher may find this general procedure a good one:

1. Fix clearly in mind the object of the demonstration.
2. Select the apparatus and materials best suited for the demonstration.
3. Determine the beginning point of the demonstration. The beginning is based upon what the teacher assumes that the pupils know.
4. Analyze the difficulty into steps of learning. Perform the parts of the demonstration to meet these difficulties.
5. Perform the techniques so that they may be observed in all parts of the room. The steps should follow some order in relation to the steps of learning.
6. Give pupils an outline of the steps to be used. Mimeographed outlines may be used, or an outline may be put on the blackboard.

The following procedure will illustrate how a silent demonstration may be carried out. The difficulty to be solved is:

"Why does water circulate when it is heated, or what causes convection currents?" The teacher assumes that the pupils know how to weigh, and how to read thermometers.

The Teacher Does	*The Pupils See*
1. Fills with water two flasks of the same size. Fits each flask with a one-hole stopper and a glass tube about ten inches long. (The water should rise in the tubes when the stoppers are forced into the flasks.) Heats one flask. Cools other flask in ice water. Lets both flasks return to room temperature.	The controls—flasks of the same size, tubes of the same size, the same volume of water in each flask. Water moving up the glass tube when it is heated. Water moving down the glass tube when it is cooled. (If the temperature of the water should go below 4°C., it would begin to expand.)
2. Places two 250 cc. graduates on scale pans of a balance. Places balance in equilibrium. Fills one graduate to the 250 cc. mark with cold water, the other to the same mark with hot water.	The apparatus and its arrangement. The same volume of water used in both graduates. Cold water overbalancing the hot water.
3. Fills a large beaker with water nearly to the top. Places beaker on tripod. Places Bunsen burner underneath and near one side. Suspends four thermometers in water, one near bottom, one at top of water above burner, and two on opposite side in similar positions. (Thermometers whose readings are not more than one-half degree apart must be used.)	The apparatus and its arrangement. The readings on the thermometers. (If the water is heated gradually, the changes in temperature may be noted from time to time.)
4. Adds fine pieces of sawdust or a crystal or two of potassium permanganate to the water in the beaker (see 3 above). Continues to heat.	The change in arrangement. Material rising above the place where heat is applied, crossing over the top, going down near the opposite side and across the bottom toward the burner.
5. Asks pupils to consider what they have observed and to draw their own conclusions.	(Since each pupil draws his own conclusions, the wording will differ, but the main ideas are likely to be the same.)

General Conclusions Based on Observed Data

Water expands when heated and contracts when cooled.

Warm water is less dense than cold water. If water expands when heated, and the total weight remains the same, then the volume of a unit of warm water must be lighter than the volume of an equal unit of cold water.

If water is heated in a container, the warm water moves toward the top and the colder water toward the bottom. The water circulates until all of it becomes heated.

Water circulates because its density is changed when it is heated.

6. Asks pupils to use their general ideas in explaining such applications as the hot-water heater, the hot-water heating system, and the like.	(Each pupil formulates his own explanation and submits it for examination by teacher and fellow-pupils.)[1]

Silent demonstrations should not be used frequently because there is no way the teacher can determine whether the students are reaching the objectives while the demonstration is being given. Silent demonstrations can, however, provide a welcome change in the routine activity of the class. They can be used effectively, provided an instructor accentuates his movements in the demonstration so the students can see and have some hints about what is relevant. In a silent demonstration, visibility is extremely important and must be insured; otherwise the students will quickly become frustrated, and this will lead eventually to discipline trouble.

EQUIPMENT AND STORAGE OF DEMONSTRATION EQUIPMENT

Equipment made by you or your students can lend an added fascination to a science demonstration, because students are often more impressed by homemade equipment. Parents, industrial companies, and students often can construct or provide apparatus for the school without cost. Having students build equipment involves them in improving the science instruction of the school. This personal investment helps to build student morale and to show the community that the science department is an active and dynamic part of their school.

Considerable thought should be given to storing equipment after use so it may be found easily in the future and set up again with little effort. One way to do this is to establish a list of headings

[1] E. S. Obourn, *Aids for Teaching Science Observation—Basis of Effective Science Learning* (Office of Education Publication No. 29024 [Washington, D.C.: U.S. Government Printing Office, January, 1961]).

under which to store materials. For example, in physics, storage areas might be labeled: "electricity," "magnetism," "heat," "light," "sound," "atomic structure," etc. In biology, storage categories might be: "glassware," "chemicals," "slides," "preserved plant and animal specimens," etc. The next time you wish to find the equipment, it can easily be located under the proper storage title. Such a system also makes it easy for students to assist you in storing or obtaining equipment for use in demonstrations.

An efficient way to store small demonstration materials for future use is to obtain several shoe boxes. Place all of the materials you need for a demonstration in the box and label the end of the box. For example, a box might be labeled "electrostatic demonstration materials." You might also include in the box a sheet of paper describing the demonstration. This procedure helps you lessen next year's preparation time when you want to give the same demonstration. A student laboratory assistant can get the box down, read the included sheet describing the demonstration, check to see if all of the equipment needed is present, and replenish needed supplies. The box then will be ready for use, and practically no preparation time will be required of you. This storage procedure works particularly well with general science materials, and simple physical materials. It has a drawback in that when many materials and articles of equipment are stored in the boxes they are not then easily available for other demonstration work during the year.

Special Equipment

Science courses often require special science equipment. Some of this specialized equipment may be available to the teacher without cost if he goes through the proper channels. For example, the West Coast Electronic Manufacturers' Association will provide electronic components to science teachers without cost in the San Francisco Bay region. In other areas of the country there are various companies which will donate materials to the schools upon receiving a written request from the teacher. Consult with experienced teachers or professional scientists in your community to find what is available.

Every science class should have an overhead projector with suitable transparency supplies. An overhead projector can become a valuable teaching aid for giving a demonstration or discussion. For example, in biology, a teacher may want to show how to make a wet-mount slide. This can not be demonstrated easily except by using an overhead projector. Many of the properties of magnetism can be demonstrated to good advantage by the use of such a projector.

Another special piece of equipment of particular value to biology classes is the microprojector to project slide material. The advantage of this projector is that the teacher and the student view simultaneously the same material. An alternative to the use of the microprojector is a closed-circuit television camera adapted for use over a microscope; the students view the material on a television console. These microprojectors cost over $2,000 and are beyond the reach of most schools. Amplifiers can be used to good advantage to study heart beats of various animals and to let the class hear them. Some teachers have a small tape library which may contain information that can be used as an actual part of a demonstration. In the study of sound in general science or physics, tape recorders can be put to good use.

DEMONSTRATIONS VERSUS INDIVIDUAL EXPERIMENTATION

A planetarium provides unique facilities for demonstrating various aspects of astronomy.
Photo courtesy of Clark Science Center, Loomis School, Windsor, Conn.

Educators have stressed the importance of self-instruction with less reliance on large-group or class instruction. Education should be preparation for life, and part of that preparation must be to insure that the individual continues his education long after formal education ends. It is important that the school reinforce habits and patterns of learning which will prepare the individual to continue his education many years after he leaves organized instruction. Laboratory work, because it involves the individual directly in the learning process as well as imparting working skills, is thought to be a superior way to teach. A person working on a laboratory problem has learned far more than just the answer to the problem. He may learn to be efficient, self-reliant, and analytical; to observe, manipulate, measure, and reason; to use apparatus; and, most importantly, to learn on his own. Individual laboratory experimentation helps to facilitate the attainment of these goals better than demonstrations do; however, demonstrations have certain advantages over individual experimental work. They are:

1. Lower cost. Less equipment and fewer materials are needed by an instructor doing a demonstration. This is, therefore, cheaper than having the entire class perform experiments. However, it should be remembered that cheap education is not necessarily better education.
2. Availability of equipment. Certain demonstrations require equipment not available in sufficient numbers for all students to use. For example, not every student in a physics class needs to have an oscilloscope to study sound waves.
3. Economy of time. Often the time required to set up equipment for a laboratory exercise cannot be justified for the educational value received. A teacher can set up the demonstration and use the rest of the time for other instruction.

4. Less hazard from dangerous materials. A teacher may more safely handle dangerous chemicals or apparatus requiring sophisticated skills.
5. Direction of the thinking process. In a demonstration a teacher has a better indication of the students' thinking processes and can do much to stimulate the students to be more analytical and synthetic in their reasoning.

A DEMONSTRATION SHOULD STRESS THE HIGHER LEVELS OF LEARNING

A demonstration should contribute to the objectives of the course and school. It should be used to stimulate critical thinking and offer opportunities for manifesting creativity. A demonstration may further be used to develop understanding of the philosophical basis of science. For example, the instructor may ask, "How certain are we of our data? Does science constantly strive for certainty—is there certainty in science? How did we fractionate knowledge in order to find answers to a bigger problem? Will the sums of our fractional bits of knowledge equal the whole? I have just produced chlorine. Chlorine is a poisonous gas. Am I immoral for making chlorine? Am I moral if I use chlorine to purify water? Is science moral, immoral, or amoral?" Questions of this type can be used discriminately throughout a series of demonstrations to build a philosophical awareness of the foundations of modern science. The responsibility to impart knowledge of this sort offers great challenge to the teacher in formulating lessons.

A demonstration technique which embodies higher understanding, more students' individuality, and creative reactions is shown below:

EVALUATION OF STUDENT UNDERSTANDING
OF A BASIC PHYSICAL PRINCIPLE

Each student is to be given a Mimeographed sheet containing the information that follows:

Part I
1. Show an arrangement of tubing and water within the cans by which you can explain why the water started running from the glass tube when a small amount of water was poured into the funnel.
2. In a few sentences, explain why you think the water started to run and why it continues to run.
3. How long (in terms of what is happening within the cans) will the water run?
4. What basic physical principle is illustrated by this demonstration?

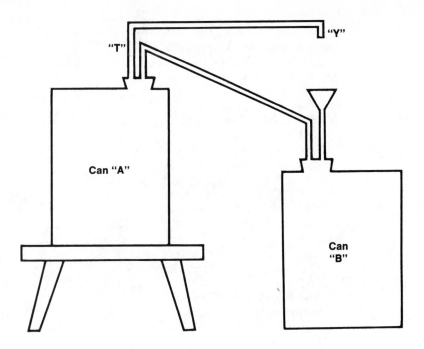

Part II

The questions on this part of the test refer to the diagram below. Assume: (1) that can "A" and can "B" are identical, (2) that all parts of the apparatus remain unchanged unless a change is specified in the statement which you are answering.

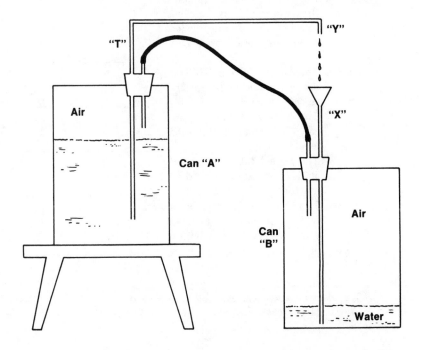

Directions:

In the blank to the right of each statement place an (X) in the column indicating the effect which the given change would have upon the rate of flow.

How would the rate at which the liquid flows from the glass tube be affected if:

The liquid would:

Not Flow	Flow Slower	Flow at Same Rate	Flow Faster

1. The top of the funnel was only one half as far above can "B" as it was in the diagram?

2. Can "B" was lowered until the top of can "B" was level with the bottom of can "A"?

3. The glass tube "T" was lengthened so that it extended twice as far above can "A"?

4. The funnel was replaced by a thistle tube extending to the same height above can "B" but having a bulb volume three times as great?

5. The tip "Y" of the glass tube from which the water is flowing was lengthened until it was level with the top of the funnel?

6. Kerosene, which is less dense than water, was used instead of water? (Neglect differences in viscosity and vapor pressure.)

7. The volume of can "B" was doubled while its height "H" remained constant?

8. The bottom of can "A" and can "B" were at the same level?

9. The funnel tube was cut off at "X" and did not extend below the stopper in can "B"?

10. The glass tube in can "B" to which the hose is fastened was extended to the bottom of the can?[2]

---

[2] This demonstration and evaluation guide was prepared by Dr. Gene F. Craven, Department of Science Education, Oregon State University, Corvallis.

SUMMARY

A demonstration has been defined as showing something to a person or group. The techniques of planning a demonstration involve determining the concepts and principles to be taught, deciding on activities, gathering the materials, practicing the demonstration, outlining the questions to be asked, and deciding on what evaluational techniques to use.

Plan a demonstration with the intention of using it again. A teacher in giving a demonstration should be aware of visibility, audibility, and all the aspects which go with good staging. He should have zest, present the demonstration inductively, ask questions contantly, give positive reinforcement, use the blackboard or projection techniques, summarize, and evaluate the demonstration. A demonstration may be carried out by the teacher, by the teacher and students together, by a group of students, by an individual student, or by a guest. More attention should be given to demonstrations other than those presented by the teacher, with accompanying comments. Silent demonstrations offer a different approach and emphasize observational techniques.

Equipment should be stored so that it is easily located for future times when the demonstration will be given again. Special equipment often can be secured from local industries without cost. The overhead projector and microprojector are excellent teaching aids for giving certain demonstrations.

Individual experimentation generally is more desirable as a teaching technique than are demonstrations, but demonstrations have the advantage of economy of time and money and allow for greater direction by the teacher. Demonstrations should contribute to the higher levels of learning—those requiring critical thinking and creativity.

Further Investigation and Study

1. Suppose that you wanted to teach the molecular theory of matter. How would you start your unit? What demonstrations would you do and why?
2. What is the difference between teaching a demonstration inductively and deductively?
3. What does the word *demonstration* mean?
4. How does an experimental demonstration differ from a verification one?
5. What are the advantages and disadvantages in giving a demonstration?
6. How is the staging of a theatrical production similar to that of staging a demonstration? What considerations have to be made in preparation for both?
7. What can you do to determine whether you are moving through a demonstration at the right rate?
8. What advantages are there to a student demonstration?
9. How would you give a silent demonstration?
10. What are the advantages and disadvantages of demonstrations compared to student laboratory work?
11. Explain how you would give a demonstration to insure that there would be higher levels of learning.
12. How would you store demonstration equipment so that you would be able to use it with greater efficiency?
13. Two chemistry teachers were talking. One said, "I never answer questions." How could the teacher do this and still be a good teacher?

*We know too much for one man
to know much, we live too variously
to live as one. Our histories and
traditions—the very means of
interpreting life—are both bonds
and barriers among us.[1]*

J. Robert Oppenheimer

8

Discussion as a Means of Inquiry

DISCUSSION VERSUS LECTURE

June Truesdale, a first-year teacher, came storming into the faculty lounge. She said, "Wow, if this day represents teaching, you can have it!" Mrs. Pollack asked, "What happened to upset you?" Mrs. Truesdale said, "The students in my class just don't want to learn. They don't pay attention and are always causing discipline trouble. I had to send three students to the dean's office last period." Mrs. Pollack, an experienced and sympathetic colleague, said, "June, you must be doing something wrong. What did you do last period?" June replied she was lecturing to her general science classes on light. Mrs. Pollack asked, "How long did you lecture? Did you do any demonstrations? Did you allow the students to do anything?" June answered no to all of these questions. Mrs. Pollack then suggested that June not lecture to the students but have a discussion instead. She said, "Why don't you ask some interesting questions about light? For example, ask how do you know there is glass in my eye glasses? What evidence do you have that there is glass present without touching the glass? Does all the light hitting the eye lenses go through them? How do you know it isn't all going through? What causes a rainbow?

---

1 From a speech delivered at the University of Colorado, Summer, 1963.

What does a flat mirror do to light? What does a curved mirror do to light?" Mrs. Pollack then suggested the class take a mirror and discuss what happens to light as it hits it. "Don't lecture to them but demonstrate and discuss. You will find far more interest and less discipline trouble."

Most experienced science teachers would have given Mrs. Truesdale the same kind of advice. Good science teaching requires student-involved activity. The trouble with Mrs. Truesdale's using the lecture approach was that students were seldom involved except in absorbing information. In a lecture, many students "tune the teacher out," become bored, listless, and eventually cause discipline problems. The attention span of junior high school and high school students for a lecture is, at best, short. This doesn't mean that a few minutes of lecture may not be desirable. An experienced teacher can use it effectively for ten to twenty minutes, particularly if he is using several visual aids such as the chalkboard, overhead projection, models, or apparatus. A lecture on how to use the microscope, for example, may work well, especially if the students have microscopes before them and are encouraged to locate the parts being covered in the lecture.

Discussion, because it involves students more than lecture in the learning process, is a more desirable approach for class procedures. Since an objective of modern science instruction is to teach science as a process with emphasis on the cognitive development of the individual, students must have the time and opportunities to develop critical thinking. Thinking is something one does! A student can't think unless he is given opportunities to think. The presentation of problems in a discussion requires students to think in the process of formulating their answers. A teacher, on the other hand, who tells students all about a subject presents no problem to the student except boredom. In addition, the students have been robbed of an opportunity to think. All they have to do is soak up information and memorize it.

A discussion leader interested in developing inquiring behavior seldom gives answers but asks questions instead. Students in answering questions learn to evaluate, analyze, and synthesize knowledge. They also may be thrilled to discover fundamental ideas for themselves.

A discussion has another advantage over a lecture. It presents feedback to the teacher. An astute discussion leader learns quickly from the student comments their comprehension of the topic. He then guides the discussion, moving it rapidly when students understand the information and slowing it down when they have difficulty. A lecture-oriented teacher seldom knows what students are comprehending. He may belabor a point the class long ago understood or speed through information few understand. One of the greatest mistakes a beginner teacher can make is to assume that the lecture method will work well in a secondary school.

HOW TO LEAD A DISCUSSION

Leading a discussion is an art, an art not easily learned. There is nothing more exciting to see than a master teacher with a group of students having a discussion in which the students are filled with interest and excitement. But how can you bring students to this point? Excellent class discussions do not just happen. The inexperienced instructor may think he will walk into a class and talk about a subject "off the top of his head." After all, doesn't he know more about the subject than the students? It's true he may know about the material, but he is faced with the problem of getting students to discover it. This takes preparation, as much preparation as any other class procedure requires. The first step in preparing for a discussion is to determine what it is you wish to accomplish, your objectives. Next, outline questions you think may help students to reach these objectives. A good discussion leader uses the "What do you think?" approach to learning. He asks such questions as: Why did you do this in the experiment? What did the data show? Do you have sufficient data? Do you need to repeat the experiment? Why did you use this approach? How would you go about finding answers to this problem? Is there another way you could find the answer to this problem? What good is this in our daily lives? What steps did you make mentally in solving this problem? How many variables are involved? Every discussion should contribute to the development of critical thinking. Some attention should be devoted to analysis of the thought processes used in the discussion itself. That is why you should spend some time discussing the steps the students went through to reach their conclusions.

An instructor should enter the class with an attitude of letting students work out the answers. A simple design for planning an inquiring discussion is as follows:

1. Present a problem.
2. Encourage students to formulate hypotheses or give evidence for answers to the questions. For example, the problem is stated as follows: A burning candle is placed upright in a pan. There is some water in the pan. The candle is then covered by a glass container. Questions to be asked: What will happen to the candle when it is covered? Will anything else happen to the apparatus as this is done? What would happen if the candle were lengthened, the size of the jar above it were increased, the amount of water in the container holding the candle were decreased?
3. Review the cognitive processes they used in solving the problem. Ask: What hypotheses were made? What was the best hypothesis and why? How were the conclusions reached? On what are they based? What is required to make better conclusions?

Instructor starting a discussion in biology.

Photo courtesy of Bob Waters, Colorado State College.

What the teacher in a situation like this is asking students to do is to formulate hypotheses. The discussion could lead to the testing of their hypotheses by doing more experiments. Involved in the discussion outlined above is an evaluation and an understanding of oxidation and gas laws. In the process of answering questions, students have to reason and apply their knowledge. Discussions of this type lead to an extension of an understanding of information and give students opportunities to practice their cognitive skills.

Another use of the discussion is to summarize class activities. For example, after several days of laboratory work the instructor may stop the class and ask them to summarize what they have done. The students make statements. The instructor may ask several questions, some of which are similar to questions used in an inquiring discussion, such as: How do you know your answers are correct? How do you know they are true? How did you go about finding out this information? Do you have ample information? How could you have improved your laboratory procedures? What did you do in your work procedures which has value in running a business, home, or raising a family?

A neophyte discussion leader often starts a discussion with too broad or too difficult a question. If there is no response to a question, the teacher should rephrase it, make it simpler or lessen its depth. This procedure may have to be followed several times before there is any response. A question implies an answer. If the question is too vague the students may not respond; rephrasing a question may give them some insight. Leading a discussion by questioning and giving no answers is a skill which brings with it great satisfaction, but to be an astute questioner requires practice and a keen awareness of the students' comprehension. The sophisticated discussion leader is able, by the questions he asks, to guide students toward the understanding of the concepts and principles involved in the lesson or experiment. The questions must be of sufficient depth to require critical thinking and not so simple as to require only a yes or no answer.

Eye contact is an important aspect in leading a discussion. A teacher's eyes should sweep a class like a searchlight, constantly looking for boredom, a student with an answer or a question, or one with a puzzled look. Eye contact helps to give the instructor feedback as well as to motivate students to think and participate in the discussion. Another motivational technique useful in beginning a discussion is to start it with a demonstration. For example, a bottle of blood sitting on a demonstration desk can do wonders for beginning a discussion about blood or the circulatory system. Burning a candle can lead to a discussion of a number of scientific concepts and principles. A good rule to follow is to start a discussion with a percept if possible. Not all discussions will lend themselves to this procedure, but those that involve the discovery of a concept almost always do.

The use of overhead projection with transparencies helps to concentrate the class's attention on clarifying a problem. For example, focusing students' attention on some of the approaches to devising a classification scheme can be done easily on an overhead projection. Use different-colored paper cut to various sizes and shapes and ask students how they would group the materials. A discussion can arise from the demonstration of such cognitive processes as analysis, discrimination, and ordering. Another demonstration using the overhead projector might include a discussion of magnetism and magnetic lines of force; using a magnet and iron filings sprinkled on top of transparent plastic sets the stage for a discussion of the properties of magnetism.

Some general rules to follow in giving discussions are:

1. Create an atmosphere in the class in which questions are not only welcomed but *expected.*

2. Try to bring in the interests of the students as much as possible in the discussion.

3. Give positive reinforcement as much as possible. Seldom use negative reinforcement. Say: "That's a good answer, that's right, you have the idea," "Good, you're thinking; keep it up, you have something there," "Who would like to react to this answer?" Do not ignore the answers of students; always give some recognition to their answers. No response by the teacher is a form of negative reinforcement. If students have the wrong answer, do not say, "That's wrong; no, that answer is no good." But rather say, "Well, that is not quite right," "You may have something there, but I am not sure I understand the point," or "Good, you are thinking; but that is not what I was thinking about."

4. When you encourage a student to think, evaluate the product on the basis of his level of comprehension. Even when you, with a more extensive background, are aware that the idea given is either incomplete or incorrect, accept it or even praise it, if it indicates that the student has made effective use of the information he was expected to know at that stage of the course.

5. When a student calls attention to a mistake you have made, praise him.

6. In leading the discussion try to remember previous comments and interrelate them. If at all possible give recognition by referring to the name of the student who made the comment. For example, a teacher in responding to the idea of a student says, "John believes there are other factors determining the rate of expansion of a metal beside temperature. George has just suggested that possibly humidity and air pressure may have a minor effect." The teacher has acted as a summarizer for two students' views and has given them recognition by using their names.

7. Your attitude in leading a discussion does much to determine the quality of that discussion. If you walk into a class feeling and looking very serious and with the weight of the discussion on your shoulders, the students' response will be mild. However, if you start a discussion with the attitude that you and the students are going to have fun wrestling with ideas, the response is more likely to be impressive. In leading a discussion with adolescents, you must be able to laugh at yourself. "Ham up" the situation to some extent; discrete use of humor captures interest and gains participation.

8. If questions arise for which science does not yet provide an adequate explanation, say so. This gives students insight into avenues of research which we still need to explore.

9. After a student answers a question, include the answer to the question in your next remarks as you elaborate further. There is always a good possibility that some students did not hear the student's answer. Call upon students who do not indicate a willingness to answer, as well as those who do.

Special Precautions in Leading a Discussion

At times the following suggestions are proper, but the teacher should give serious consideration to their potential disadvantages:

1. When a question is asked of you, toss it back to a student in its entirety. Have another student repeat the question in its entirety. Ask a student to speak up so that the entire class can hear. Ask a student to research an answer to the question on his own.

2. The teacher obviously wants an answer to a question to benefit the entire class. Some techniques to aid this are: Encourage the entire class to take notes. Avoid the appearance of carrying on a private conversation with the person who asked the question. Deliberately let your eyes roam over the entire class while giving the answer. Use the hypothesis-forming technique.

3. The easiest way to kill a discussion or possibilities for further discussion is to be sarcastic or to belittle students' ideas. If this has been done often in the school, it may be difficult to get a discussion started. One way to overcome reticence of this nature is to say, "Don't be afraid to answer the question. Even if you give the wrong answer, I shall cover up for you so that the rest of the class will never know." A statement like this often breaks the ice and conveys to the students your true purpose in trying to get them to learn.

4. Don't permit students to answer questions without proper recognition, to break into the answers of others without proper recognition, or to make derogatory remarks about another student's question.

5. The following indicate when to show displeasure with the person asking the question: The student's tone of voice implies sarcasm or antagonism. The student is obviously using delaying tactics to avoid an impending quiz. (This is difficult to judge.) The student obviously had not studied or participated in discussion, but just before the examination he wishes to ask questions. The question was asked and answered previously.

6. The following indicate when to suggest that the answer can best be delayed for an individual conference with the student: The degree of difficulty of the answer is above the level expected of the class as a whole. The subject matter involved bears little relation to the key ideas being stressed. The answer is both detailed and lengthy. The time spent in answering the question may destroy the sequence of thought being developed.

TESTING YOUR JUDGMENT

Secondary students are similar to college students in that they are continually trying to psychoanalyze the instructor. "What does he know?" "Is he smart?" "Does he really like this material we are studying?" "How sharp is he?" These questions are constantly in the minds of the students until they come to know the instructor as a person. An instructor should be cognizant of the fact that students sometimes are testing his judgment. They may ask questions to which they already know the answers to see how he will respond. They may try to deviate from the purpose of instruction to see whether they can get the teacher off the track. They may try to bring up controversial subjects not because they are interested in them but to see the teacher's reaction. Students will not generally do this; most of the time they are sincerely interested in learning. However, an instructor who does not recognize these deviations or who reacts poorly to this type of questioning usually is poorly prepared in subject matter and in educational psychology, lacks awareness, or is an authoritarian who feels he must know everything. A well-prepared teacher with a sense of direction and purpose will have little trouble recognizing these attempts and will laugh at the situation. He might say, "I know what you're doing. You're trying to get us off the subject, and that's OK for a little bit; but let's get back to the problem. The problem was . . . ." An instructor should not feel that he must know the answers to all questions. It is impossible for a teacher to know all about his subject. When asked questions he cannot answer he can ask the class whether any of them knows the answer or how the answer could be determined and admit to the class he doesn't know it. Students don't really expect the teacher to know everything, and in fact they enjoy having the teacher learn with them.

SPECIAL DISCUSSION TECHNIQUES

Invitations to Inquiry

The Biological Science Curriculum Study has produced in its *Biology Teachers' Handbook* forty-four class-discussion outlines under the title "Invitations to Inquiry." The purpose of these outlines as expressed by the BSCS is to show the student that knowledge arises from data and is constantly changing. The invitations engage students in the process of solving a problem by involving them in problems worked on by scientists. A typical outline presents a problem to the student and invites him to devise an experiment, make hypotheses, draw conclusions from data, interpret data, or understand the factors involved in the problem. The BSCS authors state, "The primary aim is an understanding of inquiry. It is mainly for the sake of this aim that the active participation of the student is invoked. Both practical experience and experimental study indicate that concepts are understood best and retained longest when the student contributes to his own understanding."[2] An example of a simple invitation, similar to one produced by BSCS, inviting students to form hypotheses and design experiments is given below:

> A farmer had a reasonably high mortality rate among his chicks. He wanted to decrease this rate but was not sure what to do. What would you do to insure that fewer chicks died?
>
> [Student discussion then is invited by the teacher. More text is given after the discussion.]
>
> The farmer came to the conclusion that the possible cause of death might be related to the heat source keeping the chicks warm at night. He suspected that some of them got cold, but there was ample room for the chicks to get near the white lamp heat source. He wondered whether the lamp itself might have something to do with the death of the chicks. What would you do to test this idea?
>
> [Student discussion ensues.]
>
> After a period of time he decided to use different colors of light bulbs in the lamp to see what happened. If you were going to test this hypothesis, how would you go about it?
>
> [Student discussion.]
>
> Out of a flock of twenty-five chicks in each of the incubators he obtained the following mortality over a three-day period.

Red Light Source	Blue Light Source	White Light Source
1 chick died	2 chicks died	3 chicks died

> What do the above data indicate?
> Can you definitely conclude anything from this data?
> How could you be more certain of your answers?

---

[2] Joseph J. Schwab *et al., Biology Teachers' Handbook* (New York: John Wiley & Sons, Inc., 1963), p. 47.

Are you certain from this experiment that light was the cause
of the mortality?
Are other factors involved?
What are some of the other factors that might have caused
chick mortality?

The above invitation involves students in understanding a problem,
outlining an experiment, forming hypotheses, interpreting data,
and drawing conclusions. It illustrates the application of the scientific method to a realistic situation.

How to design an invitation to inquiry.

You can easily make your own "invitations." The steps are as
follows:
1. Decide what your objectives are, either in subject matter or
   understanding science as a process or both.
2. State a problem related to your objectives. The idea for problems can come from actual scientific research reported in
   journals.
3. Devise questions which give students opportunities to set up
   experiments, make hypotheses, analyze and synthesize, and
   record data. Stress the understanding of science as a process
   and the cognitive skills involved.
4. Write the invitation as a series of steps. Insert in different
   parts of it additional information to help the student progress
   in depth into the topic or methods of research.

Invitations to inquiry can be written for various levels of learning. They should stress as much as possible the development of the
students' cognitive abilities. Students should derive from them an
understanding of the necessity for a control, of cause-and-effect
relationships, of when to use quantitative data, of how to interpret
quantitative data, of the role of argument and inference in the
design of the experiment, of the fractionating of a question for
study and the problem involved in summing these fractions to
give understanding about the whole.

The first invitation you write probably won't be very sophisticated, but in the process of writing it you will gain insight into how
to write them plus a better understanding of how to involve students in understanding science as a process.

Invitations can be open-ended and can suggest project research.

Invitations to inquiry can be used to suggest open-ended experiments. For example, if a class goes through an "invitation" project
concerned with whether seeds require light to germinate and they
determine that their seeds do not need light, the teacher might
ask, "Do you think other seeds need light to germinate? What other
factors might affect germination? Do you think there would be
any difference in the germination if we changed the temperature,

humidity, type of light, intensity of light, air pressure, withdraw air, increase the oxygen present, use a magnetic field, etc." In devising questions of this type the instructor should attempt to have students learn what factors may be involved in an experiment. They may include the following:

light	food supply	electricity or
heat	gases present	electrical field
sound	pressure	pH
humidity	magnetic field	etc.
numbers and types	motion	
of reactants	gravity	

Invitations to inquiry are vicarious experiences in how a scientist goes about solving problems. By studying these projects the students gain insights into the limitations of science, see science as a process, and develop confidence in their own ability to become scientific. The vicarious activities of the inquiries can be changed to active involvements in research activities by having students become aware of the number of variable factors involved in an experiment and how they can be modified, and by then having them devise an experiment to do in the laboratory.

Single-topic film invitations to inquiry.

Single-topic films have been produced by BSCS as "Invitations to Inquiry." These films, which have no sound, present a problem and ask questions. The students use the visual material to discover the answer to the problem. The single-topic film *Social Behavior of Chickens,* produced by BSCS, shows a group of chickens in a cage. A problem is posed: Is there social behavior in chickens? Questions are asked by the teacher from time to time about what the students are viewing. Students can spend considerable time viewing a frame, since these are produced in eight-millimeter cartridges for the small eight-millimeter projector, and a single frame can be stopped for an extended period. As the film progresses, the chickens are paired in ten possible combinations. The students observe each of these combinations and record their information. They are then asked to make interpretations. The class discusses the results. The films may be rerun to verify the conclusions or to answer some question or doubt. The role of the teacher is essentially that of questioner and leader of a discussion, aided by the projection of visual material. The visual material is the inquiring medium.

Pictorial Riddles

Another technique for developing motivation and interest in a discussion is to use pictorial riddles. These are pictures or drawings made by the teacher to elicit student response. A riddle is drawn on the blackboard or on poster board or is projected from a transparency, and the teacher asks a question about the picture.

For example, an instructor may show a picture of a tropical rain forest and one from a desert and ask, "What relationships do you see in each picture? Why are there different forms of life in the pictures?" A pictorial riddle can show a situation, as in Figure 17, and the teacher can ask why it occurred; or it can have something wrong with it, as in Figures 18 and 19, and the teacher can ask what is wrong with the picture.

Figure 17

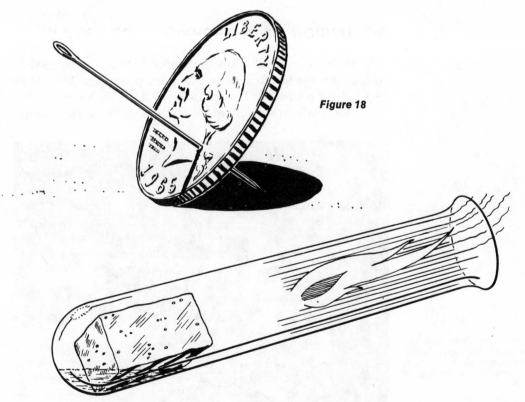

Figure 18

Figure 19

Case Histories

Another technique to motivate discussion is to use case histories in science. These are stories about the development of concepts in science. The instructor may tell the students part of what was done and then ask what they think was the next step in solving or developing the scientific scheme. Case histories can be integrated with a demonstration of a classic experiment which was actually done in the development of a theory. The Science Research Associates publish a collection of these case histories in science for high school use.

Covers of Science Magazines

An activity to supplement a science lesson can be constructed around magazine covers depicting various aspects of science. *Science,* the journal of the American Association for the Advancement of Science, has some very interesting covers which lend themselves well to this approach. The instructor holds the cover picture up and asks questions to give students hints about the topic represented.

DISCUSSION AS A TECHNIQUE OF REVIEW

All of the discussion techniques outlined above can be used to good advantage for class review. Discussion may also be used as an excellent review for laboratory work. After an instructor has had a class perform several experiments in a unit in the laboratory,

Junior high and elementary students in an outdoor camp discussion sponsored by the school. School camping is gaining in popularity.

Photo courtesy of Bob Waters, Colorado State College.

time should be taken to discuss what conclusion can be drawn from the laboratory work. Consideration should also be given to how the information was obtained, what types of problem-solving and cognitive behaviors were involved in determining the answers, and with what assurance the students know their information is correct. A discussion of this type can do much to reinforce learning and divide the trivia from the really important aspects of learning.

A teacher never quite perfects his ability as a discussion leader, but he should never stop trying to improve this ability. Excellence in discussion comes only with wisdom, not only in subject matter but in educational psychology as well. To a dedicated teacher there is probably no greater satisfaction than to be able to walk out of class knowing that he has developed the students' mental abilities to the point where his presence is practically unneeded except as an organizer. To acquire this facility requires preparation and constant self-analysis, but it is one of the intellectual satisfactions that come only with good teaching.

SUMMARY

The lecture method should play a relatively minor role in instruction in the secondary schools. Inquiring discussions motivate students and involve them more in cognitive processes than do lectures. There are definite techniques to be used in leading discussions which are inquiry-oriented. The instructor should mainly question and give little or no information; the type of question asked by the teacher helps students discover the concept or principles involved in the learning situation. To lead a good discussion requires extensive preparation. The discussion leader should know the objectives he wishes to attain, have a series of relevant questions outlined, and spend time at the end of the discussion analyzing how the conclusions were reached. Part of the discussion should be devoted to reflecting on the thought processes used in arriving at the conclusions involved in the discussion. In this way better understanding and development of the cognitive processes will be insured.

A discussion leader should give positive reinforcement as much as possible. He should compliment students on good ideas and suggestions and seldom deride or make sarcastic remarks about poor suggestions. Regardless of the answers given in a discussion the teacher should try to react positively to the participants; ignoring a response is a poor procedure. Eye contact is important as a motivator and a means of receiving feedback. A good method of starting a discussion is to use a demonstration or overhead projection pertaining to a subject or topic of interest to the student. In leading the discussion, attempt to recall previous comments and interrelate the suggestions with the names of the individuals who made them. Remember that students will from time to time test your judgment to determine your competence as a teacher.

Some special techniques used in stimulating discussion are: "invitations to inquiry," single-topic films, pictorial riddles, case histories in science, and questions organized around covers of science magazines. All of these can be used to suggest open-ended experiments if students are aware of the factors involved in experimentation. Discussion is also an excellent vehicle for review, both in class and laboratory work.

Further Investigation and Study

1. What are the advantages of discussion over the lecture method?
2. How can a discussion be used as an approach to inquiry?
3. How can you motivate students during a discussion?
4. Choose some topic and outline how you would present it in a discussion.
5. How does an inquiring discussion differ from one used to summarize? Can a discussion used as a summary also be inquiring in nature? Explain your answer.
6. List some of the positive things you can do to develop a good discussion technique.
7. List some of the things that tend to stifle a discussion.
8. What does your attitude have to do with setting the stage for a good discussion?
9. Why do students sometimes test your judgment while you are leading a discussion? How can you indicate that you have good judgment?
10. What should you do when you don't know the answer to a question?
11. Write an "invitation to inquiry." After writing it summarize the cognitive processes required in the invitation.
12. How can an invitation to inquiry be used to suggest some open-ended experiments?
13. How is a single-topic film used as a method of inquiry? How does it differ from the traditional film?
14. What is a pictorial riddle? Design three pictorial riddles and write an analysis of what is required in solving the riddles. Cover both subject-matter comprehension and cognitive abilities.
15. What are case histories, and how may they be used as methods of inquiry?
16. What is meant by the statement that "a teacher never quite perfects his ability as a discussion leader"?
17. What is the main role of an inquiring discussion leader?

Evaluation has five functions:

It helps the learner realize how he should change or develop his behavior (feedback to learner).

It helps the learner attain satisfaction when he is doing as he should (reinforcement).

It provides a basis for subsequent decisions about the learner: what courses he is ready for, what remedial treatment he needs, what job or college to recommend him to.

It helps the teacher judge how adequate his teaching methods are (feedback to teacher).

It provides information for administrative judgments.[1]

9

Evaluation: Evaluating the Total Person's Behavior

Probably nothing is so well known and so little understood by teachers as evaluation. Evaluation involves the total assessing of a student's learning by the instructor. It includes evaluating understanding of the processes of science, subject-matter competence, scientific attitudes, laboratory skills, and ability and willingness to work. Not only the progress of the students toward the objectives of the course and school but also the effectiveness of the instructor are considered. Good evaluation indicates the strengths and weaknesses of instruction. Once he has made a thorough assessment, the teacher has an indication of how to improve his teaching. Evaluation acts as the feedback in the experimental process of teaching. A teacher must be experimental if he is to progress and try to become more skilled. He must be willing to try new methods and new techniques and in so doing evolves toward true teach-

---

[1] Lee J. Cronbach, *Educational Psychology* (New York: Harcourt, Brace & World, Inc., 1963), p. 539.

ing mastery. Science teachers above all should be experimental, not only in the laboratory but in their daily approaches to teaching; however, an experimental approach assumes collection of data to verify the success of the method used. The data in this case must come from the evaluating techniques. The more sophisticated the evaluating instruments the greater the information available to the teacher for improving his course and instruction.

Listed below are general evaluational techniques used by teachers. It must be emphasized that testing is only a part of evaluation and probably receives too much attention at the expense of other methods:

Tests

1. Standardized tests. There are several standardized tests in science. All of the new curriculum studies have produced standardized tests or are in the process of doing so. These tests include (a) achievement tests in specific subject areas, (b) aptitude tests, (c) understanding-of-*science* or critical-thinking tests, (d) tests to determine creative ability.
2. Essay tests. These should require a sufficient sample of the subject matter. A teacher should refine his essay questions by studying student performance on past tests.
3. Problem tests. A problem or a situation is presented, and the students are asked to suggest plausible answers. This type usually involves experimental procedure or judging information from an experiment.
4. Simple recall tests.
5. Multiple-choice tests.
6. Matching tests.
7. Self-tests.
8. Completion tests.

Non-test evaluations

1. Behavorial records. These are based on laboratory or field work. The teacher prepares a checklist of how the individual functions in these situations.
2. Analysis of creative work. This may involve the production of some piece of apparatus, art work, or a science project.
3. Student self-evaluation of performance in the course or unit.
4. Interpretation of written and oral presentations.

Because of the complexity of evaluation it is strongly urged that science teachers get some advanced special training, particularly in testing and measurement. Some states now require this before a teacher can be certified. In the sections to follow, only two aspects of evaluation are considered because of economy of time and space. Those selected are (a) evaluation of laboratory work and (b) testing, because these are of greatest importance to science teachers.

EVALUATING LABORATORY WORK

Laboratory work is an important part of all new science programs; however, evaluating lab work presents a difficult task. Science teachers generally require students to hand in reports on their laboratory work. This has value as long as the laboratory manuals do not require cookbook answers, simply filling in blank spaces. All the new curriculum-development laboratory manuals stress guiding questions rather than those requiring fill-in answers; however, the techniques of reporting in the new curriculum laboratory books is left to the discretion of the individual instructor. All students should have some experience in reporting laboratory work as scientists report theirs in journals. The criticism of the cookbook approach is that it is unrealistic. Scientists do not have an outline of questions to answer or simple small spaces to fill in when they actually do research. Scientific research is reported in the following manner: Statement of the problem, hypotheses, experimental designs, data, conclusions. Following this format or some modification of it gives the student actual experience with the problems a scientist confronts in writing up his own work. This approach, furthermore, because it is less structured, requires the student to think more and to reason about what he has done. Particularly in summarization, the student recalls better what he has done, gains better understanding of his work, and learns more.

A science teacher who has five classes (150 students) a day cannot, because of sheer numbers, correct all laboratory work reported in this form. Many schools enlist student assistants to check laboratory work for the teacher. The science teacher occasionally then only spot-checks the reports. However, the first written reports should be gone over in detail so that students start with a better understanding of what is required and know that their work may be critically evaluated. Teachers who have no assistants usually spot-check reports and spend more time in discussion covering the laboratory work.

Practical and written examinations covering only laboratory work are used as a means of evaluation. Practical laboratory work involving the testing of materials, determining unknowns, recognizing and classifying organisms, and outlining experimental procedures is valuable. The problem with practical laboratory examinations is that they take a considerable amount of time to set up. Student laboratory assistants or one or two A students can be of considerable help in setting up the examination before or after school.

TESTING

Look over a segment of the following test. Consider what is good and bad about this test.

Part of evaluation in science is observing how students function in the laboratory.

Photo courtesy of Bob Waters, Colorado State College.

Select from Column *B* the answer which best fits Column *A*.

Column A	Column B
1. Roundworms	a. Mammalia
2. Flatworms	b. Echinodermata
3. Snakes	c. Aves
4. Birds	d. Platyhelminthes
5. Paramecium	e. Nemathelminthes
6. Dogs	f. Protista
7. Starfish	g. Porifera
8. Sponges	h. Reptilia
9. Whales	i. Protozoa
10. Fishes	j. Rotifera
11. Diseases and pathogens able to pass directly from one host to another within a population	k. Anopheles Mosquito
	l. Mosquito (Aedes)
	m. Contagious
12. The parasite which is the causative organism of a disease	n. Aerobic
	o. Anaerobic
13. The insects which, along with man, are alternate hosts for malaria	p. Pathogen
	q. Slime mold
14. The vector insect of yellow fever	r. Louis Pasteur
15. Oxygen-requiring bacteria	s. Charles Darwin
16. A visible living protist which glides along using an amoeboid movement	t. Animalcule
	u. Pasteur
	v. Protista
17. The scientist who definitely killed the idea that microbes might arise spontaneously from dead materials	w. Euglena
	x. Rickettseae
	y. Anticoagulent
	z. Leeuwenhoek
18. Discovered the world of microscopic life in the 1670's.	aa. Linnaeus
	bb. Salivary glands
19. The name which represents the whole group of subvisible creatures	cc. Denitrification
	dd. Nitrogen cycle
	ee. Vector
20. Means *little animals*	ff. Flagellate
21. The man responsible for the great classification system in 1750's	gg. Noctituca
	hh. Rickettsibe

22. Proved that microbes always have   ii. Pathogen
     ancestors   jj. Temporary immunity
23. Name given to organisms   kk. Dinoflagellates
     between virus and bacteria   ll. Answer not listed
24. A common flagellate
25. Makes a mosquito bite itch
26. Ancestor of man by theory of evolution
27. All disease producers
28. Phosphorescent ocean tidal disturbances
29. Deadly oceanic "red tides"
30. Anaerobic activity in swampy or packed soils
31. Lighting and legumes participate in this
32. Virus influenza and colds return year after year to an individual
33. A per cent within the total mosquito population
34. Causes of tick fever
35. Are quite mobile
36. Pied Piper of Hamelin

Refer to the test again. What is wrong with the format of the test? Where will the students place the answers? What of the number of answers to match the questions? Does it test for scientific principles, understanding of science as a process, or simply recall of information?

Just as there are levels of learning, so are there levels of testing. This test does not test for the important objectives of science. A teacher trying to evaluate the quality of his instruction from this test has little indication of how well he is teaching. The test clearly indicates that the teacher, as he wrote the test, did not consider his objectives or the scientific principles he wished to teach. The first principle of test construction is to use your objectives and scientific principles as a guide in making a test; otherwise, there is little use in having them. It is worth repeating that students tend to learn the way they are tested. Are the things this test emphasizes really the important goals of the course?

Levels of Testing

1. Recall.

The test above mainly requires recall. Simple recall is the lowest level of learning. It requires only memorization of information—and information is not knowledge in the broad sense. Animals can memorize. To teach mainly for recall is the lowest level of instruction, but teachers have often devoted too much time to this level because recall questions are simple to write. Other levels must become a part of all tests. No more than 20 per cent of any test should consist of simple recall questions.

2. Ability to indicate relationships.

Questions involving an understanding of relationships of knowledge can be easily written by constructing questions which include the words *significance, compare,* or *relationship*. One caution should be noted: questions of this type should not be too vague or general. For example, "What is the significance of hormones to plants?" is too vague. Better to limit the question to "What is the significance of hormones to flowering or stem growth?" Listed below are examples of relationship questions.

1. What is the significance of DNA to evolution?
2. How is heat related to the kinetic theory of matter?
3. In what way are hydrogen bonds related to the boiling point of water?
4. What is the significance of indol-acetic acid to stem morphology?
5. How are the digestive systems in roundworms, flatworms, and segmented worms similar or dissimilar?

3. Application of knowledge.

The purpose of education is to be able to transfer knowledge to new situations. Giving opportunities to use this ability in testing helps to insure that this skill will be used later in life. Questions that test for application of knowledge can be easily written if you (1) determine what scientific principle you wish to teach, (2) present a problem which requires the application of the principle, and (3) ask questions requiring application of information.

Example:
1. Principle to be taught
   a. Metals expand when heated
2. Problem requiring application
   a. A student noticed that the telephone lines in front of his house sagged more in the summer than in the winter
3. Question
   a. What explanation can you give for this fact?

Questions involving applications of knowledge can have answers in essay or multiple-choice form. Examples of both types follow. Read the following questions, giving particular attention to the format:

Objective-Type Questions

Questions 1-6 relate to the following situation:

    I. Robert Johnson, a rancher, organizes a wolf hunt to kill wolves preying on his sheep. He also has several acres of alfalfa. Some time later, he notices an increasing amount of damage to his alfalfa field. Upon investigation he discovers large numbers of rabbits and deer eating his alfalfa.

_____1. The increased numbers of rabbits and deer would indicate that the balance in nature tends to be:
   A. Permanent
   B. Fixed
   C. Constantly changing
   D. A perfect balance

_____2. Which of the following best describes the wolf in the above situation?
   A. Producer
   B. First-order consumer
   C. Second-order consumer
   D. Key-industry animal

_____3. Which of the following best describes the sheep in the above situation?
   A. Producer
   B. First-order consumer
   C. Second-order consumer
   D. Key-industry animal

_____4. The deer and rabbits increased because:
   A. The supply of alfalfa was plentiful.
   B. There was less competition from sheep.
   C. Parasites were reduced.
   D. Predatory animals were reduced.

_____5. The basic source of energy for the food web in this problem would be:
   A. Alfalfa
   B. Sunlight
   C. Minerals
   D. Water

Essay-Type Questions

6. In a short paragraph, state how you would explain to Mr. Johnson how he should reestablish a simple balance in nature to save his alfalfa crop.

Multiple-Choice Type of Questions

II. In Michigan there are two subspecies of deer mouse, one of which inhabits the shore line of the Great Lakes, the other the wooded areas. Nearly everywhere between the shore and the woods is a zone of meadowland that both subspecies avoid. So they rarely meet. If they were to meet more often, there is good reason to suppose they would interbreed.

_____1. What type of barrier is presented here? (a) oceanic, (b) partial, (c) complex, (d) food

_____2. Which of the following environmental changes will probably cause these animals to interbreed? (a) development of a new species of mouse that can live in the meadow and interbreed with both, (b) a forest fire that destroys all the forest area, (c) a gradual succession of the shore line to form a bridge between the two areas, (d) a change in the route of prevailing westerlies, bringing more rainfall to the area.

The following diagram shows four different locations on the surface of the earth. For each numbered statement mark, in the space provided, (a) numbers which designate(s) the location for which the statement is true. If the statement is true for none of the locations, write "f" in the space.

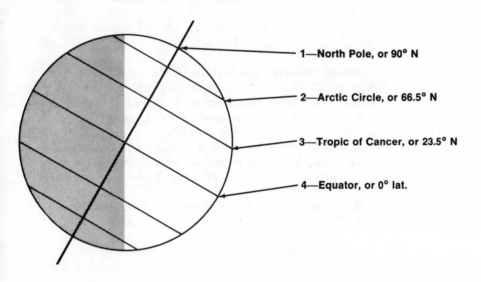

1—North Pole, or 90° N

2—Arctic Circle, or 66.5° N

3—Tropic of Cancer, or 23.5° N

4—Equator, or 0° lat.

_____ 1. All Southern Hemisphere stars could be seen from this point at some time during the year.

_____ 2. The acceleration of gravity is less here than at any other point on the earth.

_____ 3. The Foucault pendulum would not demonstrate earth rotation here.

_____ 4. The Aurora Borealis would frequently be visible here.

_____ 5. When the sun is overhead at noon here, it is September 22.

_____ 6. This point has six consecutive months of darkness each year.

_____ 7. When the sun is overhead at noon here, every place on the earth has days and nights of equal length.

_____ 8. Stars are visible only at night from this point.

_____ 9. Malignant diseases are most common at this latitude.

_____10. This location is closer to the center of the earth than are any others.

_____11. When the sun is overhead at noon at this location, the earth is at its greatest distance from the sun.

_____12. The sun's rays are most direct in December at this location.

_____13. Polaris (the North Star) would appear to be 23.5° from the vertical at this point.

_____14. What would happen to the earth's seasons if the earth's axis were changed from 23° to 90° straight up?
  A. The poles would become warmer.
  B. Denver would have two winters.
  C. Fall weather in New York would be lengthened.
  D. The equatorial region would become colder.

Essay-Type Questions

III. Meat markets age fresh beef for a variable period of time, usually three to seven days optimum. They say this aging period accomplishes two functions: (a) gives the meat more flavor, (b) makes the meat more tender. Assuming that this is true, answer the following questions.
  1. What reasons can you give to support this statement?
  2. If you decided to design an experiment to prove the above statement, what problems would you expect to encounter?
  3. In what ways would temperature be an important factor?
  4. What would you expect to happen if you ran the experiment for ten to thirty days?

QUANTITATIVE TERMS

All sciences use mathematics. The use of mathematics insures more accurate communication and brings exactness to science where vagueness once flourished. When we describe phenomena, we may do so by use of dichotomous or metrical terms. A dichotomous explanation is of the "either-or" type, such as: it is tall (or short), small (or large), heavy (or light). Science strives to escape from explanation of this type because it contributes to ambiguity; what may be tall to one person may be small to another. Scientific explanations are usually given in metrical terms. Instead of saying a person is tall, a scientist says he is 6 feet, 4 inches tall. Instead of stating, "Place some glucose in water" he is more likely to say, "Place 10 grams of glucose in 100 cc of water." The use of metrical terms insures exactness.

Exactness in science is important not only for insuring better communication but in replicating research as well. It is the nature of the scientific enterprise to have one scientist check the results of another. This would be impossible without the use of exact metrical terms. Compare the following and this becomes obvious.

A non-metrical explanation: "A small amount of penicillin was injected into a human organism suffering from a bacterial infection. The infection was cured in a short time."

A metrical explanation: "Sixty subjects and ten control patients infected with streptococcus were administered 500,000 units of penicillin. On the third day, forty of the patients no longer evidenced the infection in the nasalpharyngeal passages."

The importance of metrical terms can be easily pointed out to a class by holding up an eraser and having them describe it in complete detail so that it could be produced by some African tribesman who had never seen one. Students will often write down a description without giving exact dimensions. An instructor can then discuss the necessity of giving the dimensions, thereby emphasizing the place of math in science. There are other uses of mathematics in science aside from those discussed here, but the important point is that mathematics become a part of each examination and students gain insight into its association with science.

Graphing

One quantitative tool used to a considerable extent in science is graphing. Graphing has the following advantages: (1) It conveys a tremendous amount of information in a small space. Try to describe verbally all the information depicted by a curved line on a graph, and this point immediately becomes apparent. (2) It helps the viewer to see quickly relationships which are not so apparent when one looks at a set of numbers. (3) A pictorial representation of data is retained more easily by students than are other forms of data. Below are examples of graphing exercises used in secondary science:

Graph Interpretation

I. This graph represents data collected on *E. coli* bacteria in the laboratory. *E. coli* is found internally in a symbiotic relationship with man.

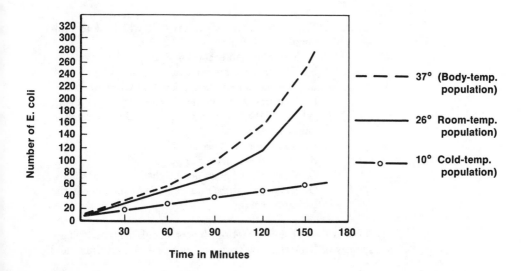

1. From the data given, what are your conclusions about the effect of temperature on *E. coli* population?
2. At 37°C approximately how long does it take for *E. coli* to double its population? at 10°C?
3. Why do you think *E. coli* is successful in its relationship with man?
4. What would be the approximate population of *E. coli* in 4 hours at 37°C? at 26°C?
5. Each population is in 100 ml. of nutrient. What could you predict about the eventual curve of bacteria populations at 37°C? at 10°C?
6. Which of the three populations will reach its maximum growth development first? Why?

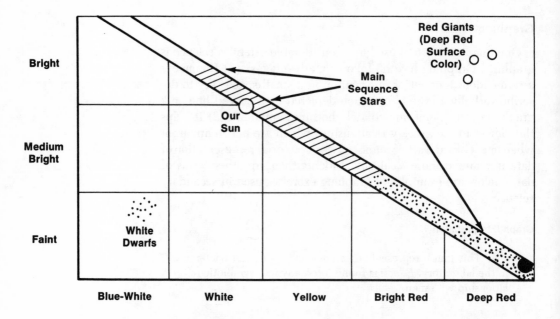

_____1. The graph above indicates that which of the following is not true?
   A. The sun is an exceptional star.
   B. The sun is a medium bright star.
   C. The sun is between yellow and white in color.
   D. The sun will some day become a red giant star.
_____2. Which of the following is true of the information found in the graph?
   A. Red giant stars are faint
   B. The sun is a main sequence star.
   C. White dwarf stars are brighter than red giants.
   D. Deep red stars and red giant stars have the same weight.

II. A flask of sterile beef broth was inoculated with a single species of bacteria. The flask was not sealed, and thus mold spores were able to enter. The growth patterns for the bacteria and mold are shown in the graph below.

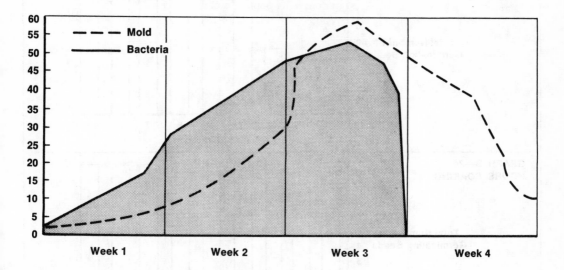

From the graph above answer the following questions:
1. Why do you think the bacteria flourished at first and then all died by the end of the third week?
2. Why do you think the mold population decreased so rapidly during the fourth week?
3. Notice the shape of the growth curve for the mold during the first two and a half weeks. What important concept of growth rate does this illustrate?

III. Answer the following questions in relation to conclusions that can be drawn from the graph. Before being tested for germination, corn seeds represented in Graph A have been soaked 0 hours; in Graph B, 24 hours; and in Graph C, 72 hours.
1. Farmer Brown wants to plant corn seeds and get them up as soon as possible. From the graphs, how long would you advise him to soak the seeds prior to planting? (a) 0 hours, (b) 24 hours, (c) 72 hours
2. Which of the graphs shows maximum germination after three days? (a) Graph A, (b) Graph B, (c) Graph C
3. How many days does it take for 50 per cent germination of seeds soaked for 24 hours? (a) 1 day, (b) 2 days, (c) 4 days, (d) 10 days
4. Moisture applied to seeds for 24 hours before planting has a greater effect on seed germination than soaking them (a) 0 hours, (b) 36 hours, (c) 72 hours, (d) 100 hours
5. From the graphs above, which group of seeds would be considered the control? (a) that in Graph A, (b) that in Graph B, (c) that in Graph C

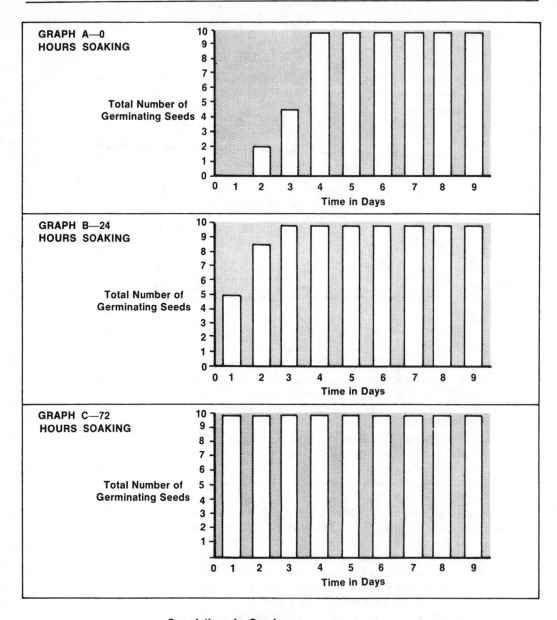

GRAPH A—0 HOURS SOAKING

Total Number of Germinating Seeds

Time in Days

GRAPH B—24 HOURS SOAKING

Total Number of Germinating Seeds

Time in Days

GRAPH C—72 HOURS SOAKING

Total Number of Germinating Seeds

Time in Days

Completion of a Graph

Another way to determine students' understanding of graphing is to have them complete a graph. The graph test on page 157 can be used in a regular assignment or done as homework:

The following graph applies to the red-fox population on an island which is 10 miles long and 20 miles wide. It is located in the center of a very large lake in central Canada. This island supports several species of animals; however, detailed population studies have been conducted only on the fox population. These population studies began in 1958 and continued for six full years.

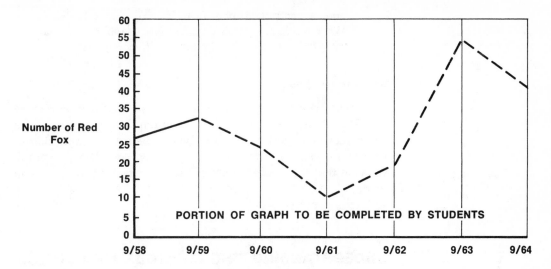

During part of the year, October to May, the lake is frozen over. This allows a fluctuation in the fox population due to immigration and emigration across the ice. The breeding population for each year was determined in late May, as soon as the lake thawed. The young are born in early June and are counted in early July.

Total population counts were continued for six full years. These counts were always made in late September by elaborate trapping methods. Immigration and emigration counts were determined by tagging the foxes as they were trapped and counted.

In September of 1958 the total population of foxes was 27. In September of 1959 the population was 31 foxes. In the years from September, 1959, to September, 1964, the following data were compiled for each one-year period:

	9/59–9/60	9/60–9/61	9/61–9/62	9/62–9/63	9/63–9/64
Breeding population	20	14	8	22	41
Natality	24	17	16	26	59
Mortality	11	16	4	6	43
Immigration	1	0	7	16	3
Emigration	9	5	3	6	15
TOTALS	25	10	24	52	45

From the above data, compute the total population for each year and complete the following questions:

1. Plot your computed populations on the graph for each year and then complete the graph by drawing the line from point to point.
2. What was the density of foxes in September of 1960?
3. From September, 1961, to September, 1963, there is a rise in population; however, you notice that there is a very high rate of mortality during the same period of time. Can you

offer a valid conclusion about this high mortality rate? What would the graph probably look like if the population studies had been continued for 10 more years?

Student-drawn graphs

Another way to test for understanding of graphs is to require the students to devise a graph. For example, students could be given these instructions: "Graph below the rate of expansion of copper for temperatures $-10°C$ to $100°C$" or "Draw a graph showing the rate of absorption of the red wavelengths of light in water."

UNDERSTANDING THE METHODS OF SCIENCE

Special efforts should be made to evaluate students' understanding of science as inquiry, since this understanding is one of the main objectives of science instruction. This evaluation involves testing for numerous skills and attitudes. An extensive list of these, as formulated by Dr. Obourn, is included in the appendix; however, a few of these skills and attitudes—those involved in the steps of the scientific method—are considered below, with examples of questions for each category.

1. Recognizing a Problem

a. A student goes to Mexico for three days of vacation. After he returns to the United States he becomes nauseated. What would a scientist do when confronted with this situation—and why?

b. A student set up a science demonstration consisting of a coffee can, a spark plug stuck in the top of the can, and a spoonful of gasoline. The gasoline was placed in the can and the plastic lid attached with the spark plug gap end hanging down inside the can. The student connected the spark plug to some dry-cell batteries. Nothing happened. The student didn't know what to do. What do you think the demonstration was supposed to show? What would you do in such a situation and why?

2. Learning to Make Hypotheses

The following questions require students to make hypotheses:
1. High in the mountains a dam suddenly breaks. What possible hypothesis could you give for such an occurrence?
2. A candle is placed in a tray. Water is added to the tray so that it is two inches deep. The candle is lit. The candle

is covered with a jar. What will happen and why? Which of the following hypotheses do you think to be valid?

a. The water level will remain the same in the jar.
b. The water level will be lower in the jar than in the tray because the heat of the candle will cause water to evaporate.
c. The water level will rise because all the oxygen will be burned up, causing less gas pressure in the jar.
d. The water level will be lower because when the candle burns it produces carbon dioxide in the jar, which will cause greater gas pressure, forcing water out of the jar.
e. The water level will rise because the candle gives off heat. This causes expansion of gases around the candle. When the jar is placed over the candle, the candle goes out, the air cools, and has less pressure than room-temperature air. The water level then rises.

4. Interpretation of Data and Making Valid Conclusions

I. In a controlled experiment involving the effect of Gibberellic acid on the growth of Alaska peas and Little Marvel peas, from the period immediately after germination to 8 days of growth, the following data were observed:

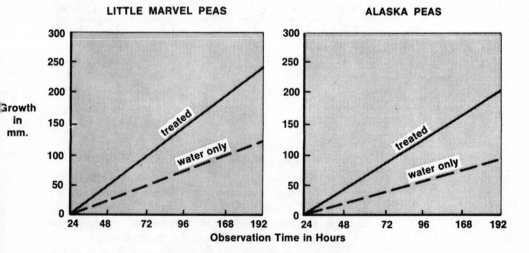

From the data in the graph, which of the following conclusions are (a) reasonably certain, (b) supported by experimental evidence, (c) not confirmed by experimental data? Mark your answers a, b, or c.

_____ 1. Gibberellic acid is a strong growth-stimulating factor.

_____ 2. Gibberellic acid is the only auxin that acts on pea plants specifically.

_____ 3. Gibberellic acid has marked effect on dwarf-type pea plants.

_____ 4. Gibberellic acid acts specifically on the stems but has no effect on growth of roots.

_____ 5. The function of using plants treated with water was to justify the factor that growth was not due entirely to water.

_____ 6. The effect of Gibberellic acid is the same on other dwarf plants as it is on dwarf peas.

_____ 7. Had the experiment been continued for longer than seven days the Gibberellic acid would have had no effect.

_____ 8. Straight-line growth is the only effect that Gibberellic acid has on peas.

II. During controlled experiments, the effects of various concentrations of auxin indole acetic acid on the growth of oat coleoptiles from which the tips have been removed were measured. The coleoptiles selected from seedlings germinated in darkness were placed in sugar solution with indole acetic acid as indicated in the table below. Growth effects were observed at the end of 24 hours.

COLEOP-TILE	CONCENTRATION MG/L. AV. CHANGE IN LENGTH				
Initial Length	Sugar 290	IAA .01	IAA 0.1	IAA 1.0	IAA 10.	Unknown IAA Sol.
2.0	2.8	3.4	5.1	7.0	2.1	6.3
2.1	2.6	3.0	4.9	6.8	2.1	6.2
2.2	3.0	3.3	5.2	7.0	2.3	6.0
2.2	2.8	3.3	5.1	7.2	2.3	6.1
2.0	2.4	2.8	5.0	7.1	2.1	6.0

Does the analysis of the experimental data seem to indicate that the following are true or false?

_____ 9. From the data in the table it is indicated that the optimum concentration of IAA is between 0.1 mg and 1 mg/liter.

_____10. Increasing concentration from zero produces the same proportional increase in growth rate.

_____11. Concentration of IAA influences cell division but has little effect on cell growth and elongation.

_____12. Removal of the coleoptile tip removes the source of plant auxin.

_____13. Coleoptiles are selected from seeds germinated in darkness because light greatly increases the production of plant auxin.

_____14. Above a certain concentration of IAA growth is actually inhibited.

_____15. Based on the growth rate of the various concentrations, the unknown solution is about 0.05 mg/l.

5. Devising Experiments

    a. How would you find out whether soda pop is harmful to your teeth?

    b. How would you determine which metal is the best conductor of electricity?

    c. You suspect that a special plastic material used to coat floors might cause lung cancer. How would you go about proving this?

    d. You suspect a certain chemical is a stimulant. How would you find out?

    e. You believe you have a mutant mold strain that has lost the enzyme capable of digesting certain carbohydrates. How would you prove this?

SOME GENERAL CONSIDERATIONS IN TEST CONSTRUCTION

This section contains some suggestions for constructing tests. These are not exhaustive, but they are fundamental for any test constructor.

True-and-False Test

If the examination is limited to true or false, seventy-five or more items are needed, statistically, to overcome the guessing factor. On a 100-question true-or-false test, students should be able to get about fifty questions right without knowing anything about the subject if they just guess. Some instructors help to eliminate this problem by subtracting the number of wrong answers from the number of right answers to determine the score and penalize for guessing. This procedure is not recommended, because students usually think the instructor is using this technique for malicious reasons. It is undesirable also because the student is penalized for guessing. In science we wish to have students make hypotheses—good guesses.

Avoid overbalancing the test with too many true-or-false questions. Try to have these fairly even in number. This prevents a student who knows little about the material from getting a high score simply by assuming that more questions are true (or false).

Avoid using statements that might trick students.

Don't use the same language found in the text. This suggests to students that they should memorize.

Don't use double negatives in a statement. For example, do not write "Methane does not have no hydrogen in its molecule."

Avoid ambiguous statements. For example, do not write "Erosion is prevented by seeds."

Avoid using complex sentences in your statements.

Don't use qualitative language if you can possibly avoid it. Do not write, for example, "Good corn grows at a slower rate than hybrid corn," or "The better metals conduct electricity faster."

Arrange your statements in groups of ten to twenty. This helps to relieve tension for those taking the test.

Place the responses for answering the questions on one margin so that they can be easily checked by using a key.

Multiple-Choice Test

A multiple-choice test is made of items having more than three responses. If there are not at least four possible responses to each question, a correction formula should be used. A multiple-choice test differs from a multiple-response test in that only one answer is correct for each question in the former type of test.

In a multiple-choice test, make all responses plausible.

All answers should be grammatically consistent.

Attempt to keep all responses about the same length.

Randomize the correct answers so that there is no pattern in the examination. Students often look for a pattern.

Remember that the correct response often can be arrived at by a process of elimination as well as by knowing the correct response. Try to prevent this in your phrasing of the answers.

Present first, in the question, the term or concept you wish to test for.

Test for the higher levels of understanding as much as possible.

Require a simple method for the response. Place the space for the answers all along one margin of a page, so that they can be easily keyed. This can be done by providing short lines on the margin.

Group your items in sections. This makes it easy to refer to various sections of the test and helps break monotony in taking the test.

Group together all questions with the same number of choices.

Completion Test

Completion tests usually emphasize recall. For this reason, use them sparingly.

Limit the number of blanks in a sentence. Many blanks make the question too indefinite.

The answers should be written on the margin for ease in correcting. Leave a small space in the body of the question but a large space at the margin where the student will write the answer.

Avoid giving grammatical hints. For example, do not use only *a* or *an* before a space—include both words.

Limit your questions so that a short answer and only one correct answer is possible. This insures greater objectivity.

Don't have students complete a statement lifted from the text. This stresses memorization and not understanding.

Matching Test

Matching questions should be grouped. When there are more than fifteen matching items in a group, the test becomes cumbersome.

Number your questions and use letters for your answers, or the reverse; but be consistent.

Although matching tests have traditionally stressed simple recall, they can be used to test for recognition or application of principles. Three sample matching questions follow:

Questions	*Answers*
_____1. A machine which would require the least amount of friction on it to move it 20 feet.	a. Pliers b. Wheelbarrow c. Ice tongs d. Seesaw
_____2. A machine which could best be used to pry open a box.	e. Doorknob f. Pencil sharpener g. Saw
_____3. Which of the listed devices is made up of the greatest number of simple machines?	

Self-Test

A self-test is similar to any other test in its construction, but it is taken by the student mainly as a learning device. It usually has questions on one side of a page and the answers on the other side. The student takes the test; then he turns over the page and checks his answers. The instructor can use the completed test as a means of stimulating discussion.

Teachers usually set up self-tests on Ditto masters and run off enough copies for their students. A suggested format is shown in Figure 20. The back page should contain a detailed explanation for each answer so that students learn from the test. The student folds under the answers on the right side of his page. The answers then are next to the correct answers and explanations on the *left* margin of the back page. This makes it easy to correct the test.

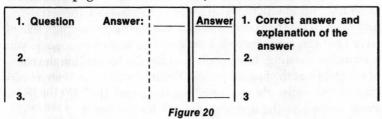

Figure 20

A Problem Test

This kind of test presents a problem and asks the students to work on it. The test usually contains a series of questions the students are supposed to answer in solving the problem. A problem test can be constructed with relative ease if it is based on a problem that has actually confronted a scientist. These problems can be easily obtained from a scientific journal. Give the students information about the problem and have them devise their own hypotheses, research designs, or methods of collecting and recording data. A problem test can best be used to acquaint students with scientific processes. The test may have an answer sheet similar to that for a self-test, or it may be used to stimulate discussion. Scientific problems which are open-ended in nature are preferable for this kind of test.

GENERAL STATEMENTS ABOUT TESTS

Tests bring out only a sample of what has been learned. One which tests for understanding of the principles taught in a unit and of the processes of science is a good test. As we have pointed out before, students learn the way they are tested. If tested for rote memorization, they will memorize. Teacher-prepared tests have traditionally sampled rote memory to a large extent. Modern tests emphasize reasoning, critical thinking, and problem-solving skills.

The more frequently students are evaluated the better they achieve. Quizzes should be given rather frequently, at least once every two weeks. A large test probably should be given at least once every three weeks.

All tests should contain questions which vary in difficulty. The easier questions should be placed in the first part of the test to give the students confidence and to minimize frustration and nervousness.

Consider the time factor. How long will it take students to complete the test? Some students will finish much sooner than others. What will you do then? If they do not have some work outlined, they are likely to present discipline problems.

Discourage dishonesty. Attempt to remove the temptation to copy by spreading students out or by making two versions of the same test and alternating these when you pass out the tests. You may wish to try the honor system; some instructors in high school have used this with success. Caution the students as soon as you see anyone cheating. It generally is better not to mention the name of the culprit at the first infraction. You might just say, "I see cheating" or "Some people are stretching their eyeballs." If you really stress honesty in the first tests your task of trying to prevent dishonesty will be lessened during the rest of the term. Set a pattern of honesty immediately in your classes. Be present while students take tests, and discipline a pupil if he is guilty of continued dishonesty.

SUMMARY

Evaluation involves the total assessing of a student's learning by the instructor. Science teachers evaluate students mainly by tests and laboratory reports. Just as there are levels of learning so are there levels of testing. Modern teacher-made tests should devote less time to recall questions and more to the applications of knowledge. Application questions can be easily devised by determining the principle to be evaluated, stating a problem involving the principle, and asking questions to see whether the student understands the principle. Because mathematics and graphing are so much a part of science, tests should incorporate many graphs and mathematical data. A good technique to use to see whether students understand graphing is to have them complete a graph or devise one.

Each test should contain questions that will enable the teacher to evaluate students' understanding of the methods of science. Students should know how to recognize a problem, make hypotheses, interpret data, draw valid conclusions, and devise experiments.

Certain features of each type of test must be considered before tests are constructed. Completion and matching tests, because of their emphasis on recall, are to be discouraged. Self-tests and problem tests place more emphasis on self-instruction and can be used to motivate class discussions. A teacher should consider how long a test will take and should provide assignments for those who finish before the class ends. The incidence of discipline problems is lessened in this way. Cheating must be strongly discouraged early in the term.

Good test construction requires considerable sophistication if sole dependence upon memorization is to be discouraged; therefore, teachers are urged to get further training in this very important part of their professional competence.

Further Investigation and Study

1. What does evaluation involve?
2. What do you know about a test if a student passed it by only reading the book the night before the test?
3. Describe what you consider to be a weak test; a strong test.
4. What are some principles to consider in constructing a test?
5. What is meant by the statement "A test is only a sample"?
6. How would you evaluate laboratory work and why?
7. What are the levels of testing?
8. What are the steps you should take in writing a question requiring application of knowledge? Write three examples of this type of question.
9. What is the function of mathematics in science?
10. Devise three questions involving understanding of graphing.
11. Make four questions which test for understanding of science processes.
12. Write two questions requiring a student to use his creative ability.
13. What is the purpose of a self-test and how is such a test constructed?
14. Write a problem test and describe its objectives.
15. What are some general considerations to be kept in mind when making: a true-false, a multiple-choice, and a completion test?
16. How will you operate in the classroom to insure honesty?
17. What considerations about time and individual differences are necessary for giving a test?
18. What were the three main ideas discussed in this chapter?
19. It is said that a teacher who uses evaluation well is more scientific. What is meant by this statement?
20. Read Chapter 16, "Constructing the Classroom Test," in *Biology Teacher's Handbook* (New York: John Wiley & Sons, Inc., 1963), pp. 455-87.

Learning in science requires an
adequate experience background.
This applies equally well to the learning
of facts and the understanding of
principles. It applies to the
development of skills as well as
to the development of habits
and attitudes.[1]

Thurber and Collette

10

Materials of Science Teaching

The science teacher is fortunate in having an abundance of teaching materials to draw upon. His problem is selecting the proper materials and techniques for accomplishment of his task. Recent years have seen a proliferation of teaching materials of every description; the display areas of any large convention of science teachers present an overwhelming variety of these materials.

With the availability of teaching aids in great variety, it is well to consider the purposes they serve in the process of educating science students:

1. More of the students' senses are stimulated by teaching aids. They frequently activate the avenues of learning involving sight, sound, touch, smell, and taste. Combinations of senses are appealed to more often.
2. Teaching aids maintain interest. Students are likely to be in a receptive frame of mind for maximum learning.
3. Teaching becomes less fatiguing when a variety of methods and materials is used, and the teacher's enthusiasm is maintained.
4. Individual differences are most adequately served by a variety of teaching aids. Students frequently learn better by one method than by another.

---

[1] Walter A. Thurber and Alfred T. Collette, *Teaching Science in Today's Secondary Schools* (Boston: Allyn and Bacon, 1964), p. 80.

Science seminar library with current published materials.

Photo courtesy of Clark Science Center, Loomis High School, Windsor, Conn.

5. Teaching aids provide opportunities for frequent changes of pace. This is particularly useful in junior high school teaching.
6. Specific materials designed for specific teaching tasks are more effective because of their refined nature. For example, a well-designed model of certain geological features may illustrate a point better than a photograph or in some cases better than an actual field trip to the scene.

Printed materials will continue to retain their role of importance in science teaching. Textbooks are still a basic source of information in science classes; and when they are used judiciously and with realization of their limitations, textbooks contribute substantially to the teaching-learning situation.

USE OF TEXTBOOKS

The science teacher must place the textbook in its proper perspective in his classes. Students generally feel more comfortable with a textbook than without one. It serves to organize information, stress important concepts, direct activity, and set goals for the study of a particular science. All of these are important contributions. It must be remembered, however, that a textbook alone cannot achieve even a majority of the objectives of science teaching. It cannot provide laboratory experiences, develop true inquiry skills, or teach self-reliance in the solution of problems. These are objectives which are achieved best by other methods and materials. But in collaboration with a variety of other materials, the textbook is an important contributor to these objectives.

The selection of a textbook for a given science class is frequently a haphazard affair. Textbooks are often chosen after superficial inspection. Color may influence one's choice more than content; photographs may carry more weight than organization of subject matter; advertising appeal may be more of a deciding factor than usefulness to students.

In selecting a textbook in science, criteria should be established against which competing books can be rated. A list of these criteria follows:

A. Factors which deal with the subject matter content and organization:
   1. Logical organization, sequence of difficulty, groupings of topics
   2. Emphasis on principles and concepts
   3. Accuracy of information
   4. Usefulness of information, applications, and functional nature of the material
   5. Recency of information, modern concepts, theories and applications

B. Factors which deal with development of non-content objectives:
   1. Attention given to development of interests, appreciations, and attitudes
   2. Attention given to problem-solving approach
   3. Attention given to skills of science learning
   4. Attention given to role of science in society, scientific literacy
C. Factors which deal with experiments, demonstrations, and activities:
   1. Inquiry or verification approach
   2. Student participation, activity, and investigation
   3. Use of simple materials, degree of structure in laboratories
   4. Emphasis on drawing conclusions on basis of observation and experimentation
D. Factors which deal with mechanical features of the textbook:
   1. Binding, size, durability, attractiveness
   2. Size of type, level of reading difficulty, summaries, glossaries, index
   3. Illustrations, maps, charts, graphs, captions
   4. General ease of usage of the book for purpose intended
E. Factors which deal with authors of the textbook:
   1. Qualifications (experience, level of preparation)
   2. Quality of writing, interest, and readability
   3. References to purposes of the book and intended use
F. Factors which deal with prospective useful life of the textbook:
   1. Copyright date, revisions, and reprintings
   2. Nature of material, rate of obsolescence, years of usability

It is suggested that the foregoing criteria be used with a rating scale for comparison of competing textbooks. A number scale like the one that follows might be used:

   0—Book totally lacking in the characteristic
   1—Occasional evidence of the characteristic
   2—Greater evidence of the characteristic but below average
   3—Reasonably frequent evidence of the characteristic
   4—Excellent evidence of the characteristic
   5—Superior in all aspects of the characteristic

OTHER PUBLISHED MATERIALS

A large number of resource books in physical science, earth science, and biological science are now available. (See list in the Appendix.) These books are designed to help the science teacher plan experiments, demonstrations, and student activities. Categories of activities in various subject areas are usually provided. Lists of materials, diagrams of apparatus set-ups, and suggestions for use of simple materials are included in the resource books. Many of these books are suitable for student use with little if any assistance necessary from the teacher.

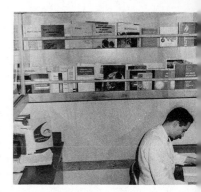

Effective teaching depends upon many current periodicals and other materials.

Photo courtesy of the Biology Dept., Oak Park and River Forest High School, Illinois

A well supplied reference library near the science room is an effective means of stimulating learning.

Photo courtesy of Wayne Taylor, Michigan State University.

Another type of published material in common use in science classes is paperback monographs (and pamphlets or bulletins on special topics). Excellent examples of this type of publication are those in the Science Study Series of Educational Services, Incorporated. These are inexpensive pocket books on a variety of scientific topics, designed to supplement the PSSC physics course or to provide general scientific reading at a non-technical level. Another excellent series is the BSCS Pamphlet Series, which consists of single-topic booklets designed to develop one or more of the nine BSCS themes. The pamphlets provide a rich source of reference materials in depth and breadth for student and teacher use. Reprints from the *Scientific American* serve a useful purpose in science classes, particularly at the senior high school level. Articles are written for the non-technical reader yet present material of current scientific interest at the research edge of science.

AUDIO-VISUAL MATERIALS

Recent years have seen the development of numerous audio-visual aids for the science teacher. These materials have not always enjoyed the best possible usage because of certain limiting conditions. It is important for the science teacher to have a good working knowledge of a number of audio-visual devices and to be aware of their teaching possibilities.

In the use of an audio-visual aid, the teacher's most important consideration is: "Is this the most effective method at my disposal for teaching these concepts?" If the answer is yes, every effort should be made to incorporate the aid into classroom planning. Mental inertia or unwillingness to try a new device should not remain a deterrent to good teaching in science.

Films

Motion-picture films have been used with varying effectiveness for many years. Limitations are:

1. Poor scheduling or inability to secure the film at the optimum time or place in the course.
2. Poor showing techniques—unfamiliarity with the equipment, inadequate room darkening, or general ineptness resulting in wasted time.
3. Poor choice of film. Films thirty minutes long may have only five minutes of appropriate learning material in them. The intellectual level of the film may not be appropriate for the class.
4. Indiscriminate use of films that do not contribute to attainment of the course objectives.
5. Cost of rental or purchase, which may be prohibitive for some school systems.

Advantages of motion-picture films are numerous. They include:

1. Close-up sequences, which may be superior to a live demonstration.
2. Organization of content in succinct and capsulized form.
3. Showing of experiments not feasible in the average laboratory because of time and expense.
4. Slow-motion or time-lapse photography, which demonstrates phenomena too rapid or too slow for first-hand observation.
5. Showing of natural scientific phenomena from places not accessible for class visitation.
6. Animated sequences which help to clarify difficult concepts.
7. Creative sound and visual effects for dramatic reinforcement learning.

Variations on the standard film techniques are becoming more common. Single-concept films are produced by several companies. These films are brief and develop a single important idea which can be pursued further in class discussion.

Teacher's guides for films are frequently provided. They give a résumé of the major film ideas, suggestions for use, questions raised in the film with possible answers, and a list of supplementary reading materials.

Eight-millimeter film loops are now available in a number of areas in biology, chemistry, physics, and general science. Fitted into a small cartridge with a specially designed silent-film projector, these film loops can be operated by individual students when the need arises. Since they are usually less than ten minutes long, they can be run repetitively until the concepts are thoroughly understood.

Film loop projectors fitted with removable cartridges containing five to seven minutes of continuous film are useful teaching aids in meeting individual rates of learning.

Photo courtesy of Bill Tillery, Colorado State College.

Film strips have a number of advantages in science teaching:

1. They are relatively inexpensive and can be purchased by a

library or science department for a permanent collection. The projectors are correspondingly less expensive than motion-picture projectors.

2. When used as a class-teaching technique, they can be stopped at a given frame for whatever time is needed to discuss the ideas presented.

3. Students may study these films individually with minimum disruption of other class work. They are noiseless and require only a moderately darkened area.

4. Film strips are frequently available at no cost from industry and government sources. These are usually accompanied by a printed narrative guide or lecture for use when showing the film.

There is no single rule for best usage of films. The science teacher must be free to use films creatively and flexibly, as they can be fitted into his teaching objectives.

Slides present innumerable opportunities for good teaching. Their relatively low cost and flexibility in use are points in their favor. A science teacher may acquire a highly effective teaching aid by making a collection of his own photographs on colored slides. The purchase of a tripod and inexpensive close-up lens enables a teacher to make pictures of plant and animal life for purposes of illustration in the classroom. The slide collection acquired in this way becomes more valuable each year. Students frequently can produce their own slides for reports, projects, or classroom research activities.

Overhead Projection

Science teachers are making increasing use of overhead projection as an aid to teaching. The versatility of this instrument makes it an extremely useful tool for everyday classroom use. Some teachers consider it an indispensable piece of equipment.

The cost of an overhead projector is relatively moderate, much less than a motion-picture projector, for example. The cost of transparencies, or the materials for making them, is likewise low. Only moderate darkening of the room is needed for satisfactory visibility. The instrument is quite as convenient to use as the chalkboard and is frequently used as a replacement for it.

Materials that can be used with the overhead projector in science teaching are contained in the Tested Overhead Projection Series (TOPS) produced by a project of the National Science Foundation.[2] In this series, a large number of chemistry demonstrations were designed to be carried out on the overhead projector in full view of the entire chemistry class. Other adaptations for physics

---

[2] Hubert N. Alyea, "Tested Overhead Projection Series," *Science Teacher,* March, April, September, October, November, December, 1962.

and biology have also been designed.[3] In many cases, demonstration apparatus is designed to be used with standard overhead projectors.

Other Audio-visual Aids

Radio and television have not yet fulfilled their promise as teaching aids for the science teacher in the average classroom. Ordinary A.M. radio has occasional use as special programs in science or science related areas are broadcast, but these at best are of a general nature for lay consumption. A few educational F.M. stations have produced science programs, but the average science student has not benefited perceptibly from them. Probably the most direct benefit has been derived from on-the-spot news reports of scientific events such as space shots, natural disasters, or scientific breakthroughs.

The dream of television as an effective teaching tool has still to be realized. However, news coverage of scientific events has become immeasurably more dramatic since the advent of television and probably has contributed to vastly improved understanding of these events. The opportunity to witness the launching of a manned satellite or final photographs from a television camera crashing on the moon is tremendously stimulating. It undoubtedly molds public opinion in regard to scientific problems and progress. In this respect, one of the objectives of science teaching, development of scientific attitudes, is being met by forces outside the control of the science teacher. It remains to be seen whether this is beneficial in the long run. A false impression of science as a gimmick-filled world of spectacular advancements in technology may be created at the expense of a sound understanding of the role of science in society.

As a direct teaching tool, television has yet to come into common use. The technical problems and expense of installation and upkeep are formidable. Closed-circuit television may become the tool of the future, but it has not yet received wide acceptance; too few science teachers are trained to use it and explore its many possibilities. Furthermore, very few schools are equipped to make use of it on a planned and regular basis.

Some of the advantages which may be realized when television comes into full use are:

1. Direct teaching to large numbers of students by a well-prepared master teacher with access to adequate demonstration equipment.
2. Opportunity for close-up viewing by the television camera, giving optimum visibility to all students.

A telemicroprojector serves an invaluable purpose for making small things clear to a large class.

Photo courtesy of Wayne Taylor, Michigan State University.

---

[3] Walter Eppenstein, *The Overhead Projector in the Physics Lecture* (Troy, N.Y.: Rennselaer Polytechnic Institute, May, 1962).

3. Opportunity for on-the-spot viewing of scientific events.
4. Opportunity for training science students in television techniques and familiarizing them with its teaching and learning possibilities.

Desirable as these outcomes are, it is important to realize that television has limitations as well. It cannot replace the science teacher. It cannot develop laboratory skills or replace the difficult, repetitive problem-solving practice necessary for mastery of certain science concepts and skills.

Tape recorders are gaining popularity as teaching aids in science as well as in other subjects. In biology, for example, they might be used to record sounds of nature such as bird calls and other forest sounds. Classroom use of the tape recorder might include taping student reports, interviews with community resource people, or scientific programs on radio or television. The tape recorder is an instrument most science students take to readily. Their resourcefulness in its use may surprise the science teacher at times.

A technique which has come into recent use is the telelecture. Arrangements are made with a scientist or other resource person to speak via telephone with a science class; full-class audibility is provided, and students are permitted to ask questions or otherwise converse with the speaker. The cost for telephone connections for a half-hour session may be $50, but the per-pupil cost may be quite moderate when evaluated in terms of motivation and scientific learning involved.

Ample and easily accessible equipment provides more opportunities for student experimentation.

Photo courtesy of the Biology Dept., Oak Park and River Forest High School, Illinois.

MATERIALS FOR THE LABORATORY

One of the major problems for the junior and senior high school science teacher is the procurement and maintenance of equipment for the laboratory. Questions of what and how much to order, how to use the apparatus most effectively, and how to store it conveniently for future use are difficult ones, especially for a beginning science teacher. Frequently it is the teacher moving into a new position who faces these problems in their most acute form. If the preceding teacher has not kept careful records of apparatus and equipment and maintained them in good working order, the job of inventorying can be overwhelming.

If possible, it is wise for a teacher beginning a new science position to plan to spend several days in advance of the regular opening of school to work on inventorying equipment, checking its condition, and preparing orders for needed supplies for the year. This preparation will contribute to more effective teaching throughout the year. Teaching plans may be built around certain materials that are available in sufficient quantities for classroom demonstrations and experiments.

Adequate supplies of materials facilitate better physics teaching.

Photo courtesy of Harold Pratt, Science Supervisor, Jefferson County, Colorado.

Purpose of Laboratory Materials

Science deals with phenomena of nature. The study of these phenomena can not be conducted effectively through abstract or theoretical discussion alone, although this may be necessary at times. For most science students, a presence of actual objects, models, or living specimens makes a phenomenon sufficiently concrete to be understood. Science materials and apparatus—demonstration equipment as well as materials for experimentation—are designed to fulfill this function.

Ordering and Inventorying

Several laboratory-supply companies are listed in the Appendix. Several smaller companies which specialize in types of materials not generally available from the larger companies are also listed. Various types of models, audio-visual aids, and electronic and optical equipment are frequently obtainable from those smaller companies. It is advisable for the science teacher to become familiar with these sources as well as with the names of the standard laboratory-supply companies.

A useful publication has been produced by the Council of Chief State School Officers for assisting science teachers and school authorities in ordering equipment.[4] Planned to give help in adminis-

---

[4] *Purchase Guide for Programs in Science, Mathematics, and Modern Foreign Languages* (Boston: Ginn & Company, 1959).

tering Title 3 of the National Defense Education Act, the publication establishes master lists of desirable equipment and supplies for science subject areas as well as for elementary general science. Minimum specifications for equipment in basic, standard, and advanced programs in each of these areas are established.

Factors to be considered in purchasing equipment and laboratory materials are:

1. Is this the best available item for the teaching purpose intended? Because of the importance of the teaching task and the limitations of time, it is essential to have the best possible tools at hand. The equipment must be basically simple, be capable of illustrating the intended principles, and be engineered to work well.

2. Will the materials serve their intended purpose for a reasonable length of time? Classroom equipment and other materials receive hard use as successive classes work with them. They must be designed to withstand rough handling for several years. Poorly engineered and constructed apparatus, though possibly less expensive to purchase, is rarely economical in the long run.

3. Are the materials functional? Can they be stored easily without excessive disassembly? Do they lend themselves to student use? Generally the purchase of overly delicate apparatus or equipment with unnecessary precision capabilities for the secondary science class is a mistake.

4. Is the cost reasonable for the quality of equipment purchased? Comparison of catalog prices from several companies can result in savings. It is essential to check the specifications carefully on all apparatus ordered, to insure that they meet the requirements of the situation.

New equipment and materials of the non-expendable variety should be inventoried upon receipt. A three-by-five card file system is a useful method to keep a record of new purchases and

---

Inventory for (subject) ....

Item: .... Catalog No: ....

Company: .... Cost: ....

Storage Code: ....

DATE	NUMBER	CONDITION	REORDER DATE	COST

Figure 21

current stock of materials and apparatus. A suggested form for an inventory card is shown in Figure 21.

Each non-expendable item in stock should be inventoried on a card of the type shown. Expendable items should be inventoried on a longer form of the checklist variety. With a well-kept inventory checklist, it should be possible to ascertain the amount and condition of expendable items at a glance. Since the preparation of such a list and the effort required to keep it current is quite time-consuming, it is desirable to assign this task to student laboratory assistants if possible. An inventory checklist might look like the one shown in Figure 22.

Proper storage of materials increases laboratory efficiency.

Photo courtesy of the Biology Dept., Oak Park and River Forest High School, Illinois.

Inventory of Expendables (Con't.) Chemistry					
DATE	ITEM LIST	CONDITION	ON HAND	NEEDED	COST
4/65	Tubing, glass (4mm)	Ex.	10 lbs.	None	
4/65	Tubing, glass (5mm)	Ex.	10 lbs.	None	
4/65	Tubing, glass (10mm)	Ex.	None	5 lbs.	$.40/lb.
4/65	Tubing, rubber (4mm)	Good	50 feet	None	
4/65	Tubing, rubber (5mm)	Good	10 feet	40 ft.	$2.75/100'

Figure 22

SUPPLEMENTARY TEACHING AIDS

The sources of supplementary teaching materials are multiplying year by year. For the science teacher, a major problem in using them is proper selection.

Educational departments of industrial companies have created or made available to teachers innumerable aids for the teaching of science. Many of these materials are free or obtainable at minimal expense. The Appendix gives a list of catalogs of free and inexpensive teaching aids. Many kits and project materials for the use of junior and senior high school students are now available. Some of these are free of charge if ordered in small quantities. See the Appendix for lists of such materials.

A very useful type of supplementary teaching aid is student science periodicals such as *Science News Letter, Current Science, Science World,* and *Science and Math Weekly.* Subscription rates to students are nominal. In addition to highly informative articles on current science topics, these publications frequently contain suggested activities and experiments for students. A teacher's edition, containing suggestions on how to use the activities and other materials, is sometimes provided. The science teacher of today would be remiss if he failed to make use of these very teachable materials of science.

As with the standard equipment and materials discussed earlier, storage and availability for effective use is a problem in the classroom. A storage file for printed materials, indexed by subject, is a necessary item; and periodic up-dating is required.

SUMMARY

The science teacher in today's schools has almost unlimited choices of materials with which to enhance his teaching. Wise selection of appropriate materials is a major problem. In making these choices, it is important to recognize the basic reasons for using a variety of materials in science teaching. Individual differences among students demand variations in methods and materials. The psychology of learning supports the thesis that variety of materials promotes better learning. More of the senses are stimulated, and more avenues of learning are activated. Availability of many materials gives opportunity for individual work and experimentation.

Published materials form a large segment of today's science-teaching arsenal. Textbooks continue to be essential tools, although there is greater recognition of their limitations than formerly. It is still important to select textbooks in science carefully and with understanding of their contribution to the learning situation. Many supplementary monographs and pamphlets are now available. These are usually written at a level suitable for junior and senior high school students. Authors of these publications have done an excellent job of communicating difficult concepts at the research frontiers as understandable science for the non-technical reader. At the same time, they have demonstrated the processes of science admirably and conveyed realistic ideas of the role of science in society.

Audio-visual equipment and materials continue to gain in sophistication. Although radio and television have not yet realized their potential as teaching aids in the average classroom, increasing strides are being made in their use. New techniques with over-head projectors, film-loop projectors, and single-concept films are finding increasing popularity. Individual differences are being served better by these materials, and individualized instruction is enhanced by more flexible audio-visual aids.

Science teaching depends greatly on laboratory work. Materials for the laboratory are increasing, both in variety and in abundance in science classrooms. The National Defense Education Act of 1958 has assisted tremendously in the improvement of laboratory facilities and equipment. The science teacher must become familiar with sources of laboratory apparatus and supplies. In the choice of equipment, educational value must be considered above all. In addition, durability and functionality are important considerations. Once purchased, equipment must be maintained in usable condition. An up-to-date inventory is necessary, and an adequate budget for purchase of new materials must be available.

The future of science teaching in secondary schools looks good. One of the bright spots in this picture is the increasing awareness of better and more abundant materials available for student and teacher use. No other factor is of greater importance in the advance of the current philosophy of learning through inquiry. Students must have the motivation, the time, and most of all the proper materials for effective learning by inquiry methods.

Further Investigation and Study

1. Select three textbooks for secondary science teaching in your field of preparation or interest. Evaluate them using the criteria in this chapter. What are the major strengths and weaknesses of the books you have chosen?
2. Begin a file of free and inexpensive materials related to your teaching area. Arrange an indexing system for easy access and location of items when needed. Sources of free and inexpensive materials are given in the Appendix.
3. Survey the current research in science education for information on the effectiveness of teaching by television. On the basis of your findings, what conclusions do you draw concerning the future of educational television in the field of science?

By that part of our plan which prescribes the selection of the youths of genius from among the classes of the poor, we hope to avail the State of those talents which nature has sown as liberally among the poor as the rich, but which perish without use, if not sought for and cultivated.
Thomas Jefferson,
Letter to M. de Marbois, 1781

11

Teaching Science for Individual Differences

The bell rang, and students filed into class. Several went to the study carrels and began organizing the material they were to use for that day. Two boys went over to a corner, selected two film cartridges, and were in the process of getting ready to view them on the small rearview screens. Several other students were busy at the laboratory desks setting up their equipment. They were preparing to do a number of different experiments. One student went into the growth laboratory to check on his project.

The initial impression of this class might be one of chaos, but upon closer observation it would become apparent that the students were working but working in a way very different from that in the traditional class situation. The activities of the class had been organized by the teacher so that each student could progress at his own rate.

The classroom organization portrayed above is somewhat idealized in the extent to which instruction has been adapted to individual differences. Today, however, more and more school systems are endeavoring to modify their instructional program so that greater attention is given to these differences. Research in psychology has long indicated that there are human differences which have implications for teaching. This research indicates that:

1. Individuals come to the classroom with varied backgrounds and experiences. Because the experiences vary and because of genetic differences, not all students readily learn in the same way.
2. Individuals vary in the rate at which they learn concepts. Some individuals must have a relatively prolonged contact with concepts before they grasp them.

Teachers, although mindful of these facts, traditionally have done little to adjust for individual differences other than to give an extra reading assignment to the more advanced students. Teaching to challenge the individual potential of students generally has not been done, for several reasons:

1. Tradition and traditional ways of instruction and teaching have been the primary barriers to such a change.
2. There have been logistics problems. If students can progress at their own rates this necessitates the addition of more courses, materials, and equipment. The class period may have to be lengthened, particularly in a laboratory-oriented situation. Adopting a scheduling system which allows variations of time spans, depending upon the activity or class assignment of the student, presents fantastic logistics problems particularly in the larger schools.
3. Teachers, for the above reasons and because they have been trained for group instruction, often feel insecure when confronted with the idea that not all students in a class will be performing tasks at the same time.

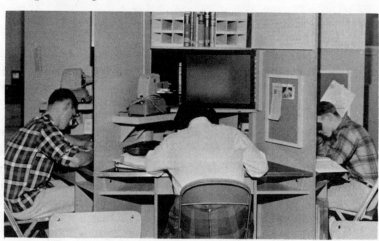

Biology students working individually in a study carrel arrangement.

Photo courtesy of Littleton High School District, Littleton, Colorado.

4. Group instruction is cheap and easy to direct and control. When a body of students progresses through a curriculum at varied rates according to their ability, there must be more automated resources and equipment for them to use.

5. Facilities for individualized instruction are more costly because they require more space.

In spite of these resistances to change, there are patterns of instruction which have received acceptance because of a belief that they will offer a greater chance for each individual to realize his potential.

INDIVIDUALIZED STUDY AND CONTINUOUS PROGRESS

There is an exciting development in American education which changes instruction from a teacher-centered to a student-centered endeavor. This approach is to let each student progress through the course work at his own rate. The anecdote on the first page of this chapter describes a class which has been organized for student-centered instruction. In it, not all members of a class are doing the same thing at the same time; this is truly the essence of individualized study. The schools using the individualized approach generally employ one of three plans.

In one plan, the students are grouped according to ability. They are assigned so many units of work to complete, and when they finish this work they may be moved at the end of the semester to another group of higher ability and achievement. This plan has met with considerable success at the Melbourne High School in Florida. It is a form of homogeneous grouping.

A second approach is called the continuous-progress plan. It allows students to progress from subject to subject with no time restriction. If a student finishes biology in six weeks and passes an examination, he then moves into chemistry. This approach has been worked out in mathematics at the Laboratory School at Brigham Young University and at Bryce Valley High School, Tropic, Utah, as well as at several other schools.

A third approach is called individualized instruction. It lets students work at their own rate, but when they finish the normal work required they remain in the same class and progress to enriched material. This plan is being tried at several schools in the country. It has the advantage of eliminating scheduling problems found in the other plans when students are allowed to pass from subject to subject during the school year. Schools trying modifications of these plans are Cape Kennedy High School and Nova High School in Florida, Meeker High School in Colorado, and Middletown High School in Rhode Island. Mr. Gerald Einem of the Cape Kennedy High School says of the individualized plan:

> Until you break up a grade, you don't realize how futile it
> is to be teaching a group of kids the same material merely be-
> cause they are the same age. Slow and fast students live in a
> separate world. Even the teacher doesn't know how different
> they are until he teaches them separately. We haven't begun
> to realize how imaginative the fast student can be—how much
> challenge he needs to keep him interested—and how much
> specialized help the slow student needs to keep him from
> closing his mind and quitting. I am constantly surprised in
> both directions.[1]

The advantages of individualized instruction have been outlined
by Dr. Sidney Rollins of the Middletown Project in Rhode Island:

1. Pupil progress ranges from a year or more ahead of where
   pupils would be if they attended a graded school to half a
   a year behind the usual achievement of a given grade level.
2. Dropout rate (less than one per cent at Middletown) is
   drastically lower than the national rate of 30 per cent.
3. Pupils recover from extended absences from ungraded
   schools more quickly and easily than from graded schools.
4. Pupils stimulate themselves to greater effort—even in
   April, May, or June when they normally begin to ease up
   on studies.
5. Pupils seem to appreciate the opportunities for avoiding
   the boredom and frustration that the ungraded structure
   can offer.[2]

The ungraded continuous progress or individualized approach
to the curriculum allows for individual differences and permits students to progress at their own rate. The bright are not held back,
and the slow are not frustrated by levels of achievement out of
their grasp. Before classes can be organized for individual study,
three factors must be considered. These factors are facilities, materials, and procedures.

First, how can the facilities be adapted to allow students to
progress at various rates? Some students may be doing laboratory
work. Others may be taking tests; reading; watching a film strip,
film, or slides; listening to a tape recorder; taking a program; using
a teaching machine; or discussing in groups. The facility must be
designed or remodeled to encourage all of these activities and the
use of all of these materials.

In the past, a teacher was hindered in organizing classes for individualized instruction mainly by an insufficient supply of educational materials adapted for various ability levels. Since the
advent of programmed instruction and teaching machines, plus

---

[1] Bernard Asbell, "High School for Sky High Learning," *Education Digest*,
March, 1964, pp. 26-28.
[2] S. P. Rollins, "Ungraded High Schools: Why those Who Like Them Love
Them," *Nation's Schools*, LXXIII (April, 1964), 110.

the wealth of materials produced by the national science curriculum projects, this problem has been considerably lessened. For example, in BSCS biology a student could finish reading the text, do all of the laboratory exercises, and then progress to doing a number of the Laboratory Blocks such as "Complementarity of Structure and Function," "Animal Growth and Development," "Plant Growth and Development," "Microbes: Their Growth, Nutrition, and Interaction," "Field Ecology," and "Regulation in Plants by Hormones." He could read any of several of the BSCS pamphlets, such as *Guideposts of Animal Navigation, Biological Clocks, Bioelectricity, Courtship in Animals, Biomechanics of the Body, Metabolites of the Sea,* and *Blood Cell Physiology.* Having finished these he could progress to the second-level BSCS course. The wealth of materials makes it possible to provide enough work to keep even the most able student active for at least two academic years. Other curriculum projects have similar possibilities. These abundant materials were not available until rather recently. Before their publication, a teacher was faced with innumerable problems in devising activities for students, and this difficulty practically prohibited any experimentation of the type possible in the BSCS course.

In designing instruction for individual progress, the teacher becomes mainly an organizer and a counselor rather than a teller. The problem of organizing the materials so a student knows what he is to do each day is considerable; however, once plans are worked out and perfected, the classes run with a minimum of organizational duty. The teacher then is free to give his time where it is most needed. The teacher will have to produce a syllabus outlining the progression of class assignments. The syllabus may outline a general number of laboratory, reading, and film assignments to be required, plus supplemental assignments for enrichment and depth.

Storage and organization of equipment for each of the laboratory exercises presents a problem. The instructor must anticipate problems in laboratory organization. For example, in laboratory many students may want to do a certain activity at the same time, while there may not be enough equipment. Alternate program paths should be suggested for the student to follow until the material is available.

The advantage of individualized instruction is that a student is not held back by a class average, if he is advanced, and the slow learner is not frustrated by trying for attainments far beyond his grasp. Furthermore, there is a shift in emphasis from extrinsic to intrinsic rewards. A student doing an assignment at his own rate receives self-confidence and a sense of competence which may not manifest itself so easily in group instruction. The real joy of learn-

A biology teacher gives a large group lecture in a room specifically designed for that purpose. She is using an overhead projector which projects images that can easily be followed by everyone in the room.

Photo courtesy of Educational Facilities Laboratories report, "High Schools, 1962," Wayland, New Jersey.

ing in this manner comes in the student's completing the task on his own, not from an *A* given by the teacher.

Another attempt to give greater attention to individualizing instruction is to use some large-group instruction in a team-teaching situation on certain days, with small-group and individualized instruction other days. This is a compromise between having traditional group instruction and individualized instruction. This approach has the advantage of releasing teachers during the time the large-group instruction is taking place to better prepare and organize materials. When this method is used, there is no reason why the students can't be taught on an individualized basis when the group is broken down into smaller ones. One danger in this approach is that the large-group instruction may be overemphasized. Overemphasis on group instruction is antithetical to the philosophy of the modern science course and can not be justified with our present understanding of the learning process in science.

A small group meets in a seminar room.

SPECIFIC SEMINAR OR INDIVIDUALIZED FILM INSTRUCTION

In small high schools with fewer than 300 students, where it is impossible to offer courses in all the sciences, film instruction supplemented with laboratory work and an occasional discussion by a teacher has been successful. The Harvey White, the Baxter Chemistry Series, and the American Institute of Biological Sciences films have been used as the main basis for instruction. Each of these series offers a complete course on film. The students observe all the films in sequence on their own, read the text, and do some laboratory work. Better achievement has resulted when the films have been followed by laboratory experiences. The students can if they wish see the films several times. Although film courses have drawbacks, they make it possible for a student to receive training in areas for which a qualified teacher is not available. The Western States Small School Project, financed by the Ford Foundation and involving eleven western states, found that the film courses have worked well particularly for the above-average student.[3]

A filmed course has the added advantage of serving as an inservice course for the teachers viewing it. During the second year when such a course is used teaching can be much more effective, since the teacher is better prepared and is probably more willing to improvise in teaching the class. One danger in using film instruction without correlated laboratory experiences is that the students soon become bored and lose interest.

---

[3] Colorado State Department of Education, *Colorado Western States Small Schools Project* (Annual Report, July 1, 1962-June 30, 1963), p. 73.

GIFTED STUDENTS

Traditional economics held that a country was richly endowed if it was rich in raw materials. This outlook was modified when it was realized that some countries lacking rich resources, such as Switzerland, had a comparatively high standard of living. These countries were rich because they possessed one of the most important resources—creative and gifted manpower. A country's survival and development is dependent upon its caliber of manpower. This is most apparent in modern technology. In order to maintain a high standard of living, more and more raw material must be withdrawn from poorer raw resources. The genius of the scientist and technologist must be brought to bear in order to accomplish such a feat. It is primary, if we are to maintain our standard of living with an increasing population and decreasing raw materials, that we utilize to a greater extent our potential of gifted manpower.

A gifted student working in a project area as a member in a science seminar.

Photo courtesy of Bob Waters, Colorado State College.

Educators and national leaders aware of the importance of this have for many years endeavored to discover and offer special enrichments for the gifted students. In large schools special homogeneous classes for the gifted have been devised, or individual attention has been given to gifted individuals in regular classes. Many extra-curricular activities have been specially designed for the gifted in science. These have been supported by school districts, business, industry, and state and federal governments.

Gifted students—or, as some psychologists and educators prefer to call them, the academically talented—are generally defined as individuals who are in at least the top 20 per cent of their class and have an I.Q. above 120. They are good in reading and abstract reasoning, spatial visualization, memorization, ability to apply knowledge, and persistence in solving problems. The gifted in science usually have a hobby associated with science. The Joe Berg Foundation has established special seminars in high schools for gifted students in science. Students are selected from the tenth and eleventh grades to start in the program. They suggest that the selection of the gifted should be based upon results from the Terman-McNemar Test of Mental Ability, the Primary Mental Abilities Tests (SRA), the General Education Achievement Tests, the Gates Reading Test, and the California Arithmetic Tests, plus grades and teachers' recommendations. Because this selection process is rigorous, a relatively low number of students are selected, seldom more than fifteen to twenty students in large metropolitan high schools. Most school districts in choosing students for gifted classes use some variation of the selection process described above.

Business and Industry Support Gifted Students' Programs

Business and industry, because of the wide concern for improving the quality of the manpower supply and a greater realization of

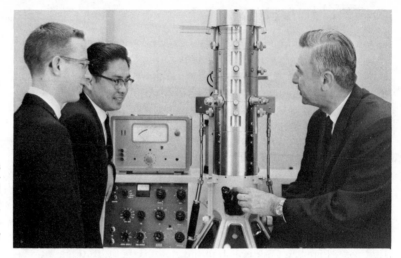

A recipient of a Future Scientists of America Award visiting the Research Facilities of the Ford Motor Company with his teachers. A scientist is explaining the operation of the electron microscope.

Photo courtesy of the Ford Motor Company.

community responsibility, have fostered many programs for the gifted student. Often these have been developed in cooperation with the public schools or with a professional science group such as the American Chemical Society. The Future Scientists of America—sponsored by the National Science Teachers' Association and financed by the Ford Motor Company, the American Society for Metals, the American Dental Association, and other societies—is an actively supported special program for students in science. Although the program is not limited to gifted students, many of the awards usually go to the gifted. The requirement for entering this program is that students in grades seven through twelve submit to panels of scientists in each of the twelve regions of the country research papers of 1,500 to 5,000 words. These papers are read by the panels. The best papers are selected from each region and submitted for national judging. The several scholarship awards are given to each of the regional winners and to the national winners. The program has been in operation since 1961 and has met with wide acceptance. It is the consensus of the regional directors of this program that the caliber of the papers submitted has definitely improved since its inception. Presumably the science teachers involved have become more aware of the processes of science and of the characteristics of a good experiment and have as a result been more helpful to their students.

Science Fairs

Science fairs are usually supported on the local level by business-industry and the schools. Nationally, Science Service operates and encourages the program.[4] There is wide acceptance of

---

[4] Science Service, 1719 North Street, N.W., Washington, D.C. 20036, sponsors Science Clubs of America and science fairs and publishes *Science News Letter*, as well as booklets on science projects and experiments.

the science-fair program. Most science fairs are open to students from all grade levels. Students from the junior high school should especially be encouraged to submit a research project. Students at this level who are annually involved in science fairs become very sophisticated in their research by the time they are seniors in high school. Submitting a project is in itself a learning experience which can contribute considerably to giving students a better understanding of science as research.

The Westinghouse Science Talent Search is sponsored by the Westinghouse Foundation in cooperation with the Science Clubs of America. Students take a science aptitude test, submit a report on a science project, and provide records of grades and other data. Forty students are invited to Washington, D.C. where they are guests of Westinghouse. They tour the city, hear and meet top scientists, and receive scholarship awards.

The San Bernardino City Schools, in cooperation with local industries, developed a special summer program for its gifted students as early as 1957. Twenty students participated in the first program. They were organized into a class, given instruction, taken on comprehensive tours of laboratories, and were later assigned for work experience with one of the participating companies. These industries attempted to match students with specific jobs in their plants. The initial experiment was so successful that the program has been amplified to include more participants.

New York City formed a committee to help gifted students obtain work experience in laboratories during the summer. The employed gifted students were usually given preliminary lectures about the plant in which they were going to work and then assigned to a member of the scientific professional staff. Each student received a modest salary plus considerable help and guidance from the staff. The general program has met with wide acceptance and has been enlarged since its inauguration.

In the upper part of New York State, industry has also been active. Industrialists in this area have supported special weekly meetings for high school students selected from thirty-four high schools in the area. These programs have been held throughout the semester for the group. The typical program has been a dinner and lecture-demonstration on some scientific subject.

Hughes Aircraft Company established a program in 1957 for a team of gifted students to work on a group project in their plant. The students toured the plant, heard lectures given by various staff scientists, and worked on the designated research project. A spokesman for the company has said that the "cost of the complete program has been more than compensated for by the inspiration and guidance that these students have gained from their experience on the team."

In addition to the activities mentioned above, business and industry have made surplus equipment available to schools and have provided scientists and engineers to act as consultants for gifted students working on research projects.

Many Chambers of Commerce and local branches of the National Association of Manufacturers have now appointed educational representatives from their membership. These representatives when contacted endeavor to meet requests for science consultants, speakers, surplus equipment, or other services that the members of their organization can provide.

The San Francisco Regional Branch of the West Coast Electronic Manufacturers' Association has gone as far as to appoint one of its members as sponsor for each of the high schools in its area. The schools can call the sponsor for any assistance they might need in the field of electronics.

Many other parts of the country now have industry-education councils which give educational aid and are also especially interested in helping gifted students. The Southern California Industry-Education Council, the Mid-Hudson Science Advisory Council, the Indianapolis Industry-Schools Committee on Science and Mathematics, Science Pioneers Incorporated of Kansas City, The Washington Joint Board of Science Education, and the Frontiers of Science, in Oklahoma, are but a few of the organizations formed for this purpose.

The activities mentioned above indicate that business and industrial groups are, more than ever, willing to give special assistance to science and mathematics teachers; however, the first step toward a cooperative relationship between an industrial group and the school must usually come from the educators. School districts can enrich their course offerings, have extra-curricular activities such as science clubs and science fairs, and better their supply of scientific equipment if they will make an effort to determine what their local industries are willing to contribute to the school. Science instructors, because of the present deep concern over science and science instruction, never have been in a better position to obtain assistance from industry to enrich gifted-student activities.[5]

School-Supported Programs for the Gifted

The school programs for the gifted in the larger schools usually consist of special homogeneous gifted classes. The general pattern of these classes includes more advanced subject courses or a seminar arrangement. The Advanced Placement Program consists of college-type courses offered on the high school level.[6] The program is operated by the College Entrance Examination Board, a nonprofit organization founded in 1900. Its purpose is to encourage

---

[5] Robert B. Sund, "Business and Industry Help the Gifted Student," *School Science and Mathematics*, Vol. LX, No. 9 (December, 1960), pp. 707-8.

[6] College Entrance Examination Board, *A Guide to the Advanced Placement Program*, 1964-65 (Berkeley, Calif., 1964), p. 4.

college-level courses for advanced students in high school, make suggestions for these courses, provide examinations, and urge colleges to grant credit to freshmen who have completed such a course in high school. The science courses for which the College Entrance Examination Board provides recommended programs and examinations are physics, biology and chemistry. Most colleges recognize these courses and accept a completed course as work for college credit.

Some schools have offered advanced or gifted-student physics courses using the Special Topics in Physics. These are materials produced by Educational Services, Incorporated, the same group that has produced the PSSC physics course.

Many schools give advanced or gifted-student courses in biology. These vary widely. Several simply use college-level texts and laboratory manuals. Others have used materials of the BSCS, such as the Laboratory Blocks. These have been supplemented by outside reading, such as the BSCS Pamphlet Series. The BSCS has produced a Second Level BSCS Course. The group states that this is not a gifted-student course but just another biology course for those students who want to take more biology. It has, however, served as the basis for a gifted-student program.

Some junior high schools have offered BSCS biology for the gifted on the ninth-grade level. This has been a successful innovation, and there is presently a considerable amount of interest in curriculum development at this level. Laboratory-oriented programs for gifted students in junior high school are likely to receive increased attention in the near future.

Small high schools seldom are able to offer special classes for the gifted. They have, however, encouraged students to do course work more or less on their own. The procedure is usually to have one or two students study a science film series or read the text and do laboratory experiments. The students may not have direct supervision, although a science instructor meets with them from time to time to discuss their work and assignments. This plan has the advantage of developing more self-direction and responsibility on the part of the students. Gifted students usually respond well to this type of operation.

Forest Hills High School, in New York, has had special honor classes for gifted students since 1941. Students in these classes are encouraged to work in laboratories on their own time. Gifted students also must take additional mathematics and language courses, beyond those ordinarily required for graduation. Dr. Brandwien has done follow-up studies of Forest Hills graduates and has found that over 90 per cent graduate from college as science majors. Many go on for advanced degrees.[7]

---

[7] P. F. Brandwien, *The Gifted Student as a Future Scientist* (New York: Harcourt, Brace & World, Inc., 1955).

A modification of this approach which is mainly extra-curricular has been tried in Menlo-Atherton High School in California. A special laboratory is equipped for the Gifted-Student Research Group. Each of the students is assigned laboratory space and drawers after he has submitted to the science staff an approved experimental design. Students must submit semi-annual reports of their progress if they wish to remain in the Research Group. Students may enter the program as freshman and continue their research until graduation. Monthly seminars are held at either a local scientific industry or research center, and at each seminar one or two of the students report on their research; the rest of the time is devoted to seeing the research facilities of the host institution and talking with scientists actively involved in research. The Menlo-Atherton High School from time to time prints a directory listing scientists who have been willing to consult with students on special problems, research facilities in the area, equipment available at the school, rules of membership and conduct, alumni of the progam, and awards received by members of the school's research group. The Menlo-Atherton program is mainly extra-curricular in nature.

New York City has provided a special school for those particularly interested in science. The Bronx High School of Science, which serves the entire system, has well-equipped laboratories and offers many enrichments for those motivated in science.

The San Mateo High School District, San Mateo, California, is one of the districts which have sponsored a future-teachers program. Those students interested in becoming science instructors at any grade level are encouraged to participate in the program. One activity in the San Mateo program releases students from afternoon classes for two weeks so that they may visit elementary or junior high schools. While in these schools, the high school students act as cadet teachers, give science demonstrations, and devise and have students perform scientific experiments. The reaction of the teachers and students involved in the San Mateo program has been excellent. Although this program is not limited to the gifted, it is the opinion of the faculty that it has induced several of the gifted to go into teaching.

Science Nights and Science Days

Some schools, instead of participating in science fairs, have held science nights or science days. The types of activities presented may be similar to those found in science fairs, the only difference being that more students may be involved and that the students may be present to demonstrate or explain their science projects or work. Science fairs have been criticized for emphasizing the dramatic or the "showy" part of science rather than experimentation. The science nights (or days) have been an attempt to get away from this by having the student present to explain the purpose of his research. Participation in these programs usually has not been limited to gifted students and should not be. Students of varying ability and from various science classes should be represented so that the public understands the effort of the science department to encourage the learning of science regardless of the student's capability. It is, however, natural for the science staff to emphasize the accomplishment of their best students and to give the gifted science student some special recognition.

Government Programs for the Gifted

Many government agencies have become increasingly interested in the training of scientific manpower. Because of this interest they have offered programs on the secondary level to encourage and provide enrichment for the gifted science and mathematics student. The interest of these government agencies has been kindled by their realization that they will need an increased supply of technical manpower in the future. It is in their direct interest to see that this type of manpower is available. Among those agencies most concerned is NASA. NASA, in cooperation with NSTA, has established several regional Youth Science Congresses. About 250 gifted science students are invited to attend these congresses. Students read reports about their research, hear talks by NASA scientists, and visit with the scientists.

The U.S. Army—in cooperation with colleges, universities, educational organizations, and industries—presents a number of Junior Science and Humanities Symposia for the gifted. Usually over 200 students are invited to each of the many symposia, which may last for four days. They see and hear discussions, lectures, and demonstrations; have informal chats with scientists; and tour research facilities.

The National Science Foundation Summer Science Programs

The National Science Foundation, a federal government agency, offers high-ability secondary school students over 7,000 opportunities to obtain intensive training in science and mathematics at leading colleges and universities in the country during the summer. These summer programs usually offer subject-matter courses in depth or place the student as a junior member of a team actively engaged in research under the direction of a senior scientist. Most programs involve both class instruction and laboratory research. The summer institutes last five to thirteen weeks. Students normally are asked to pay for the cost of room and board plus transportation, but there are some funds available to the director of the institute for those students who would be prevented from coming because of financial need.

Activities of Professional Groups for the Gifted

Many professional societies are actively interested in improving science instruction. They may conduct seminars, sponsor special conferences, or provide liaison personnel for school systems to help students doing project work. Most states have academies of science. A part of the program sponsored by these academies is the Junior Academy. Outstanding science students in the secondary schools, who are members of the Junior Academy, are invited to the conventions of the state academy, where a time is set aside for the junior members to report their research. The state academies of science also oversee a program financed by the National Science Foundation, which absorbs the costs of scientists' visiting schools to give talks on their field and research activities.

Junior Engineering Technical Society

JETS is organized to encourage interest in engineering and allied technical fields. Publications which show how to organize JETS clubs are produced by the group's national office. The clubs are usually sponsored by professional engineering societies or industries on the local level.

THE SLOW LEARNER AND THE CULTURALLY DEPRIVED STUDENT

Educators have become increasingly concerned about what the school does for the academically poor student. There are a number of reasons why students do not do well in school. They may come from disadvantaged homes; they may have low academic potential; or they may have the potential but, for emotional and other reasons, underachieve. This group does not include the mentally retarded. The majority of the slow learners in science have I.Q.'s under 90 and usually do not exceed the fiftieth percentile of the DAT Verbal Reasoning and Numerical Ability Tests. This group of individuals would fall within the lower 20 per cent of student population; however, this is a national figure. In a slum-district school over 50 per cent of the students may be in this category, whereas in an upper socio-economic area the proportion of students in this category may be less than 5 per cent. The number of students in this group nationally is about 3 million.

Students in the lower 20 per cent of the student population do not achieve well in the traditional science courses, and they have difficulty with the modern curriculum courses. BSCS has done an extensive evaluation of students taking its courses and has concluded that BSCS does not work well for the lower 20 per cent of the student population. Because of this fact, BSCS has produced the Special Materials in Biology, which include text material, laboratory activities, a teacher's manual, and programmed learning activities. The philosophy of the Special Materials course follows the traditional BSCS approach. That is, the course emphasizes laboratory work and learning by inquiry. Many of the laboratory exercises are similar to those found in the other versions of the BSCS course. They differ, however, in their reading level and in the amount of material covered. The students progress at a slower rate but are taught more thoroughly; important concepts in modern biology are explored. Most of the work is done in class, with little or no outside assignments.

The Special Materials Committee, in charge of producing the course under the auspices of BSCS, has emphasized the importance of having teachers who are especially interested in working with this type of student. They state:

> Those of us who are familiar with the instructional situation for unsuccessful learners in some of our high schools, observe that these youngsters are placed at a further disadvantage by rotation of these classes within the staff of the science department. From year to year, the teachers take turns teaching these "unwanted classes," and often new, inexperienced teachers are assigned to them. No one is skilled nor does any one take time to become skilled in teaching the slow learner. However, there seems to be a trend, probably influenced by the increasing work being done on the education of the exceptional students, toward the appearance of more and more teachers who find teaching these students rewarding. Some of these teachers actually prefer the slow classes to the regular ones. . . .[8]

The Special Materials Committee is convinced that the unsuccessful learners deserve teachers who:

1. Consider the teaching of unsuccessful learners important
2. Have some competency for teaching unsuccessful learners
3. Understand the importance of laboratory experiences for unsuccessful learners
4. Have little doubt that these youngsters can learn and appreciate the concepts within modern biology
5. Have a good background in the principles of modern biology

The suggestions of the Special Materials Committee have implications for other courses and grade levels of science instruction. Often slow students have not been allowed to do laboratory work. Science teachers lectured, conducted discussions (although this was often difficult), or demonstrated. Experienced science teachers who have worked extensively with the slow learner and experimented in their teaching approach have discovered that one of the

---

[8] Biological Sciences Curriculum Study, *BSCS Newsletter* (Boulder, Colo.), No. 24, 1965, p. 27.

best ways to teach this group is, in fact, by laboratory work; however, these students need some initial guidance relative to the freedom they have in the laboratory situation, especially if they have never experienced this type of freedom in the school. With understanding, direction, confidence in their potential, frequent encouragement, and real enjoyment in working with them, teachers do succeed in having these students learn reasonably well. The teacher in the Special Materials course, as in other BSCS courses, is supposed to act as a sympathetic guide and to help students learn by getting them actively involved in the learning process.

Slow learners have difficulty sometimes because of reading problems. The advantage of the laboratory-oriented class is that reading is placed in perspective as an aid in discovering fundamental information in science but not as the sole means to this end. Academically poor students traditionally have caused the most discipline problems and have been more likely to become drop-outs. An activity-centered classroom, although it may not cure this situation, does lessen both of these problems.

Greater efforts must be made to educate academically poor students. More experimentation with new courses organized to give these students opportunities to inquire in all areas of science and in all grades are needed. The need is particularly apparent on the junior high school level where the drop-out rate is relatively high.

SUGGESTED TEACHING ACTIVITIES FOR INDIVIDUAL DIFFERENCES

Listed below are some suggestions on how to give better individual attention in teaching science. The list is not exhaustive; a wise and creative teacher not afraid to experiment in new approaches will undoubtedly discover many more:

1. Individualize the class instruction as suggested in the first part of the chapter.
2. In a traditional class framework have students make an extra-credit file. Allow them to include in it reports about all types of science activities in which they participate. For each project the student should place in the folder a note about what he learned. The following activities might be included: (a) A report of having completed some "programmed" science unit. Presently many companies are producing programs and teaching machines for use in science and mathematics. Since a student can progress through these at his own rate, they allow for individual differences. These materials, however, are only aids to instruction; they should in no way lessen the importance of laboratory experiences. (b) Science book reports. Credit should be given for having read newspaper ar-

ticles, journals, and books. We have tried this approach and have found that the bright students may read as many as thirteen books a quarter and that the average number of books read is seven. (c) A written report on some problem. These can be library-research problems; problems in the community, such as conservation, water contamination, or smog; and other field problems. (d) Making a collection—classifying and keying the items in it. (e) Special demonstrations presented to the class. (f) Reports on special additional experiments done at home, in the field, or in the laboratory. (g) Reports on trips to museums, planetariums, observatories, parks, or research facilities. (h) A written summary of an educational-television science program. (i) Participation in science fairs, science nights, or science days. (j) A study of the natural areas near the school.

3. Offer individualized period assignments whereby the students progress at their own rates and at the end of the period hand in what they have accomplished. This may be a laboratory assignment or a written assignment.

4. Specify a minimum acceptance level for laboratory reports and extend special recognition to a student who goes beyond this requirement and reports in depth.

5. Have multiple texts available in the class. If a slow student has difficulty reading one text endeavor to find another for him. The College Outline Series or other similar publications may prove helpful.

6. Offer special activities for the academically talented. (a) Let them assist you in preparing solutions and materials for laboratory work. They should be involved in experiences which are educationally desirable and not just in "janitor" work. (b) Encourage gifted students to do research. They should consult with a scientist or engineer in the community on their research problems. Local industries, museums, zoos, botanical gardens, and hospitals have resource people who will often help. (c) Have the gifted students from the upper grades go to some of the lower grades and demonstrate a scientific principle or explain a science project. This technique is especially appreciated by the students in junior high school classes, who enjoy watching students from the upper grades with high status present activities. This approach also has the advantage of giving recognition to the able student and motivating him to greater achievement. (d) Obtain special equipment needed for experiments and other work to be done by the gifted. Local industries are often willing to give or lend such equipment. (e) Encourage the parents to obtain books and to take trips which have advantages for science students. Parents often welcome a suggestion from the teacher about

A student teacher taking a small group for specialized study.

Photo courtesy of Bob Waters, Colorado State College.

books and types of trips to help enrich their children's science education.

SUGGESTED SCHOOL-WIDE ACTIVITIES FOR INDIVIDUAL DIFFERENCES

The school can (1) establish science fairs, science nights, displays, and assemblies, like those sponsored by the National Aeronautics and Space Agency, the Atomic Energy Commission, General Motors, and other government and industrial groups; (2) have students of various abilities give presentations to the PTA; (3) produce a science newspaper for the school; (4) encourage science clubs and science research groups; (5) provide special science seminars for interested students; (6) offer special summer school classes and seminars; (7) offer students research experiences as aides to scientists.

RECOGNITION

High school science teachers have given too little consideration to the importance of recognizing achievement. They should learn from their colleagues, the coaches. Coaches award pins, blankets, cups, and ribbons; make news and see that the activities of their teams are publicized; put on athletic shows; etc. They are masters in the techniques of giving and getting recognition. All students, not only athletes, like to receive some recognition for their work. The science teacher's team is his students. A science instructor should utilize the techniques of public relations and adapt these methods for giving recognition for achievement in science. Science fairs and science nights do as much for the science achievers as a football game does for the football player. Write-ups in the local newspapers and school paper on what is happening in science are as important to the science student as the sports page is to the athlete. Display cases containing student projects, science-club pins, science blocks similar to the athletic letter blocks worn on sweaters, plaques, and certificates are all forms of recognition used by schools. Creative, well-trained teachers will find many ways to motivate students by the use of proper recognition. Regardless of how learning is stimulated, it is mandatory that the teacher constantly be aware of the importance of reinforcement and recognition.

Leaders in the science teaching profession all use varied methods of giving recognition. The end result of their efforts is a contribution to better science. How wonderful it must be to a student to be able to progress according to his ability, not devalued but given recognition for contributing as best he can. A teacher who creates this kind of climate in his classes separates himself from the less effective technicians of teaching and is on the way to becoming a master teacher.

SUMMARY

Students come to the classroom with varied backgrounds and experiences. They vary in the rate at which they learn concepts and in the way they learn them. Schools ordinarily have not taught for individual differences because of tradition, problems of scheduling, poor teacher preparation, instructional costs, poor facilities, and poor equipment. In spite of these problems, several schools are endeavoring to change the traditional pattern of instruction. Individualized study, continuous progress, and homogeneous groups in science classes have been tried with success. In individualized instruction a student works according to his ability at his own rate; he remains in the class throughout the year. In the continuous-progress plan a student stays in a class until he has finished the required work. He may finish an entire year's work in a matter of weeks; if so, he takes another subject. Homogeneous grouping classifies students according to their abilities; the gifted or slow learners may be grouped into special classes. The ungraded continuous-progress or individualized approach to instruction makes allowance for individual differences.

The advent of new curriculum developments with a wealth of materials has made it possible for teachers more easily to adapt classes for individualized instruction. These materials make it possible for the gifted student to study a subject in depth.

In designing courses for individualized instruction the teacher becomes mainly an organizer and a counselor rather than a teller. Some schools have taught for individualized differences by making available one of the science film courses in biology, physics, or chemistry. These courses are often arranged on a seminar basis, or there may be some extra laboratory sessions to supplement the film instruction. Students may view these film courses several times if they wish to.

Educators and government, professional, business, and industrial leaders have become concerned about motivating the gifted. As a result of this concern, several programs have been specifically sponsored for gifted students. These programs include, among others, special seminars, work experiences, summer institutes, scholarships, congresses, junior academies, and advanced placement. Other programs in which gifted participate are science days, science nights, and science fairs.

Greater efforts are being made to help the culturally deprived or slow learners in science. This group constitutes about 20 per cent of the student population and numbers about 3 million. The BSCS has produced the Special Materials in Biology, a course specifically designed for the slow learner.

There are numerous, diverse activities that can be used to teach for individual differences. These may include—in addition to total individualized instruction—programmed instruction; book reports; written reports; collecting; performing special demonstrations or experiments; reports about trips to museums, planetariums, observatories, or research facilities; special studies of live area; reports of research, production of a science newspaper; and participation in science fairs or science nights. Recognition should be given for student accomplishment, and there should be an active public-relations program emphasizing achievement in science. Scholarships and awards of all types are encouraged as a means of giving extrinsic motivation for outstanding science achievement.

Further Investigation and Study

1. Suppose that you are head of a large science department in a large metropolitan high school. Your department is fairly traditional. What would you do to get the department to teach more effectively for individual differences?
2. What is the difference between individualized instruction, continuous progress, and homogeneous grouping? Which of these do you think is the best approach and why?
3. Describe a class designed for individual achievement. Assume that the class has thirty students.
4. Why hasn't there been more attention given to individual differences?
5. How does the traditional role of the teacher change in teaching for individual differences?
6. What are the advantages of individualized instruction in science?
7. How have the modern curriculum developments contributed to the possibility of better individualized instruction?
8. What are some of the ways in which you would try to give the gifted student a better education?
9. What would you do for the slow learner?
10. What kind of teachers do slow learners require?
11. What is done in some of the small high schools to teach more effectively for individual differences in science?
12. In what ways has the government tried to improve the education of the gifted?
13. In what ways have businesses tried to improve instruction for the gifted?
14. What are the advantages and disadvantages of science fairs, science nights, and science days?
15. If you were going to provide a gifted-student course in physics or chemistry what would you do?
16. Suppose that you are a science supervisor who is convinced that little is being done for the slow learner. You are responsible for the science instruction in five high schools and eight junior high schools. What would you do to overcome this problem?
17. How would you design a class situation so that there would be no recognition given to individual variation?

12

Creativity: Our Most Valuable Resource

A newly appointed science supervisor in the Platte School District decided to see some science classes. He notified the science teachers that he would observe and help them in any way he could. The first visit he made was to Mr. Wiley's junior high school science class. Upon entering the class, the supervisor noticed that several students were working with microscopes, studying pond water. Four were working in the greenhouse on a project with hormones. Most were doing the laboratory exercises outlined in their BSCS laboratory manual. One was working in a space reserved for him in the stock room. This student was working on the BSCS "Complementary of Structure and Function" block. He had before him the plans and materials for constructing a chimograph. Another student was setting up a demonstration to be used in the class the next day. He had designed the demonstration and was obviously excited about it.

The tenor of the class was activity. The students were all involved in performing some task, experimenting and learning about their biological world. Some students worked in groups, others individually. There was diverse activity; yet it was purposeful. It was apparent that the students were allowed a considerable amount of freedom and respected their freedom. For example, observing pond water had not been planned for that day; but the students brought the materials into class, and Mr. Wiley encouraged them to study the pond water and make a report of their findings.

---

[1] Phillip H. Abelson, "Creativity in the Sciences," *Science*, Vol. 140 (June 21, 1963), p. 171, Copyright 1963 by the American Association for the Advancement of Science.

Contrast this class with another, a physics class, the supervisor visited:

> The instructor was lecturing to the class about magnetism. He explained magnetic domains, lines of force, fields, etc. He stopped and scolded one student for not paying attention. Several students squirmed in their seats. Two looked out the window, one looked occasionally at the clock, another was drawing pictures on a piece of paper.

In which of the classes was there greater learning? In which do you think creative ability had the better chance to manifest itself? How would you teach biology creatively? What would you have done in the physics class to make it come alive and contribute to the development of a student's creative abilities?

In the world market, the United States competes economically not so much with material goods as it does with brainpower— creative brainpower. Our labor is too expensive for competition. Almost every country in the world can beat us in this respect; they can supply labor at a lower cost. We produce products which are conceived in the minds of creative individuals. American industry increasingly relies on creative minds to solve problems with less expenditure of time and labor. By being inventive and efficient our industry has managed to remain productive and support a high standard of living. We export creative genius in the form of our industrial products. Because of the complexity of modern industry and because of the advent of automation, the demand for creative individuals will accelerate. No longer will a problem be attacked by large masses, as was the case in the building of the pyramids, but rather by a few creative minds and a minor force of technical assistants. Taylor says in this respect:

> In the future, our nation cannot depend on sheer quantity of manpower, but must strive to find high quality personnel, especially creative persons, to deal with its vital problems. In fact, an approach utilizing sheer quantity of men and facilities can be unduly expensive, so much so that we would probably find on careful analysis that we cannot afford such wasteful and inefficient approaches. Since scientists are basic to scientific progress, there may be no potentially greater payoff per unit of expenditure than from continuing to investigate the nature of creative talent and creative performance, preferably more energetically than in the last few years.[2]

The science professions are manned by individuals with various capacities and endowments. One can find widely diverse kinds of science professionals, from the simple technician to the creative scientist pushing the knowledge of his discipline beyond the fron-

---

[2] From *Creativity: Progress and Potential* by Dr. Calvin Taylor, p. 3. Copyright 1964 McGraw-Hill Book Company. Used by permission of McGraw-Hill Book Company.

tier. It is the creative scientists who are the pathfinders for the entire scientific enterprise; however, many individuals with the potential to become creative scientists remain undiscovered and unkindled. Clearly the demands of a society moving rapidly toward the twenty-first century can ill afford to let such a waste continue.

The study of creativity has received increasing attention from psychologists over the last decade. They have spent a considerable amount of time setting up criteria for defining creative endeavor. One psychologist who has been active in this effort is Dr. Ghiselin. He suggests that "the measure of creative product be the extent to which it restructures our universe of understanding."[3]

Another psychologist, Dr. Paul Torrance, says of creativity, "I have chosen to define creative thinking as the process of sensing gaps or disturbing missing elements; forming ideas or hypotheses; and communicating the results, possibly modifying and retesting the hypotheses."[4]

Creativity is generally thought of in two ways. Some think that the only true creativity is the production of some new entity or idea never before known to man. Others believe in a more inclusive definition which would allow for inventions which are unique to the individual; these inventions would not be new to mankind but *would be* to the individuals making them. This latter view is the more useful for teachers trying to develop creative ability.

CHARACTERISTICS OF CREATIVE INDIVIDUALS

Creative individuals vary in motivational, intellectual, and personality traits. Individuals with creative potential can most easily be recognized by the following characteristics:

1. Curiosity. This probably is one of the easiest signs by which a science teacher can discover creative individuals.
2. Resourcefulness.
3. Desire to discover.
4. Preference for difficult tasks.
5. Enjoyment in solving problems.
6. Drive and dedication to work.
7. Flexible thinking.
8. Rapid response to questions and habit of giving more answers to questions than do most students.
9. Ability to synthesize and see new implications.
10. Pronounced spirit of inquiry.
11. Breadth of reading background.

---

[3] *Ibid.*, p. 86.
[4] *Guiding Creative Talent* (Englewood Cliffs, N.J.: Prentice-Hall, Inc., 1962), p. 16.

Creative people have a marked ability to form abstractions and to analyze and synthesize information. In science, they demonstrate persistent and sustained concentration on trying to get a piece of apparatus to work or to solve some particular scientific problem. They are usually sensitive and individualistic. Given freedom as well as direction, creative students often surprise the instructor with their capabilities and interests.

ARE I.Q. AND TEACHERS' GRADES GOOD PREDICTORS OF CREATIVE ABILITY?

Considerable research has been done on the identification of creative individuals. Research indicates that I.Q. tests generally do not reveal creative ability and are, in fact, not good instruments for this purpose. Traditional measures of intelligence generally evaluate only a few of an individual's abilities. Dr. Paul Torrance states, "If we were to identify the children as gifted on the basis of intelligence tests, we would thereby eliminate approximately 70 per cent of the most creative."[5] He says further, "If the intellectual capacities of the individual are to be fully developed, the abilities involved in creative thinking cannot be ignored. The traditional measures of intelligence attempt to assess only a few of man's intellectual talents."[6] Because traditional tests do not reveal creative potential, psychologists have devised a number of tests which attempt to identify creative ability on the junior high and high school level.

Although creativity and intelligence do not necessarily have a high correlation, there is some indication that creative scientists do have high intelligence. Ann Roe found that the minimum intelligence required for creative production in science was higher than the average I.Q.[7]

Attempts to identify creative individuals by the use of school grades generally have been unsuccessful. Grades are usually given in school for mastery of information, and Taylor reports that "sheer mastery of knowledge does not seem to be a sufficient condition for creative performance." He found, in a study of creative scientists, little correlation between academic achievement in school and production in industry.[8] MacKennon in studying adults with outstanding creative ability found that the majority received C's and B's in school rather than A's. The fact that creative students did not

---

[5] *Ibid.*, pp. 4-5.
[6] *Ibid.*
[7] "The Psychology of the Scientist," *Science*, Vol. 134, (August 18, 1961), pp. 56-59. Copyright 1961 by the American Association for the Advancement of Science.
[8] *Op. cit.*, p. 110-111.

receive high grades indicates that schools either have not recognized this ability or have not rewarded it.

Hutchinson reports a study in which two methods of teaching were compared, using the same group of students. In one class the subject was taught by the "receive and reproduce" method, and in the other class a "think and reproduce" approach to teaching was used. When the latter method was used a different group of students emerged as the achievers in the class.[9] Mueller, in reviewing the problem of whether the schools can foster creativity, states that there is

> a formidable paradox in current research on creativity in the classroom: studies of the creative process stress the view that truly creative minds are invariably free minds—free to make choices and hold convictions in the face of society's restraints. Yet the public schools are a myriad of controls and forces that necessarily restrict the learner to culturally prescribed and approved learning tasks.[10]

Research in creativity indicates that if this valuable human resource is to be encouraged there must be a modification of present teaching practices and methods of operation.

RESEARCH IN CREATIVITY: IMPLICATIONS FOR THE SCHOOL

An accumulation of psychological research in the field of creativity has attracted the attention of educators to the problem of improving the possibilities for manifestation of creative ability in the secondary schools. Findings of this research are:

1. All people of all ages and races are creative to some extent.
2. Individuals differ considerably in the degree of their creative ability and expression.
3. Freedom to be creative has an effect on mental health. Torrance emphasizes this point when he says:

> Scattered evidence from a variety of sources leaves little question but that the stifling of creative desires and abilities cuts at the very roots of satisfaction in living and ultimately creates overwhelming tension and breakdown. There is little doubt that one's creativity is an invaluable resource in coping with life's daily stresses, thus making breakdown less likely.[11]

---

[9] Discussed in Calvin Taylor, "Creativity and Science Education," *News and Views*, Vol. VII, No. 4 (December, 1963), p. 1.

[10] Richard J. Mueller, "Can the Public School Foster Creativity?" *Saturday Review*, December 19, 1964, p. 48.

[11] Taylor (ed.), *Creativity: Progress and Potential*, pp. 51-52. Used by permission of McGraw-Hill Book Company.

4. Students can learn more effectively in a creative situation. Taylor says in this respect, "Recent experiments have suggested that many things can be learned more economically in a creative situation than in an authoritarian one and that some people who learn little by authority can learn much creatively."[12]

WHY DO SOME SCHOOLS NEGLECT OR DISCOURAGE CREATIVITY?

The research findings on creativity summarized above have great implications for the schools; however, there have been few modifications in schools as yet to insure greater creative activities in science classes. Why is this so? Probably the greatest reason is that there is an educational lag. Many educators are completely unaware of the research findings. Some believe creative ability is endowed and that the educational environment can have little effect on it. Others are not sure how to modify the present methods and materials to encourage creative pursuits. The general pattern of the school, educational philosophy, and teacher orientation may be such that the amount of energy required to modify the traditions of the institution is extremely difficult to muster. The social constructions of teen peer groups with their emphasis on acceptance, undoubtedly inhibit divergent ways of thinking and acting. All of these are forces resistant to change. A science teacher who wishes to spark the creative potential of his students and modify his department to encourage creative endeavor must counteract these forces if he expects to cause change.

HOW CAN THE CLASSROOM ENVIRONMENT CONTRIBUTE TO CREATIVE ACTIVITIES?

The environment plays a large role in stimulating creative endeavor. A traditional class—hostile to divergent thinking, structured, and almost completely directive—does not allow for the manifestation of very much creative ability. A class which encourages self-direction and divergent activities and patterns of thought, and reinforces these, is more likely to stimulate this type of ability. The organization and operation of a creatively oriented class environment departs considerably from the traditional. It does not restrict students to traditionally prescribed and approved learning tasks.

Ample equipment and facilities foster creative enterprise.

Photo courtesy of Clark Science Center, Loomis School, Windsor, Conn.

The facilities and equipment necessary for students to move out of prescribed lessons and laboratory procedures must be abundant

---

[12] *Ibid.*, p. 53. Used by permission of McGraw-Hill Book Company.

and available to the students. Students should not be held under strict security control. Creative enterprise can not and should not be limited to the class environment. Field study and continuance of a project type of work at home should be encouraged. Field study in the environs of the school on an individual basis may present supervision problems, especially if students are allowed to engage in this activity during schools hours. But this is precisely what is meant by changing the constrictive structure of the school. Certain students can handle this freedom well and should be encouraged to be self-directive and responsible in doing research in the field. The value of creative enterprise to the student is worth breaking out of the restrictive structure of school operations. Needless and sometimes unwarranted restrictions do great harm to the development of creativity. A permissive atmosphere of encouragement and a spirit of enthusiasm in making discoveries is contagious. It is a contagion well worth kindling!

Research indicates that creative potential will not manifest itself unless it is presented with stimulating environments. Dr. Hess has experimented with rats to determine how experience affects later behavior.[13] He took two groups of rats and blindfolded one group from infancy. He allowed the other group to develop from infancy to three months without blindfolds. Then he blindfolded them. Both of these groups were then allowed to run free in cages containing a number of objects. At the age of five months the two groups of rats were confronted with maze problems. The group which had not been blindfolded until three months achieved significantly greater success in solving maze problems.

Dr. Hess did another experiment in which he took one group of rats home and raised them as pets. They were allowed to run about the house a considerable amount of time. The other group was left at the laboratory in cages. After several weeks, tests were given the rats. The performance of the rats raised as pets was significantly higher than that of the laboratory rats on ability tests. Other research in anatomy and biochemistry on similar groups of animals indicated that those with enriched experiences showed an increase in cortical tissue and in the cholinesterase activity of the brain.[14] Dr. Hess states the implications of his research as follows:

> (1) There is reason to believe that the potentialities of the human mind as genetically determined do not unfold naturally and inevitably, but require active participation of a stimulating environment in order to attain normal development. (2) It is important that this stimulation occur as early as possible in the child's experience. (3) The range and variety

---

[13] Robert D. Hess, "The Latent Resources of the Child's Mind," *Journal of Research in Science Teaching*, Issue I, Vol. I (1963), p. 21.

[14] Edward L. Bennet *et al.*, "Chemical and Anatomical Pascity of the Brain," *Science*, 146 (October 30, 1964), pp. 610-19.

of early experience directly affected the possibilities of later learning and set limits to the flexibility and adeptness of the adult mind by limiting or expanding the network of concepts, meanings, and symbols through which the individual experiences his world. (4) The early deprivation of suitable stimulation probably results in some permanent loss of mental ability. (5) One of the primary purposes of elementary school education is the maximizing of mental capabilities by systematic stimulation and exercise of mental faculties.[15]

Although what Dr. Hess has to say pertains directly to the elementary school, it also has relevance to junior high and high school education. The research reported above clearly indicates the role science teachers should play. They have the responsibility to insure that students have numerous opportunities to develop their creative faculties in order to unleash dormant creative potentials. Creative instruction requires a greater awareness of the creative abilities of individuals, of the developmental nature of creative potential, and of how to provide the learning environment conducive to its expression. The teacher who strives to develop creative ability is more likely to succeed than one who does little about it. At this time, no one can stipulate a definite set of procedures which will positively produce creative persons. You will have to be a creative teacher yourself and discover your own abilities in unlocking creative potential in students. Listed below, however, are a few suggestions which can contribute to the manifestation of creative ability:

1. Give positive recognition for creative work—reinforce this type of work as much as possible.
2. Encourage new ideas.
3. Give demonstrations and experiments requiring creative responses.
4. Give problems or home assignments that require creative endeavor.
5. Let students design experiments or demonstrations.
6. Encourage project work or research requiring creative responses. In several National Science Foundation-supported summer institutes many students produce papers which are published in competition with scientists' papers in science journals. An awareness of this has caused some school districts such as Pittsburgh, San Francisco, and Menlo Park to encourage students to do research throughout the school year as well.
7. Do not rush pupils just to cover material. Give them time to work on science projects or think out how a problem could be solved.
8. Encourage them to write an "invitation to inquiry."

A project type of activity gives opportunity to develop creativity.

Photo courtesy of Ivo Lindauer, Laboratory School, Colorado State College.

---

[15] Hess, *op. cit.*, p. 25.

9. Let your students design some science riddles. (See Chapter 18 of this text.)
10. Be creative yourself in the methods you use in teaching.
11. Let the students take some initiative and responsibility in determining some of the topics they would wish to study or do research on in the local environment.
12. Don't overemphasize teamwork. Creative individuals may want to work alone.
13. Encourage production or improvement of some piece of scientific apparatus.
14. Show the class creative work that has been done by other students.
15. Allow for diverse forms of creative expression, such as experimentation, field work, art, and writing.
16. Encourage inquiry, discovery, and invention.

DO THE MODERN CURRICULUMS INSURE THE DEVELOPMENT OF CREATIVITY?

One danger with the acceptance of the modern curriculum developments is that some teachers think they are the last word in education. Such an impression may stifle a teacher's creative ability. These curriculum projects have incorporated modern subject matter and are based on a philosophy of inquiry, but this does not mean that they will insure creativity.

Dr. Calvin Taylor has studied some of the possible negative and positive effects of new instructional media on creativity. He has indicated that it is quite unlikely that areas heretofore neglected in education will automatically receive attention with the emergence of new instructional devices, and he has emphasized the need for deliberate techniques to develop creativity and to determine which instructional media might be most effective for the purpose.

The modern curricula have not outlined techniques for the development of creative ability. It is up to the instructor to teach for this objective. A teacher can use the materials of the various curriculum projects, but it is how he uses these and the arrangement of the learning process which may kindle or stifle creative enterprise. Awareness of creative ability, and a striving by science instructors to stimulate its fruition, can do much to make this valuable human resource available to society. A teacher who accomplishes this end separates himself from a mass of instructors to become truly a master teacher. Research in creativity is accelerating; and new insights into the creative process are undoubtedly forthcoming, with implications for science educators. A science teacher should strive to keep abreast of these and translate them into action in his classroom.

SUMMARY

One of the greatest manpower needs today in science and technology is creative individuals. The United States mainly exports creative genius in its industrial products; our national survival to a large extent depends upon the use and development of this valuable resource.

Scientists demonstrate various degrees of creative ability. The man on the frontier of science usually demonstrates this ability to the greatest degree. Creativity is defined in this chapter as that process by which the individual produces something unique either to society's experience or to his own experience. A creative person is curious, resourceful, likes to discover, prefers difficult tasks, enjoys solving problems, has drive, is a flexible thinker, responds rapidly to questions, has a pronounced spirit of inquiry, and reads extensively.

I.Q. and creative ability do not necessarily correlate, although outstanding creative scientists generally have high I.Q.'s. Identification of creative students on the basis of I.Q. tests and teachers' grades is not sound.

Individuals at all ages are creative and differ considerably in this ability. Freedom to be creative may affect mental health and enable students to learn more effectively. Some students learn well only when they have opportunities to be creative. Schools have neglected creative students because of lack of information, inability to know what to do for them, excessive restrictions, and the social pressures of peer groups. Furthermore, the schools generally have not rewarded creative talent in science.

Creative enterprise should not be limited to the classroom. Students should be given opportunities to be creative outside the school environs. A creative class environment requires more facilities and equipment, a permissive atmosphere, and a spirit of enthusiasm for creative enterprise. Research indicates that if the creative potential isn't tapped in the school it might never fully manifest itself. Teachers should encourage new ideas, give creative assignments, refrain from overemphasizing teamwork, provide opportunities for students to design and improve equipment, display the creative work of students, and stimulate discovery and invention. Modern curriculum developments do not necessarily encourage creativity. The approach a teacher takes in teaching these courses may stifle or encourage creative work.

Further Investigation and Study

1. How would you design a classroom to stifle creativity?
2. In what ways does the present classroom organization contribute to the stifling of creative individuals?
3. What did Dr. Hutchinson's report indicate about the method of instruction and creativity?
4. Dr. Calvin Taylor says:

   > Let us speculate about the relationship between the amount of knowledge possessed and creative performance. If sheer volume of knowledge were sufficient for predictive purposes, the problem of identifying and developing creative potential would be near solution. If so, we could merely consider each student as a "spongehead" and do everything possible to pour knowledge into him so that he who absorbed the most knowledge would be the one who would create the most new things.[16]

   Comment on the paragraph, giving evidence to support what Dr. Taylor says.
5. Outline some ways you would encourage creative endeavor in science.
6. What reasons can you give for the schools' not particularly trying to reward creative ability?
7. How would you determine the presence of creative potential in a class?
8. Define creativity in your own words and give reasons why you consider this an acceptable definition.
9. How are creativity and I.Q. related?
10. List some known psychological principles of creativity.
11. Mr. Mueller states, "Truly creative minds are invariably free minds" and suggests that this presents a dilemma to the school. What does he mean? How much direction need there be in the school? What is the role of direction in stimulating or restricting creativeness?
12. What implications does Dr. Hess's work have for teaching?
13. Devise a lesson you think will give opportunities for creative responses.
14. It has been said that creativeness is contagious. What would you do as a teacher to insure the contagion?

---

[16] Calvin Taylor, "Cruelty and Science Education," *News and Views*, Volume VII, No. 4, December 1963, p. 1.

In our society a high value is placed on the education of youth. Their teachers are expected to perform at least two major functions: to serve youth through transmitting the cultural heritage, and to lead youth to enrich and refine that heritage. Such are the opportunity and challenge.[1]

13

The Professional Science Educator

The teacher of science today is a member of a dedicated group of professional educators which includes classroom teachers, supervisors, coordinators, administrators, and other educational specialists. This group, which numbers in the millions, has the responsibility for developing curriculum plans and carrying out the teaching process for the youth of the nation, at a time when the need for high-quality education is unsurpassed.

There are approximately 140,000 science and mathematics teachers in the United States.[2] According to the NSF report on secondary school science and mathematics, 56 per cent of these teachers were teaching five or more classes in science subjects, including mathematics. If the average class size is considered to be twenty-five students, the average daily contact load of these teachers is 125 students. Students spend an average of five hours per week in the direct charge of a science teacher whose job it is to instill science knowledges and develop science skills, interests, and attitudes.

---

[1] John Richardson, *Science Teaching in Secondary Schools* (Englewood Cliffs, N.J.: Prentice-Hall, Inc., 1957), p. 343.
[2] *Secondary School Science and Mathematics Teachers— Characteristics and Service Loads* (NSF Bulletin 63-10 [Washington, D.C.: U.S. Government Printing Office, 1963]).

Summer institute participants banding and taking blood samples of pelicans.

Photo courtesy of Colorado State College, Summer Institute Staff.

The total influence of science teachers on the nation's youth is very great. Science courses are regarded as respectable academic subjects in any secondary curriculum, along with such courses as mathematics, English, foreign languages, and social sciences. The teacher of science, by virtue of his choice of subject, is viewed with respect by other teachers and by laymen of the community.

The young teacher of science cannot help but feel pride in being a part of the science teaching profession. Now, more than ever before, science holds the spotlight in the schools of our country. It is an exciting time to be a teacher of science, and the rewards are abundant. Along with a favorable focus of attention comes responsibility for dedication to the task and for self-improvement as a teacher. It is for this reason that attention is directed in this chapter to the preparation of the professional science educator.

THE SCIENCE TEACHER

The prospective science teacher in an undergraduate program at a college or university is nearing his goal of becoming a qualified specialist in his subject. In most cases his decision to prepare himself as a teacher of a particular science subject was made early in his college career—on the basis of interest, environmental background, previous training, and prospective rewards in the teaching field. As he approaches the end of his training, the prospective teacher looks forward to an interesting and productive career as a professional educator in a challenging field of teaching. He is concerned that his training has been adequate for the task and that he will be successful in meeting the challenges ahead.

Considerable attention has been given in recent years to the training of science teachers. A study by the National Association of State Directors of Teacher Education and Certification and the American Association for the Advancement of Science has resulted in a publication entitled *Guidelines for Preparation Programs of Teachers of Secondary School Science and Mathematics.*[3] Foremost among the recommendations in this publication is that "the total pattern should provide general education, subject specialization, and professional education in such amount as to assure reasonable competence in each area and provide balance in the total program."[4] With respect to subject specialization, the following objectives are stated:

1. As high a level as possible of that scientific and mathematical literacy necessary for intelligent citizenship today
2. Development of a concept of science and mathematics as an accumulated body of knowledge and of a concept of scientific methods of inquiry
3. Development of modes of thought that encourage critical thinking and problem-solving ability
4. Understanding of the basic interrelationships within and among the various sciences and mathematics
5. Understanding of the broad conceptual schemes of science and mathematics including the concepts and principles of which the schemes are structured
6. A more penetrating understanding of the relationships of current science and mathematics to the other activities of man and his cultural patterns.[5]

A science teacher trained with the above goals in mind will be well qualified for his teaching assignment. He will be able to impart science knowledge with confidence and understand the methods of teaching most successfully used in the teaching of science. His preparation will enable him to understand the interrlatedness of science and will train him for a range of teaching assignments. He will have sufficient depth in an area of specialization to teach authoritatively and enthusiastically. With this preparation, he will be able to inspire secondary school youth and to develop science interests.

Even if one obtains the best undergraduate preparation available to the prospective science teacher, it is a mistake to assume the goal has been reached when the bachelor's degree is granted. Because of the rapid and continuing pace of science achievements and the ever-changing pattern of teaching methods and curriculum organization, the science teacher must constantly be alert to new knowledge and new techniques. For this reason, a conscientious

---

[3] Washington, D.C.: AAAS, 1515 Massachusetts Ave., N.W., 1962.
[4] *Guidelines for Preparation Programs*, p. 1.
[5] *Ibid.*, p. 4.

teacher of science will consider his education never finished as long as he wishes to remain an effective contributor to his profession.

OPPORTUNITIES FOR PROFESSIONAL GROWTH

Among the opportunities for professional growth while on the job are graduate work in a subject field or in education during the summer or at night, depending upon the available opportunities; inservice workshops and institutes; government- or industry-sponsored summer institutes; committee activity on curriculum revision or evaluation; membership in professional organizations, with accompanying attendance at regular meetings and participation in committee work; reading professional journals, scientific publications, and current books in science and teaching; writing for professional publications; keeping up to date on new materials, teaching resources, education aids, etc.

GRADUATE WORK

The National Science Foundation reports that 39 per cent of science and mathematics teachers in the United States have master's degrees and that over 75 per cent hold credits for at least ten semester hours of graduate work.[6] Twenty per cent had completed at least one National Science Foundation summer institute.

The opportunities for graduate work are abundant. The usual requirement for completion of a master's degree in education is one year or four summers of course work. Theses are generally not required, but comprehensive examinations in a major and minor field usually are. The monetary rewards for science teachers with master's degrees are well worth the time and expense involved in obtaining the degree. Most school systems have a salary differential of $300 to $500 for holders of master's degrees; furthermore, opportunities for higher-paying jobs are greater and a better selection of teaching positions is available for the applicant who holds a master's degree.

It is becoming increasingly apparent that a year of graduate work beyond the bachelor's degree is a worthwhile investment, even before starting to teach. Consider an hypothetical example: Student A earns his bachelor's degree and obtains a teaching position in a small school which pays $5,000 per year. Student B stays in school an extra year and obtains a master's degree. This year costs him $2,000. At the conclusion of his work, he accepts a position which pays $6,000 per year. (This is a reasonable expectation because he will be attractive to larger school systems, whose salary scales are significantly higher than those of small school systems.)

Teachers return to school in the summer to study ecology.

Photo courtesy of Bob Waters, Colorado State College.

---

[6] *Op. cit., Secondary School Science and Mathematics Teachers*, p. 4.

In this example Student *B* is able to recoup the additional expense of $2,000 in two years of teaching; furthermore, he is a much more desirable candidate for higher-paying jobs and perhaps will be in a larger school system with better teaching facilities, more classes in his major field, and higher annual salary increments. This statement expresses quite accurately the prevailing situation with reference to training and job seeking. It merits thoughtful consideration by the undergraduate prospective science teacher as he considers his future in teaching.

INSERVICE TRAINING

Inservice workshops and institutes are usually sponsored by public school systems for improvement of the teachers within that system. Degree credit may or may not be offered, depending on the arrangements with the colleges or universities from which consultant services are obtained. Such workshops and institutes frequently have objectives designed to stimulate curriculum improvement or to improve teacher competencies in subject-matter understandings and teaching techniques. The new teacher is encouraged to avail himself of these opportunities in order to familiarize himself with broad problems of curriculum improvement and in order to benefit from the experience of older teachers in the system.

Teachers studying at night BSCS Laboratory Blocks in an in-service institute.

Photo courtesy of BSCS, Boulder, Colorado.

INSTITUTES

Government- or industry-sponsored summer and inservice institutes provide excellent opportunities to grow professionally. More of these institutes are available each year, and while the usual requirement is three years of teaching experience, this rule is frequently relaxed for one reason or another. Typical summer institutes sponsored by the National Science Foundation provide a

Experienced teachers studying Second Level Biology in an in-service institute sponsored by the National Science Foundation.

Photo courtesy of BSCS, Boulder, Colorado.

stipend of $75 per week plus $15 for each dependent up to a maximum of four. Inservice institutes customarily pay only tuition, textbook, and travel costs.

COMMITTEE WORK

Committee activity while on the job is an excellent way to develop a professional attitude and become cognizant of the manifold problems facing the science teacher. Active school systems frequently have a curriculum committee, a professional committee, a salary and grievance committee, a textbook-selection committee, or other committees of temporary nature as the need for them arises. Participation on one or more of these committees can be enlightening and can contribute to the professional growth of the new teacher; however, committee responsibilities mean extra work, and the new science teacher should consider his total work load and weigh carefully the ultimate benefits of participation.

PROFESSIONAL ORGANIZATIONS

There are many professional organizations serving the science teacher. They are listed below along with their respective journals.
1. American Association of Physics Teachers—the *American Journal of Physics* and *The Physics Teacher*
2. The American Chemical Society—the *Journal of Chemical Education*
3. The National Association of Biology Teachers—*The American Biology Teacher*
4. The National Science Teachers Association—*The Science Teacher*
5. The Central Association of Science and Mathematics Teachers—*School Science and Mathematics*
6. The National Association for Research in Science Teaching—*Journal of Research in Science Teaching*
7. The American Association for the Advancement of Science—*Science*
8. Council for Elementary Science, International—*Science Education*

Membership in a professional organization brings benefits which are proportional to the member's active participation in the organization. Attendance at periodic meetings develops a sense of cohesiveness and shared objectives; the stimulation of meeting professional coworkers and the absorption of new ideas from meetings attended bring many rewards. Voluntary participation as a panel member or speaker at a discussion session is a highly beneficial experience. It is not necessarily true that a teacher must have many years of experience before he can be considered worthy of a presentation at a professional meeting. A young, enthusiastic new science teacher with a fresh approach to a problem can make a definite contribution to a meeting of this type.

Professional journals provide another source of teaching ideas. A science teacher should personally subscribe to one or two and make it a habit to peruse regularly others which may be purchased by the school library. Occasional contribution of teaching ideas for publication in a professional journal is highly motivating and is to be encouraged. The professional benefits of such a practice, because it helps one to become known in science teaching circles and to make valuable contacts, are unlimited.

Professional journals usually contain feature articles on subject-matter topics or educational topics of current interest; ideas for improvement of classroom teaching techniques; information on professional meetings; book reviews; information on teaching materials, apparatus, and resource books; information on career opportunities for secondary school students in science; and information on scholarships and contests for students and teachers.

THE SCIENCE SUPERVISOR

It has become increasingly apparent that a definite shortage of qualified science teachers will exist for several years in the future. Study of the numbers of teachers currently being trained in the sciences and the growing demands for science teachers because of the burgeoning school population leaves one with the inescapable conclusion that the shortage can not be overcome rapidly. Perhaps it is not unreasonable to expect that a generation of youngsters will be forced to study science in overcrowded classrooms under teachers who are somewhat less than adequately prepared in their science teaching fields.

Recognition of this condition by the American Association for the Advancement of Science resulted in a Study on the Use of Science Counselors (part of the AAAS Science Teaching Improvement Program) carried out at four universities located in the eastern, midwestern, western, and southern United States. The objectives of the study were to test a method of improving science and mathematics instruction in secondary schools through the use of teacher counselors and a method of providing inservice aid with stress on recent developments, improved laboratory and demonstration techniques, and good teaching methods.

As a result of this study, several beneficial outcomes were noted:

1. Teachers developed an awareness of the need for improved practices in the teaching of science and mathematics.
2. Teachers were stimulated to up-grade their knowledge of

subject matter and were helped to re-examine their philoso-
phies of science and mathematics teaching.

3. Counselors were of immediate and direct benefit to teachers
   because they sought out and provided useful teaching materials.

4. Science counselors were called upon to give advice in the
   design and construction of science laboratories.

5. Curriculum counseling enabled teachers and school systems
   to set up accelerated science and mathematics programs and
   to develop lists of goals and topics for high school science and
   mathematics courses.

6. Much time was devoted to supplementary and extra-curricular activities such as slide-rule groups, science clubs, projects,
   science fairs, etc.

7. There was a noticeable increase in participation in summer
   and academic-year institutes by teachers in the study schools.[7]

Other types of activities in which science counselors or supervisors might have been engaged were demonstration teaching,
inter-school visitations, and developing means of working well with
beginning teachers and with teachers with minimal preparation in
science and mathematics.[8]

In an address before the National Science Teachers' Association
in 1963, Dr. Addison E. Lee spoke on "The Science Supervisor
and the New Science Curriculums." In discussing the role of the
science supervisor, Dr. Lee cited four implications of the new curriculum programs for the work of the science supervisor:

1. Leadership in decisions affecting the selection and/or development of improved science programs

2. Responsibility for helping teachers obtain the facilities, equipment, supplies, and assistance they need to carry out new
   programs

3. Some measure of responsibility for inservice preparation of
   teachers to accept, introduce, and teach improved science
   courses

4. Responsibility to act as a spokesman for the teachers, for the
   administrators, and for science in providing an appropriate
   interpretation of current needs in science education.[9]

Dr. Lee said of the science supervisor that he is

> "a middle-man—one who must act as a spokesman for the sci-
> ence teacher, the school administrators, and at the same time
> contribute toward the interpretation of science to the public."

At another point he said,

---

[7] See *Study on the Use of Science Counselors—Final Report* (Washington,
D.C.: AAAS, 1959).

[8] *Ibid.*

[9] Address to NSTA Eleventh Annual Convention, Philadelphia, Pa., March
29-April 3, 1964.

"He can be and should be one of the most effective means of communication between the teachers and administrators and vice versa. He must be a good talker and a good listener . . . he must have patience and tolerance. But let us not forget, he must also have a great deal of knowledge and understanding of science."[10]

The role of the science counselor, supervisor, or consultant (generally considered synonymous titles) is increasing. The prospective science teacher should consider the opportunities afforded by this avenue of teaching, particularly after a few years of teaching experience and the acquisition of a master's degree. In most cases, the well-qualified science supervisor will have a master's degree or equivalent in a subject field, with additional graduate work in science education or administration. Salaries for persons in the position of science supervisor or science coordinator are excellent, frequently being nearly equivalent to those of principals or curriculum directors in the school systems concerned.

SUMMARY

Today's science teacher is in a position of respect and responsibility. The demand for well-prepared science teachers has never been greater, and the rewards are exceptional.

Proper education of the science teacher in this fast-moving scientific age is a matter of increasing concern. A suitable balance of general education, subject-matter preparation, and professional training must be achieved. The current trend is toward strengthening all of these areas, particularly subject-matter preparation. Attainment of a bachelor's degree does not end the science teacher's education. More and more, demands for graduate work, up to and beyond the master's level, are being heard. From a financial standpoint, it is generally to the teacher's advantage to obtain this advanced training as soon as possible. Better-paying jobs with other attractive features frequently await the applicant who has additional training.

Professional growth of the science teacher can occur in a variety of ways. Graduate course work, inservice institutes and workshops, summer institutes, committee involvement, membership in professional organizations, a program of reading, participation in meetings, and writing for professional journals are but a few. It is important to realize that continual growth and experience are necessary if one is to be an enthusiastic, productive teacher of science.

Recent years have shown a phenomenal growth in the number of supervisory and coordinating positions open for well-prepared

---

[10] *Ibid.*, p. 11.

science teachers. The role of the science supervisor is largely one of stimulating course improvement, arranging inservice programs for science teachers, alerting teachers to new materials and techniques, and in general acting as a middleman between the science teachers and the administrator or the public. Remuneration for science coordinators is frequently much higher than for the average science teacher. At the same time, the position usually requires superior preparation in a science subject field as well as breadth of experience.

The professional science educator of today faces a challenging future. Investment in superior preparation and recognition of the need for continual professional growth can return rich dividends: a citizenry better educated in the area of science.

Further Investigation and Study

1. Write to the department of education in your state and obtain a summary of the current salary schedules in the major cities. Compare the starting salaries for teachers with bachelor's degrees and master's degrees. Compare the annual salary increase and the number of years required to reach maximum salary.
2. Obtain a copy of *Guidelines for Preparation Programs of Teachers of Secondary School Science and Mathematics* from the American Association for the Advancement of Science, Washington, D.C. Compare the training you have received with that recommended by this group.
3. Prepare a critical analysis of two professional journals, such as *The Science Teacher, School Science and Mathematics, American Biology Teacher*, and *The Physics Teacher*. Examine the feature articles, the classroom teaching helps, the articles contributed by teachers in the field, the book reviews, and other parts of the publications.
4. Prepare a critical review of two research-oriented professional science teaching journals such as *Science Education* and *Journal of Research for Science Teaching*. Report on the results of one research study published in each of the journals reviewed.

We shape our facilities; thereafter they shape us.

Winston Churchill

14

Facilities for Tomorrow

It was rumored in the teachers' lounge that the board of education was going to purchase a large parcel of land for a new high school. The next night the board announced this fact. A few days after the announcement the faculty in this suburban school district were called together and asked to help plan the new school. The faculty accepted this responsibility with interest. Some misunderstood their task and thought they were to design the building. Some believed that the architect's job was only to insure that safe materials were used in the school's construction. Other teachers, however, saw their role as outlining the types of activities they wished to perform in the rooms and describing the facilities they required; the administration of the school district was soon to convey to the teachers that this was indeed what they were supposed to do. Appointments were scheduled for members of each department to meet with the architect to make suggestions on what they thought desirable modern facilities should include. The responsibility of the teachers, administrators, and architect for planning and developing a superb $3 million structure for future generations was great. Meetings progressed for several weeks; the teachers argued and discussed what each thought was the best facility possible. It soon became clear that what some instructors thought was modern was just a duplication of their present rooms with new furniture and plumbing fixtures.

---

[1] *Time*, Sept. 12, 1960, p. 74.

Were these teachers thinking of the future? Were they aware of how science instruction was changing? What would you suggest to an architect if you were placed in a similar situation? How would you help build a science complex that wouldn't be out of date the day it was completed?

In the next ten years the American people will spend over $40 billion building educational facilities. A large portion of this will go for science facilities. Assisting in the planning of modern science complexes and the remodelling of old facilities to meet the demands of new instructional methods in science is the responsibility of the science teacher. It is a rare teacher who will not be involved in this type of activity during his professional career.

Planning a facility that will be educationally effective and efficient for thirty to forty years requires the best minds available. Several well-qualified persons should be involved in the planning —including science teachers with vast experience; science educators; and local, state, and national science supervisors. Building a structure which may cost millions certainly warrants expenditures for planning. It is desirable that some science teachers be hired during the summer so that they can devote their full time to this task.

A teacher's philosophy of education defines activities which suggest facilities. It is important that a teacher consider what he wishes to accomplish educationally and then what type of facilities will enable him to reach these objectives. A teacher must remember, however, that he will not be the only instructor to use the plant. It will undoubtedly be in use long after he has retired. It is paramount that he think to the future, to science teaching in the 1980's and beyond, and ask, "What can I help design today that will not hinder other teachers two or three decades from now?"

Peripheral laboratory arrangement showing semi micro-chemistry materials.

Photo courtesy of Dr. S. I. Charney, Chairman, Science Dept., New Rochelle High School, New Rochelle, New York.

It is the responsibility of science teachers to outline the educational specifications for the architect. The science teacher does not design the room. The design of the science area obviously must fit into the total scheme for the school. Designing the area for optimum fulfillment of the educational specifications is the responsibility of the architect.

The science staff has a role to play in site selection. They should convey to the administration, before the site is selected, that consideration be given to how the site can add to the instructional program of the school. This is of particular importance in the area of biology where fieldwork does much to complement the class instruction. The final decision in this matter is the responsibility of the board of education and must be based upon cost and other factors. For example, a site desirable because it offers a good natural area for science work may present a problem in transporting students to and from school.

TRENDS IN SCIENCE INSTRUCTION WITH IMPLICATIONS FOR SCIENCE FACILITIES

To insure that facilities will not be outdated, the science staff must be aware of the trends in science instruction.

(1) Science education is undergoing a dynamic revolution not only in curriculum but in teaching methods and techniques as well. Modern technology and research in learning theory will alter the present methods of instruction. In order to insure that facilities do not restrict new methods of instruction they should be designed so that they are flexible, easily modifiable, and take into account the trends in science education.

(2) Two instructional approaches which are receiving greater attention are team teaching and individualized instruction. Team teaching involves some large-group instruction for 80 to 100 students with smaller laboratory sections. Provisions for large lecture-demonstration classes are provided by lecture complexes or by rooms divided by operable walls which open for large groups. Individualized instruction is designed to allow each student to progress at his own rate. This approach requires a large number of individual work areas. Both group and individualized instruction require diverse facilities far removed from those of the traditional classroom.

(3) All of the modern curriculum developments emphasize inquiry. Facilities must be provided to allow for inquiring in a number of ways, including reading, observation, experimentation, study of models, films (sixteen and eight millimeter), charts, preserved specimens, field work, slides, overhead projection, and film-strip projection.

(4) The modern curricula also emphasize laboratory approaches. These require more laboratory space and supporting facilities such as preparation rooms, live rooms, greenhouses, and student research and project areas.

(5) There is less emphasis on teacher demonstrations and more emphasis on pupil experimentation and problem-solving activities.

(6) There is more project work being done by students for science fairs, Future Scientists of America activities, NASA-sponsored congresses, etc.

(7) There is an increased use of audio-visual aids by *small* groups and individuals engaged in special work. Tape recorders are being used more to enrich class instruction. Some of the new schools have multiple tape-recording outlets and a series of tapes so that individual students can listen to various tapes at the same time. This arrangement is similar, on a limited basis, to the type of activity that goes on presently in language laboratories. Provision must be made to insure widened use of audio-visual material on both individual and group bases.

(8) Another development is emphasis on more varied instruction. Not all students necessarily perform the same experiment in the same class period. In one class students may be engaged in several different activities.

(9) There is a trend to greater use of the block approach to learning science. This is most advanced in the BSCS biology course, in which students concentrate on laboratory work in depth for four to six weeks. This arrangement requires greater storage space, as do some other modern developments in science instruction.

(10) In many schools more space for both equipment and storage is being provided. This change includes the provision of more preparation areas.

(11) Advanced science courses, such as science seminars or advanced placement, are gaining in popularity and require more work areas.

(12) More science offerings and more science for *all* students is the trend, requiring facilities that could easily expand to meet future needs.

When all the trends described above are considered, it is clear that the science complex simply has to contain more of everything and must be designed with an emphasis on flexibility. In planning science facilities attention should be given to the following principles:

1. The amount of floor space provided should be thirty-five to forty-five feet, or more, per student.

2. Those who select the school site should consider the potential contributions of the surroundings to the teaching of science. The location of science rooms within the science complex in relation to supply, outdoor areas, and sunlight

exposure needs consideration. For example, a biology class-room is best located on a ground floor with access to growing areas.

3. The number of rooms needed and what utilization they will receive throughout the day should be carefully determined. If a room will not be filled with science students all day, what other classes will be in it?

4. Planning of science facilities should include consideration of the community resources that can be used to supplement the program.

5. Planning of science rooms should utilize the ideas of many qualified individuals who have had experience in planning science facilities, not just ideas of the architect.

6. The science rooms should provide for a wide range of learning activities for individuals, small groups, and the entire class.

7. The needs of science should be considered in planning floors, illumination, ventilation, plumbing, placement of sinks, and water taps. Electric plugs for each student should be provided if necessary.

8. Rooms should be pleasant and attractive. The use of a variety of color in cabinets and display cabinets helps to give the room a pleasing appearance.

9. Rooms should be flexible, to accommodate a variety of uses. Furniture that is not permanently installed insures greater flexibility, since it can be easily moved as conditions warrant.

10. Adaptable furniture should be provided.

11. Facilities should permit students to experiment with a wealth of materials.

12. Areas should be provided where experiments and projects may be carried on for others to observe.

13. Facilities should be available for individual experimental work.

14. There should be a facility for construction and repair of equipment.

15. There should be sufficient space for projects to remain assembled for periods of time.

16. Provisions should be made for published materials to be available.

17. Sufficient space should be provided for proper storage of all materials.

18. Facilities should be provided for effective use of audio-visual aids.

19. Space should be provided for display of student-constructed and other products and devices.

20. Space should be provided for the science teacher to work on study plans and class records, and to do private counseling.

21. There should be provision for small-group or individual con-
    ferences with the science teacher.
22. Greater aisle space needs to be provided in multipurpose
    laboratories, because of greater student movement.
23. Consideration should be given to windowless classrooms,
    since they do have some advantages for storage, thermal
    control, and audio-visual programs.[2]

In planning a science complex, careful consideration must be
given to the study of space relationships. Where should the biology rooms be located in relation to the physics, chemistry, and
other science rooms? What relationship should they have to the
storage areas? Should there be a central storage area with access to
all classrooms, or should each classroom have a storage facility?
The advantage of the former arrangement is that it requires less
space and makes equipment available for multiple use. For example, a vacuum pump may be easily available to physics, chemistry, physical science, and general science classes. A central
storage area, however, requires greater organization and agreement among the faculty involved on how the equipment will be
used and returned to the storage area. An example of a space-
relationship study to be given to an architect is shown in Figure 23.

Team teaching facilities showing
folding walls.
*Photo courtesy of Barber-Greeley,
Colorado.*

FACILITIES FOR MODIFIED FORMS
OF INSTRUCTION

The traditionally designed science room was a self-contained
classroom providing for all the science activities within the con-
fines of the room. In the traditional class all students did the same
thing at the same time. With the advent of computers, flexible
scheduling was introduced allowing for a departure from the
traditional method of instruction. Students could be scheduled
in various ways with relative ease. As a result, team teaching was
introduced, allowing for a number of innovations in the normal
instructional pattern. Team teaching may involve large-group instruction for 80–120 students, instruction for small groups of 20–30
students in the laboratory, and a minor amount of individual instruction. Facilities designed for team teaching require educational
specifications which will allow for all of these modifications of
instruction.

Individualized instruction or continuous progress is another
approach to teaching science which is gaining acceptance. A curriculum organized for individualized instruction enables the student to progress at his own rate. One student may be performing

Large group instruction.
*Photo courtesy of Clark Science
Center, Loomis School, Windsor,
Conn.*

---

[2] This list has been modified, with additions from National Science Teachers
Association, *Science Facilities for Our Schools* (Publication K-12 [Washing-
ton, D.C., 1963]).

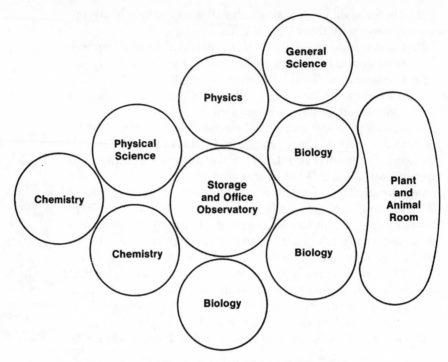

Figure 23–Science Space Relationships

Provided through the courtesy of the Educational Planning Service, Colorado State College, Greeley, Colorado.

a certain laboratory exercise while another is doing an experiment much farther along in the course. Some students may be listening to tapes; others may be observing film strips, watching eight-millimeter projections, or doing reading research. Facilities designed for individualized instruction are different from those for large-group instruction. The emphasis is upon the individual's teaching himself. The teacher becomes an organizer and a provider of activities in the learning complex. For the teacher to be effective, the individualized laboratories require more space, more flexibility, and more storage and project areas. The laboratory must provide for a variety of methods of inquiring and for as many diverse activities as there are students. Figure 24 illustrates some of the varied activities found in a facility adapted to this purpose.

Modifications of these two approaches—team teaching and individualized instruction—have been developed in a number of schools. That a school has team teaching does not mean that it can not also have some individualized instruction. For example, there could be some lecture demonstrations in the lecture complex area followed by individualized approaches used in the laboratory. Some of the modern curriculum projects such as BSCS do not consider team teaching in large-group instruction effective. Individualized instruction may involve some unique facilities such as study

or laboratory carrels. One arrangement has been tested with success in Littleton High School, Littleton, Colorado. The carrel used
there accommodates six students. It provides a quiet place in which
to work and makes available many references, audio-visual aids,
and laboratory materials.

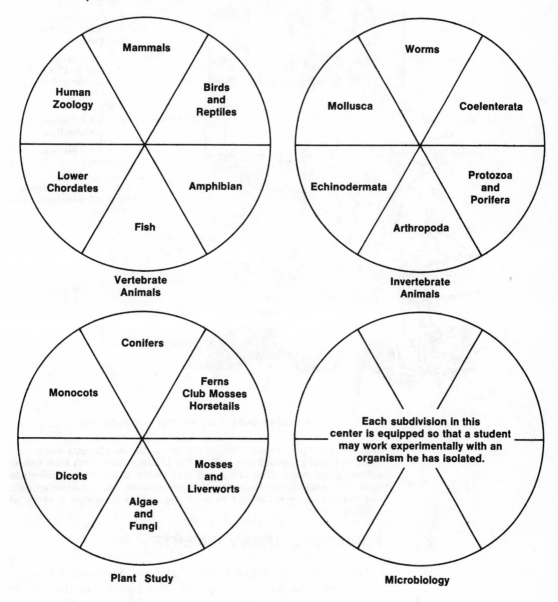

Figure 24–Individual Study Centers

Location of materials in the individual study carrels shown in
Figure 24. These sections are found at the several levels of the
Lazy Susan-like central part of the carrel.

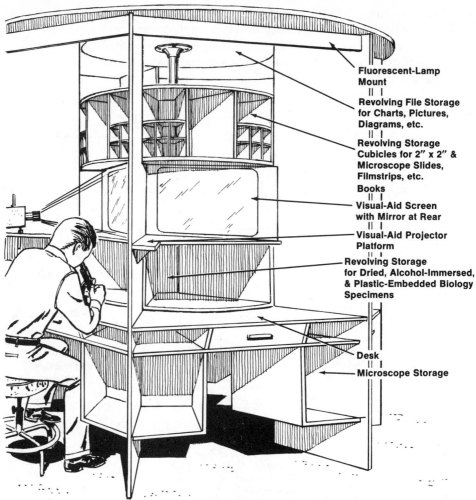

Fluorescent-Lamp
Mount

Revolving File Storage
for Charts, Pictures,
Diagrams, etc.

Revolving Storage
Cubicles for 2″ x 2″ &
Microscope Slides,
Filmstrips, etc.

Books

Visual-Aid Screen
with Mirror at Rear

Visual-Aid Projector
Platform

Revolving Storage
for Dried, Alcohol-Immersed,
& Plastic-Embedded Biology
Specimens

Desk

Microscope Storage

Figure 25–Carrel Used in Littleton High School

Four circular study centers, which accommodate six students each, have
been built and are now being used in the Littleton (Colorado) High School
science department. Each center provides a quiet place for the students to
work and makes available many reference sources and audio-visual aids.
The materials are accessible to each student by means of a series of
rotating shelves.

FURNITURE ARRANGEMENTS

One of the first things a science staff must do, in writing educational specifications, is to decide on the function of the science
rooms. Are they to be laboratories or a combination of laboratory
and demonstration-discussion room? Obviously, decisions related
to furniture needs will be quite different if the rooms are to serve
the latter function.

The choice of furniture and its arrangement presents a tremendous number of possibilities to the science instructor. Scientific-

furniture companies are producing a wide variety of pieces. These can be arranged in several ways depending on the purposes of the laboratory. The greatest concern in selecting furniture should be to insure a flexible arrangement. Figure 26 shows some of the possible floor plans for a laboratory situation. The several designs of labora-

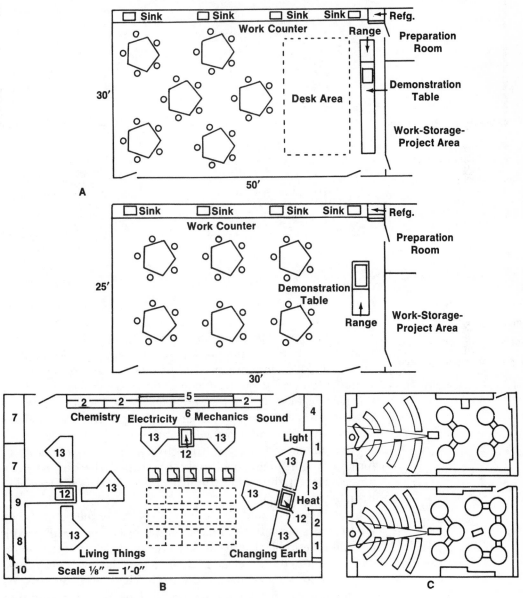

Figure 26

Source: *BSCS Newsletter*, No. 9, September, 1961.
Source: Junior high school laboratory arrangements, Sheldon Equipment Company, Muskegon, Michigan.
Source: John E. Sjöström Company, Inc., 1717 N. Tenth St., Philadelphia, Pa., 19120.

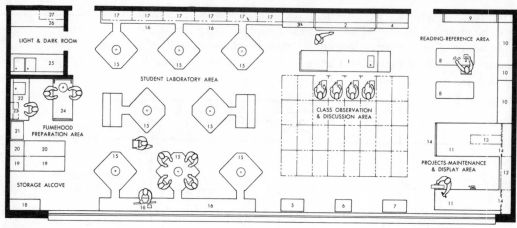

1	Demonstration Table	9	Book Shelves		Cabinets
2	Sliding Chalkboard & Storage Assembly	10	Files, Illustrative Materials, Chart Storage Cases, etc.	18	Open Shelving
3	Horizontal Demonstration Storage Unit— counter below	11	Work Benches	19	Materials, Apparatus Storage Cases
4	Vertical Demonstration Storage Unit— counter below	12	Tool Storage and Materials	20	Apparatus and Chemical Storage Cases
		13	Wall Storage Cabinet	21	Laboratory Cart
		14	Pegboard Display Panels	22	Sink Work Counter
5	Aquarium	15	Four Student Laboratory Tables	23	Wall Storage Cabinet
6	Projector Cart			24	Peninsula Fumehood
7	Climatarium	16	Work—Storage Annex Counter	25	Wet Developing Table
8	Reading—Reference Table	17	Wall Storage & Display	26	Dry Work Table
				27	Wall Storage Cabinet

Plan A

Room Size 64'-0" X 24'-0"

32 Students

This plan provides all necessary facilities when adapted specifically to Chemistry, Physics, or Biology.

tory desk and the combinations of shapes to form circles, hexagons, and rectangles enhance the possibilities for varieties of arrangement. Arranging laboratory furniture at the perimeter, with non-utility desks in the central portion of the room, gives flexibility. A number of laboratory exercises in the new science courses do not require utilities; flat-surfaced, non-utility desks can serve well for the performance of these experiments. Movable, flat desks are most important when space is at a premium. All student desks should have flat tops. Trapezoidal rather than rectangular tables provide for more flexibility, since they can be moved easily to form rectangular, hexagonal, and other shapes. They can be easily arranged in a traditional way or in a circular formation, depending upon the class activity.

Some thought should be given to the height of the desks if they are to push against the peripheral furniture as supplemental work areas; it is desirable that the desks be the same height as the perimeter laboratory furniture. Consideration must be given to the type of surface for the desks. The surfaces of chemical desks must be much more resistant than those used in biology. It is wasteful to stipulate the same type of desk tops for all classes, especially when it is more costly to install a chemically resistant table. The SAMA in their *Guide to Buying Scientific Laboratory Furniture and Equipment* include a rather wide number of items in their definition of furniture, as indicated below:

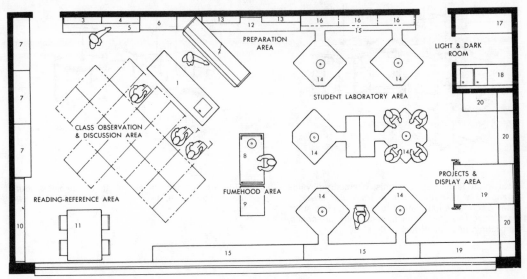

Plan B
Room Size 52'-0" X 24'-0"
24 Students

This total Experience Chemistry plan shows planning skill, ingenuity, and originality.

1 Demonstration Table
2 Sliding Chalkboard & Storage Assembly
3 Vertical Demonstration Storage Unit
4 Horizontal Demonstration Storage Unit
5 Work—Storage Counter
6 Demonstration Apparatus Panel Storage Case
7 Material—Apparatus—Display Storage Cases
8 Island Fumehood
9 Laboratory Cart
10 Book Shelves
11 Reading—Reference Table
12 Work—Storage Counter
13 Reagent Shelving
14 Four Student Laboratory Tables
15 Work—Storage Annex Counter
16 Wall Storage Cabinets
17 Dry Work Table
18 Wet Developing Table
19 Work Bench
20 General—Tool—Project Storage Cases

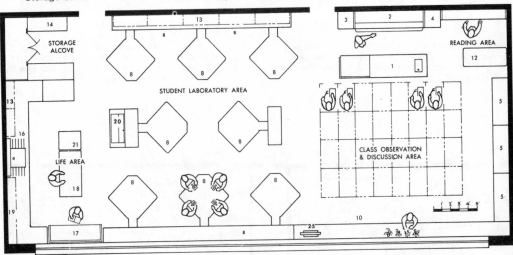

Plan C
Room Size 56'-6" X 24'-0"
32 Students

The Total Experience Biology Laboratory retains the desirable elements of the master Total Experience plan.

1 Demonstration Table
2 Sliding Chalkboard and Storage Assembly
3 Skeleton Case
4 Torso Case
5 Storage and Display Cases
6 Student Laboratory Tables 2 Student
7 Student Laboratory Tables, 4 Student
8 Annex Work & Storage Stations
9 Work and Display Counter
10 Book Shelves
11 Illustrative Materials Storage
12 Reading Table
13 Material and Apparatus Storage
14 Herbarium
15 Case front only for "rollaway" storage
16 Work Counter-Sink, Potting, Aquaria
17 Illuminated Growing Cart
18 Climatarium
19 Plant Display Shelves
20 Special Purpose Wash Sink
21 Laboratory Cart
22 Biology Fume Hood
23 Animal Care Case
24 Bio-work Center—Refrigerator & Incubator
25 Classroom Bee Colony

Photo courtesy of Sheldon Equipment Company, Muskegon, Michigan

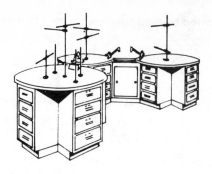

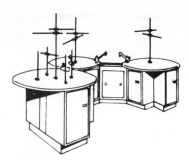

Twelve students can use this chemistry-physics arrangement of three tables in triangular arrangement. Each table has four base units. The two sinks each have two cold water faucets, four gas cocks, and four duplex electrical outlets.

This arrangement is similar to the twelve-student combination, but uses three base units with two sinks.

This eight-student arrangement for biology-physics-general science consists of two four-student tables with one inter-connecting sink. Each table has two base units and a standard leg unit.

The instructor's demonstration desk is equipped with a sink, aluminum uprights and connecting rod. Services include one cold and one hot water faucet, one gas cock, one duplex electrical outlet.

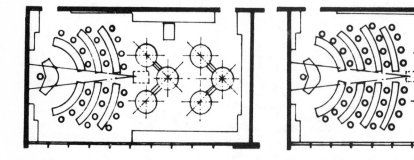

A wide variety of arrangements is possible with "science circle" furniture. Here are two typical chemistry-physics laboratories, one equipped for twenty-four students and the other for thirty-two students.

Photo courtesy of Sjostrom Company,
Philadelphia 20, Pa

Definition of Science Laboratory Furniture

Science laboratory furniture consists of the fixed and movable furniture and equipment for the laboratory designed to have a usable life approximately that of the laboratory building. Laboratory furniture is the "machinery" of the laboratory as differentiated from apparatus which is the "tool" of the laboratory. Such furniture includes tables or desks for student experimentation or demonstration; tables, cabinets and cases for storage and/or display of apparatus, chemicals, models, etc.; chemical fume hoods; sinks; service island and racks; tables for supplies, balances, dark rooms, preparation room, titration, etc.; chairs and stools; and accessory and supporting items such as but not limited to:

Animal Cages	Key Cases
Apparatus Carts and Trucks	Laboratory Carts
Aquariums	Map Tables and Cases
Balance Tables and Cases	Microscope Cases
Biological Incubators	Notebook Cases
Biological Refrigerators	Peg Boards
Biology Utility Tables	Physics Utility Tables
Book Cases	Plant Preserving Chests
Book Shelves	Portable Chalk Boards
Chalk Boards (sliding)	Portable Fume Hoods
Chairs	Portable Instructor's Desks
Chart Cases	Preparation Tables
Controlled Environment Biology Units	Safety Cabinets
	Skeleton Cases
Dark Room Tables	Soil Bins
Demonstration Trucks	Stools
Display Cases	Storage Cases
Fume Hoods	Teachers Cases
Germinating Beds	Terrariums
Glass Tubing Cases	Tote Tray Cases
Herbarium Cases	Wall Sinks[3]
Instructor's Desks	

An addition to the above list could be a small, apartment-type electric range. Schools which have them have found them to be very desirable.

DEMONSTRATION AREAS

The modern curricula stress individual or small-group experimentation. The need for having a demonstration desk in the classroom is diminishing, although occasionally there will be a need for particular demonstrations, especially where complex and costly equipment is involved. The installation of a permanent demon-

---

[3] *Guide to Buying Scientific Laboratory Furniture and Equipment* (Prepared by a committee of the Scientific Laboratory Furniture and Equipment Section, Scientific Apparatus Makers Association, Chicago).

stration desk in front of the classroom lessens the flexibility of the room and diminishes the amount of usable student space. It further limits movement and dictates methods of instruction. A permanently fixed desk prevents close contact between the instructor and students when the instructor is using the blackboard. The possibility of students' gathering around the instructor in close groups near the board for a discussion is limited by this arrangement. Presently there are several well-designed portable laboratory desks which can be moved easily and used in a number of ways. The chief detriment to the use of these desks is the problem of water supply. However, such desks usually contain a portable supply with a pump and stored water in plastic containers; the water must be replenished from time to time. Many demonstrations require little or no water, and the water that is needed usually can be easily obtained from the peripheral sources in the room. The electrical supply can be obtained from wall plugs; and gas, from portable gas burners. An instructor should seriously consider whether the convenience of a well-equipped demonstration desk warrants the lack of flexibility and the expense. A portable desk also has some advantages; it can serve as a cart to move supplies to areas of the room where they will most be needed, or it can be used as a supplementary student work area.

If a demonstration desk is permanently installed, the following utilities should be considered: hot and cold water; electricity—AC and DC; gas; vacuum and compressed-air lines; receptacles for upright rods; a garbage-disposal unit; and the proper types of drawers, with or without locks. There are movable laboratory carts which may be added to the demonstration desk. These are supplied by manfacturers in styles to match the demonstration desks. There is an increasing use of overhead projection in demonstrating; the construction of a demonstration area with a permanently installed overhead projection has advantages and may provide for a far greater use of this technique of teaching.

CLASSROOM STORAGE

A study we have recently done in the state of Colorado indicates that one of the greatest facility problems confronting teachers is insufficient storage space. There are three types of storage problems—storage of students' materials and equipment, storage of chemicals, and storage of special equipment which is especially large, such as vacuum pumps, cathode-ray tubes, microprojectors, or microscopes.

Extensive shelving is needed to provide ample storage. Open shelving in the classroom usually is desirable. Glass cases provide for easy visibility and have the added advantage of teacher control. There should be a variety of drawers and cupboards avail-

Open display shalves are convenient for displaying or storing interesting models, demonstration equipment and student projects.

Photo courtesy of Meeker School District (Jr. High), Meeker, Colorado.

able and a special place to store charts and other audio-visual aids. Display cases in the classroom can serve as display areas or as storage for models and other interesting equipment. Classroom storage should be arranged to prevent student traffic problems; for example, if all students have to move to one reagent shelf this will cause a considerable amount of chaos. Security of expensive items must be insured by seeing that they can be checked easily. Glass-covered cases for the storage of microscopes, for example, help in this respect. Storage of special items in the classroom— such as autoclaves, incubators, costly balances, aquaria and terraria, and a small, slender, counter-type refrigerator—are other considerations.

The Storage Room

The storage room should be easily accessible to the classroom. It should be provided with carts so that materials can be easily wheeled into the classroom. Constructing it so that an instructor in the classroom can see whether anyone is in the storage room insures better supervision of its use. The storage room may also serve as a preparation room for instructors; the storage and preparation sections may be separated by a wire fence or sliding doors. The storage room may contain incubators, refrigerators, autoclaves, and other large equipment. A means of storing corrosive chemicals away from the other materials in the room is necessary, particularly in chemistry storage rooms. The storage or preparation area requires utilities similar to those installed in demonstration desks.

THE CLEAN-UP AREA

Because of the emphasis on laboratory work today the problems of maintaining clean and efficient laboratories have increased. Orderly and efficient cleanliness of the laboratory can be enhanced by giving attention to designing a special area of the classroom or preparation room for this purpose. The clean-up area should be provided with waste-disposal cans, a garbage-disposal unit, and washing and drying facilities such as pegboards and a dishwasher. There should be space to accommodate a laboratory cart.

PROJECT AREAS

Senior science seminar courses, science-fair projects, and the Future Scientists of America program have all influenced students' research activities. Research often involves a project requiring the use of laboratory space for a prolonged period of time. Schools have modified old facilities or built new facilities to provide special space for students' set-up projects which do not have to be dismantled. Emphasis on project work will undoubtedly continue. No new science building should be constructed without inclusion of some space for talented science students to carry on their research. The project room should be well equipped and have sufficient utilities for research work.

The Lux Electronic Laboratory is a special laboratory provided for all gifted students in the San Francisco schools from 5th to 12th grade.

Photo courtesy of Miranda K. Lux Electronic Laboratory, Polytechnic High School, San Francisco, California.

LIVE AREAS

A live area is a compromise between a controlled environment for animals and a greenhouse. In live areas there are usually both plants and animals. For animals to live satisfactorily there can not be intense heat and light. Artificial light if properly controlled is usually satisfactory and often serves the purpose better than natural light for both plants and animals. Excessive daylight, for example, provides problems with aquaria. Live rooms generally have heat problems because they have too large a glass area. Modern live rooms use less glass and supplement growth areas with bays of daylight fluorescent bulbs.

Live areas should include a large aquarium of about fifty-gallon capacity; a salt-water aquarium with special controls for circulating and cooling the water; terraria; vivaria; growth chambers; soil areas; and equipment found in an animal room, such as various types of cages. A portion of the live area may be devoted to culturing various types of life used in the science courses, such as protozoa, invertebrates, bacteria, algae, fungi, frogs, and insects.

THE GREENHOUSE

A greenhouse differs from the live area in that its sole function is to grow plants. Greenhouses require light, temperature, humidity, and air-circulation controls. They need running water and floors resistant to slipping. There are special companies that build these, and generally the science staff need only specify the utilities and area needed, plus the number of soil bins and potting tables.

THE ANIMAL CENTER

Some schools have special animal rooms. They require considerable cleanliness and care. The room temperature must be controlled between seventy-two and seventy-five degrees Fahrenheit, humidity must be 50 to 55 per cent. Freedom from excessive noise should be assured. The live room requires cages for birds, mice, rats, hamsters, and many forms of reptiles. Care and upkeep of such a room demands time and is fairly expensive.

Science teacher's office and work area.

Photo courtesy of Bob Waters, Colorado State College.

OUTDOOR LABORATORIES

With the increased interest in ecology, many schools have embarked upon maintaining outdoor areas for study. Often these include a well-planned campus planted and maintained for the purpose of supplementing class study.

Some school systems have extensive areas which they own and students maintain as a part of ecological or conservation studies. These areas may or may not be an integral part of the campus. Outdoor areas may include potted vegetable gardens, several examples of trees and shrubs, tree-growth demonstrations, an arboretum with all the plants labeled, wildflower and rock gardens, weather stations, fish ponds, bog gardens, reptile pits, school forests, and erosion-study areas.

Outdoor laboratory area showing a greenhouse and an ecological area.

Photo courtesy of Barber-Greeley, Colorado.

THE TEACHER'S OFFICE

The modern science teacher is a professional person requiring office space for study, administrative work, counseling, and planning. A school system purchases teacher time, and it is highly inefficient not to provide the teacher with tools and space to make optimum use of this time. It is paramount that teachers have office space if they are going to be truly efficient and effective in using their non-instructional time. The office should contain a desk, chairs, lockable files, bookshelves, a bulletin board, storage space, a typewriter, a telephone, and duplicating equipment. The science complex in a large school could justify the use of photocopy machines, especially one that can copy drawings or illustrations from books on transparencies for overhead projection.

MULTIPURPOSE LABORATORIES

A multipurpose laboratory may function as a laboratory or a lecture-demonstration classroom. The term *multipurpose laboratory* also is used to refer to a laboratory designed as a laboratory-classroom for more than one type of science—biology and general science or chemistry and physics, for example. Multipurpose laboratories, if well designed, provide more flexibility for scheduling. Instructors, in outlining classroom needs for a science complex, must consider the utilization of the room. Construction of a physics laboratory to be used by one class a day in physics can hardly be justified. Rather, it would be preferable to construct a multipurpose laboratory which could serve as a physics laboratory one period and be used for chemistry or physical science classes for the other parts of the school day. A multipurpose room must be larger than a single-purpose room; but on a class-utilization basis the cost of building the larger room can be justified, since the room will be used more periods a day. Most science teachers are tradition-bound. They believe a physics room must appear to be uniquely designed for physics; in fact, a multipurpose room may be just as functional for physics. High schools have given far too little consideration to designing laboratories for multiple purposes.

Multipurpose laboratories are the most functional type and offer the most flexibility for junior high schools. With the present emphasis on laboratory work at all grade levels, it is important to construct modern junior high school facilities with well-equipped science laboratories and with support facilities characteristic of a well-designed modern high school.

SUMMARY

In this chapter we have not attempted to give an exhaustive treatment of the problems of facilities design. We have tried to show the responsibility teachers have in insuring that new facilities are an improvement over the old ones and to point out some considerations in providing modern facilities. Science teachers are the people most competent to know what facilities are needed for efficient and effective teaching. It is their responsibility to suggest that these be provided.

In writing educational specifications, teachers must take care that the facilities will not be outdated in twenty or thirty years. This can be avoided if facilities are made flexible and if teachers understand trends in teaching that have implications for science instruction. Variation in instruction such as team teaching and individualized or continuous progress, modern curricular emphasis on laboratory and project work, increased use of auxiliary aids of instruction such as audio-visual materials and programmed teaching, the advent of more advanced science courses, and more science offerings for increased numbers of students all require considerable deliberation in writing educational-facility specifications. Other factors are: site selection, amount of floor space required, the number and type of rooms required, community resources, particular chemical-resistant features required in a science room, types of furniture, storage, growth laboratories, display, library materials, windowless areas, the relationship of the science complex to the school, and the relationship of the various science laboratories to one another and to the supply area. The sophistication of the types of furniture presently produced allows for an almost infinite variety of arrangements. Instructors should seriously consider the type of furniture to be purchased, requiring and insuring the greatest flexibility commensurate with function. They should especially be aware of student traffic problems that may be caused by furniture arrangement. There are several types of furnishings to consider, and a list of these is included in the chapter. Examination of modern curriculum changes suggests that demonstration areas are less needed today and that in fact they limit the flexibility and function of a laboratory.

Auxiliary rooms requiring special consideration are storage and clean-up areas, project areas, live areas, greenhouses, animal centers, outdoor laboratories, teachers' offices, and multipurpose laboratories. Because of the financial investment involved and because of the role the facilities will play in the educational program of generations to come, a number of learned and experienced individuals should devote a large amount of time, in an unrushed manner, to outlining facilities specifications. It is suggested that the science staff be compensated by a school district to work on the planning of new facilities during the summer.

Further Investigation and Study

1. What did Churchill mean by the statement, "We shape our facilities; thereafter they shape us"?
2. What relevance does the statement "form follows function" have for science teachers?
3. Who should be involved in the planning of science facilities and why?
4. Many schools are built with little or no consultation with school personnel. Why is this an undesirable practice?
5. What does a teacher's philosophy of education have to do with facilities?
6. What trends of science education have implications for facilities?
7. What five considerations do you think most important in facility design?
8. Design a floor plan for a science complex you think will be very modern. Justify your design.
9. How do the facility requirements for individualized instruction vary from those of team teaching?
10. What is the function of a study carrel?
11. What considerations are paramount relative to choosing furniture?
12. What arguments are there for and against having demonstration desks?
13. What are some of the problems of storage?
14. How does a greenhouse differ from a live area?
15. What are the advantages of a multipurpose laboratory?

*The fundamental characteristic that is
common to both children and science
is that both are actively involved
in interpreting the objects and events
of the environments.*[1]

Gerald Craig

15

Discipline in Science Classes

Mr. Woods faced his first class in eighth-grade general science with apprehension. Taking over Mrs. Clark's class in the middle of the year was going to be no cinch, he could tell. He had heard rumors of some of the problems in this class, particularly with one or two of the larger boys.

Nevertheless, Mr. Woods determined to make a success of this assignment. For the past week, he had looked over the individual records and noted several interesting facts. Tom Drake, for example, was a troublemaker and had given all of his teachers difficulty. A file of notes on various conferences with parents, teachers, and principal filled his folder. Susan Avery's file had several references to "laziness," "inattention," and "poor attitude." Alice Hendricks' file contained notes like "not working up to her ability" and "wastes time." **A** comparison of her aptitude and intelligence scores with her science marks in seventh grade supported these statements.

For his first day of class, Mr. Woods had prepared a good plan. It included a demonstration and fifteen minutes of student experimentation to follow. Provision for a summarizing discussion concluded the plan.

The period began with Mr. Woods' introducing himself briefly. A few words about the subject, magnetism, led Mr. Woods directly into the demon-

---

[1] Quoted in Ellsworth S. Obourn and John H. Woodburn, *Teaching the Pursuit of Science.*

stration. A small magnet was fastened to a support rod about one foot above the demonstration desk. A paper clip fastened to a thin thread was brought up under one pole of the magnet but not quite touching it. The other end of the thread was thumbtacked to a small board lying beneath the support rod. To all but a few students very near the demonstration desk, it appeared that the paper clip was suspended in mid-air without support.

Mr. Woods passed a thin piece of cardboard through the space between the paper clip and the magnet. Nothing happened. A piece of plastic produced the same result. A sheet of aluminum had no effect. When Mr. Woods put the blade of his pocket knife in the space, the paper clip dropped to the table.

The class watched with rapt attention during the demonstration. The questions afterward indicated good thought. All looked forward to the experiment on magnetism which Mr. Woods had mentioned. The period progressed smoothly, with frequent changes of pace. All were surprised how soon the period was over. It was obvious from their comments as they passed from the room that they were already looking ahead to the next science class period.

Discipline problems? There weren't any. The class was too busy. No one was bored, even for a minute. There were no lists of "don't" rules. Mr. Woods just assumed that everyone was there to learn about the subject and proceeded to teach them. There was no preliminary "dead time" at the beginning of the period. The class began and ended with the bell. Even though he was apprehensive at first, Mr. Woods did not show it. He was forthright and direct. No one ever doubted who was in charge of the class.

With this successful beginning, the remainder of the year proceeded without serious difficulties. Even Tom Drake seemed to enjoy science and caused no problems. Alice Hendricks contributed good ideas during discussion periods and finally earned a *B*. At the end of the year Mr. Woods wondered why this class had had a reputation as a "tough class" to teach.

Part of the solution to discipline problems is rapport with the students.

Photo courtesy of Bob Waters, Colorado State College.

THE JUNIOR HIGH STUDENT

The seventh-, eighth-, and ninth-grade student can be described in one word—*exuberant*. The world around him is his oyster. He is quite uninhibited, but he is serious and reflective on occasion. He is trying to fit himself for the future—whatever it may be. He finds models and patterns himself after them. In some cases, his science teacher may be his model.

The junior high science teacher must be aware of the adolescent character. The classroom must be a place where the adolescent's mind can develop. This means a place for activity with its accompanying confusion, but a place where learning goes on nonetheless. Great bursts of energy can be expected from the junior high student. Also, total disdain for learning can be expected on occasion.

Discipline for this age level is largely a matter of instilling controlled self-discipline. Thus, certain freedoms must be permitted within limits so that self-discipline can be exercised. It is unlikely that the student will develop self-discipline and reliability if he is never given the opportunity to practice it. Overly rigid, authoritarian control, in which the primary motivation for good behavior is fear of the teacher's reprisal, will not develop the kind of student who is capable of self-discipline. At the same time, one cannot permit chaos to develop by allowing uncontrolled behavior. An environment must be provided in which students can show initiative and be responsible for their own actions within a framework of supervisory control by the teacher.

The junior high school youngster is usually quite responsive and sensitive to his peers. Relationships with his classmates are very important. In view of this, a positive approach to discipline is to show that his actions influence the actions of other members of his class. If he misbehaves and takes up valuable class time, he is infringing on the study time of his classmates. As a result, he is likely to lose their favor and be branded as a troublemaker, and his status among them will deteriorate.

The junior high school science teacher can skillfully use peer pressure to bring about improved classroom behavior. This is to be done, not by sarcastic remarks or public humiliation of the student, but by constant reference to the need for cooperation, the value of class time, the real purposes of the study of science, and mutual obligations to one's classmates in a classroom situation. Most classes will respond favorably to this type of adult treatment, and discipline problems will diminish.

THE SENIOR HIGH STUDENT

There is no sharp character difference between the junior high student and the senior high student. One can easily find younger students who have the maturity of those in the senior high school. The reverse is also true. In general, however, as the students mature, one finds increased inhibitions and less boisterous behavior in the classroom. This is a natural result of the student's approach to adulthood. More thought is given to his future plans, his vocational choice, or his choice of advanced education.

From the standpoint of discipline, this increased maturity has a salutary effect. In general, the frequency of classroom incidents requiring disciplinary measures decreases. The student is more likely to respond to treatment normally accorded adults, and because of the student's sensitiveness in this regard, the most effective measures the teacher can use in disciplinary matters are those which consider the student an adult with responsibilities for adult behavior. If the teacher makes it clear that he expects mature behavior and reciprocates by treating the students accordingly, he will find they respond favorably.

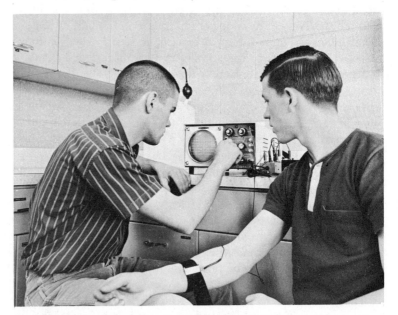

Part of the solution to discipline problems is allowing highly motivated students to participate in individual study.

Photo courtesy of Bob Waters, Colorado State College.

THE PROBLEMS OF DISCIPLINE IN SCIENCE CLASSES

The nature of science classes affects the types of discipline problems and the methods of control. On the positive side, we find that science has numerous applications to the daily lives of students. It is relatively easy to make associations of new learning with old. Every child has had contacts with his environment which show scientific relationships. Thus, motivation is an easier matter than in a more abstract course.

Science classes also have the advantage of many demonstration devices which tend to hold interest. Students may find themselves drawn away from unruly influences and toward scientific interests in spite of themselves. Furthermore, for students whose poor behavior may stem from lack of recognition, science classes may offer opportunities to gain prestige in the eyes of their peers. Currently, science rides a crest of popularity and status as a vital subject in the world of today.

On the negative side, certain unique problems exist in science classes. The laboratory by its very nature offers freedom of movement which may lead to a breakdown in discipline. Students not possessed of self-discipline qualities will find in the laboratory many opportunities to cause trouble. The teacher's control here must be completely effective, although not rigid, or the learning opportunities of the laboratory will be sacrificed. Safety in the laboratory and respect for equipment poses other problems. Horseplay cannot be tolerated. Learning requires considerable self-direction and attention to the task, and the laboratory under skillful guidance of the teacher can be a training ground for self-discipline qualities.

Certain sciences require mathematics in varying degrees of difficulty. The non-mathematically oriented student may encounter frustrations which lead to discipline problems. It is important that the teacher recognize these frustrations early and give the necessary remedial help. In some cases it may mean redirection of the student into other channels where success can be achieved.

PROBLEMS OF THE BEGINNING SCIENCE TEACHER

For the first-year teacher, handling discipline on his own is a new experience. In his student teaching days, the supervising teacher held most of the real control and was the center of discipline. Now, the beginning teacher is faced with the problems of what to teach, how to teach, and how to keep the classroom under control during this crucial period.

Paul Richard, a young science teacher, has listed, for the benefit of the first-year teacher, some school situations which give rise to discipline problems:

These school situations make it difficult for students to exert self-control:
1. The first minutes of the period
2. The first few days of school
3. Fridays in general
4. Before holidays and vacation periods
5. Report card distributing days
6. The day of the big game
7. The last five minutes before lunch
8. Last period of the day

9. Last period of Friday

Problems arise from student interactions. Some of these are:

1. Continued and disturbing conversations
2. Passing notes
3. Flirtations
4. Hostility

Other problems which occur are:

1. Failure to do homework
2. Impudence
3. Refusal to obey a teacher's request
4. Minor misbehavior for no apparent reason

The above problems are normal among students and must be identified as normal and treated with common sense. The success of a first year teacher depends on how he handles these problems.[1]

It is important to know that some discipline problems arise from personal maladjustments and may be beyond the teacher's control. In these cases, it is necessary for the teacher to recognize the problems and refer them to trained personnel capable of handling them, such as the school psychologist, principal, or counselor. Such problems are:

1. Stealing
2. Truancy
3. Destruction of property
4. Sexual offenses
5. Lying
6. Extreme aggression and hostility
7. Chronic misbehavior

Fortunately, the frequency of such problems is rather low in normal classrooms. It is advisable for the beginning teacher to become aware of their existence, however, and to plan for appropriate action if the need arises.

DISCIPLINE TIPS FOR THE TEACHER

The following list has been developed by an experienced teacher of science whose classes demonstrate a superior level of discipline and control.

Tips on Preventing Discipline Problems

1. Be firm at first. It is much easier to relax than to become more strict.

2. Make it clear at the beginning of the year what type of behavior will be tolerated and what will not. Make this ap-

---

[1] "How Should the First Year Science Teacher Handle Discipline Problems?" (Unpublished paper, Colorado State College, Greeley, Colorado, 1963), p. 2.

proach on the basis of common sense and reason; don't just make threats.

3. Direct your remarks to individuals. Do not preface your remarks with *class* or *students*. If you begin that way, the offenders rarely consider that you are really talking about them.

4. Be certain to acquaint yourself with the school policies on discipline.

5. Ascertain what type of support you will receive from the principal. Use this resource only in an absolute emergency.

6. During the first few weeks treat every violation of your rules immediately, even if it means interrupting your own sentence.

7. Cultivate the power of your voice and the ability to use it to stress important points. A thin or monotonous voice tends to convey the impression that the speaker is a weak or listless person.

8. Exhibit enthusiasm with voice and manner. A dynamic teacher conveys the impression that he has latent power he hasn't used yet.

9. Make decisions with the immediacy and confidence of a baseball umpire.

10. Be the first to admit it when you are wrong.

11. Strive to be basically congenial. Then, when you are not the effect will have more impact.

12. Be sensitive to the class tempo. Move along as fast as common sense will permit.

13. Strive for a class period which is filled with ideas and activity recognized by the students as both interesting and purposeful. The students should just not have time to get into trouble.

14. Particularly with young students, vary the types of activity within a class period.

15. Decide when to go along with a gag. There are not any real guides for this, but the result of your decision may be critical.

16. Be conscious of any forms of familiarity from students. First names and "buddy-buddy" arrangements are not acceptable. Any teacher wants to be liked, but there can be a difference between being liked and not being respected.

17. Do everything possible to achieve more than "veneer discipline." Try to achieve such rapport with a student that the mere fact that he has lost status with you makes a deep difference. Then you really have control.

18. Evaluate your group to determine which students will respond to class-pressure techniques. This may not work with extroverts.

19. Determine the dynamics of a group. Often when you have the leaders with you, they are able to assist in eliciting cooperation from a large number of students.

20. Try to develop techniques of instruction which achieve your purpose but which the students regard as fun.

21. Keep your eyes on the students and their activities. Make frequent checks on their work and avoid periods of unplanned and unsupervised time.

22. Start a class off with vigor and enthusiasm. Use a forthright approach and proceed immediately to the business of the hour.[2]

HANDLING DISCIPLINE PROBLEMS

Teacher resourcefulness in identifying potential problem situations and in applying a variety of discipline measures is an important factor. The teacher who has the greatest number of methods of control is particularly effective in quelling incipient problems before they develop into serious, disruptive situations. A number of basic requirements for successful handling of discipline problems is suggested by Knute Larson. Among these are:

1. A working knowledge of adolescent psychology
2. The ability to know where the class is going and to see to it that it gets there
3. The opportunity to visit superior schools and superior colleagues
4. Recognition that the starting point of all preventive discipline is a good lesson, carefully planned and skillfully executed
5. A sharp upgrading in the quality and quantity of classroom supervision
6. Avoidance of the use of ridicule and embarrassment
7. Opportunities for frequent changes of pace and creative pursuits
8. Insistence on quality, not quantity
9. Consistency and impartiality in application of disciplinary rules[3]

DEVELOPING SELF-DISCIPLINE

The goal of all discipline training should be the development of responsible self-discipline. Students should reach a point where they have inner motivation to complete the learning tasks of their own volition. Discipline of this type is positive and self-rewarding. Accomplishment of the task is reward in itself. To reach this goal, numerous opportunities must be provided for students to practice self-discipline or peer-group discipline. As with the development of any skill, there must be time to practice. Self-disciplined students are not likely to emerge from autocratic classrooms.

---

[2] Adapted from Lawrence Conrey, "Tips on Discipline" (Unpublished paper, University School, Ann Arbor, Michigan, 1963).
[3] "Secondary School Discipline," *NEA Journal*, September, 1963, pp. 12-17.

Teaching by inquiry methods provides a setting for development of self-discipline. Individual work in the laboratory or projects carried out in the classroom or at home give many opportunities to develop good work habits and qualities of self-reliance, persistence, and reliability. Students engaged in a task for which they have a high degree of motivation are less likely to create problems of discipline requiring action by the teacher.

The following suggestions may assist the teacher of science in providing an environment in which student self-discipline can be developed:

1. Capture interest through activities, experiments, projects, and other student-oriented learning methods.
2. Allow a degree of unstructured work commensurate with the maturity and experience level of the students in the class.
3. Give suitable guidance to students who require direction and external control, until it is no longer needed.
4. Treat students as adults from whom you expect mature behavior and evidence of self-discipline.

SUMMARY

The matter of class control is of primary concern to the beginning teacher. The multiple problems of class preparation, devising suitable teaching methods, and keeping the class under control are frequently overwhelming.

Real disciplinary control comes from the development of mutual feelings of respect between students and teacher. When this rapport is developed, discipline problems largely vanish, and the mode of control becomes student self-discipline. The beginning teacher should strive to create such rapport by taking a sincere interest in the students. At every opportunity he should give assistance generously, be fair and impartial, stress the values of learning, and demonstrate positive attitudes toward discipline. Students in junior and senior high school respond to adult treatment. The teacher's expectations in this respect will influence student response.

Science teaching has advantages and disadvantages in regard to disciplinary problems. In general, students in the secondary school are curious and interested in science. The opportunities to show science applications are numerous; experiments and demonstrations are abundant. At the same time, laboratory approaches to the study of science necessitate greater freedom and flexibility, and this may increase the chances for misbehavior. It may also, however, afford opportunities to develop self-discipline, which should be the ultimate goal.

In the handling of discipline, the application of common sense and a positive approach will satisfactorily solve most of the problems which arise. It is well to assume the attitude that discipline problems will be minimized by careful planning of daily work, use of a variety of techniques, keeping students busy, and treating them like adults. Problems that remain unsolved may require specially trained personnel; the classroom teacher should know to whom these cases may be channeled for treatment.

Further Investigation and Study

1. Make a list of ten typical discipline problems which might occur in a science class. For each, describe the measures you would use to solve the problem if you were the teacher of the class.
2. Prepare a brief annotated bibliography of recent books and articles which deal with the problems of discipline.
3. Observe a science class for a week. Keep a record of the events which in your opinion represented discipline problems. How did the teacher handle the situations?
4. Interview a science teacher and raise questions concerning the following:
   a. Discipline in the laboratory
   b. Preventive techniques for minimizing discipline problems
   c. Use of peer pressure to solve problems of discipline

*The most successful teachers are often
those who let the students behave as
practitioners of a given discipline.*[1]

Thomas Aylesworth

16

The Practice
Teaching Experience

A student nearing the end of his training to become a teacher grows increasingly anxious to get on the job. He may look forward with anticipation to "trying his wings" as a full-fledged teacher in charge of a class. At the same time, he is apt to feel somewhat apprehensive at the prospect of facing a roomful of students. Will he be able to hide his nervousness? Will his knowledge of his subject be adequate for the task? Will he be able to handle problems which require discipline? These questions and many others may give him concern as he faces the future—a future which will see him transformed from a "science student" to a "teacher of science."

WHY PRACTICE TEACH?

The practice teaching experience is designed to smooth the transition from the role of student to that of teacher. It is the student's opportunity to test his liking for the teaching task. He will discover whether he really enjoys teaching the subject for which he has prepared himself. He will learn through his close contacts with children whether he is really interested in teaching children of the particular age level for which he is assigned. Most important of all, it is hoped that he will find

---

[1] Quoted in Ellsworth S. Obourn and John H. Woodburn, *Teaching the Pursuit of Science.*

a genuine enthusiasm in the teaching task, an enthusiasm sufficient to convince him that this should be his chosen vocation.

At the same time, the practice teaching assignment will give to the training institution an opportunity to evaluate the student's teaching capabilities. A successful practice teaching experience under the supervision of a properly qualified classroom teacher will enable the training institution to place its stamp of approval on the practice teacher's work with reasonable assurance of his future success.

The prospective practice teacher in science can confidently expect to gain the following values from his practice teaching experience. These values will not accrue automatically. Much of the responsibility rests with the practice teacher himself as he attempts to profit from this culminating experience in his teacher training.

A practice teacher's experience involves out-of-door as well as classroom activities.

Photo courtesy of Bob Waters, Colorado State College.

Improvement in Confidence

Actual experience with a science class will take away the fear of the unknown which everyone experiences when faced with a new situation.

Opportunity to Put Theories into Practice

Here the new teacher will be able to test what he has learned in methods classes, and in other classes, about ways of handling various problems of teaching. Handling individual differences among students, discipline cases, techniques of presenting science material, laboratory methods, working with small groups, etc. will provide situations in which the practice teacher can apply educational theories to classroom reality.

Opportunities to Learn about Children

First-hand responsible relationships with students in his class will give the practice teacher the chance to study them, observe their behavior under a variety of conditions, and learn of motivation, competition, enthusiasm, boredom, and many other factors which make up the "climate" of a typical classroom.

A Chance to Test Knowledge of Subject Matter

Regardless of the practice teacher's self-assurance and confidence in his own knowledge of the subject he is planning to teach, there is likely to be a certain amount of apprehension about his ability to transmit this knowledge to others. Facing a class of expectant and sometimes critical students with the responsibility to teach them can be an unnerving experience, and is almost certain to convince the practice teacher of the necessity of knowing his subject very thoroughly and of the need to prepare well for his contacts with the class. One frequently hears the comment, even among experienced teachers, "I really learned my subject when I had to teach it."

The Chance to Gain the Benefits of Constructive Criticism

At no other time in a teacher's experience will he have the benefit of prolonged, intensive observation of his teaching by an experienced teacher in a position to help him constructively. This is a value not to be taken lightly. If the criticism and suggestions are taken in a receptive fashion with an intention to put them into practice, this experience can be the most valuable part of the practice teacher's assignment. It is important therefore, to select one's supervising teacher wisely. The chance to observe and be observed by a master teacher in an atmosphere of mutual respect and helpfulness is immeasurably worthwhile.

The Opportunity to Discover Teaching Strengths and Weaknesses

The practice teacher will be afforded the opportunity of discovering his own strong and weak points in the handling of science classes. He may find that performing demonstrations results in most successful teaching and gives him the most pleasure. It may be that organizing classes into effective discussion groups brings about maximum learning under his direction. The questioning technique and the Socratic method of carrying on teacher-pupil discussions may be most successful under his guidance. On the other hand, these same activities may be the least effective for him. Early knowledge of these facts may enable him to improve upon his weaknesses and capitalize on his strengths. It is certainly to the advantage of a science teacher to be highly competent in many methods of teaching, but it is equally important to recognize that individual teachers have certain innate teaching strengths and should make use of the techniques which capitalize to the maximum on these strengths.

Gaining Poise and Finesse

Because teaching is as much an art as a science, experience should bring about improvement in certain fine points of handling classes, such as anticipating student questions and problems, timing, exploiting enthusiastic and dramatic classroom events, sensing the proper time for introducing a new activity, and commending good work. These factors will contribute to smoother functioning of class activities and generally more effective learning. It is important to recognize, of course, that this kind of improvement will continue as long as a teacher teaches and that rarely, if ever, does a teacher reach complete perfection in the art.

SELECTING YOUR SUPERVISING TEACHER

Frequently, a certain amount of latitude is allowed the prospective student teacher in his choice of school, subject, and teacher under whom he wishes to work. The extent of this freedom will vary with the institution and circumstances in which the practice teaching program is operated, and it is entirely possible that assignments may be made quite arbitrarily. However, it is more likely that, within certain limitations, the wishes of the student will be taken into consideration.

It is, therefore, to the advantage of the student teacher to make a careful selection of school, subject, and supervising teacher. It is quite frequently the feeling of new teachers that their practice teaching assignment was the most valuable experience in their training program. This may be entirely true if the selection was well made and the experience fulfilled its potential.

The prospective student teacher ought to obtain the maximum advantage by teaching in his major field. It is this area for which he is best prepared and in which he will probably feel the greatest confidence. If the situation permits, teaching in his minor field at the same time under a different supervising teacher may be advantageous. This will gain for him the benefit of constructive help from two experienced teachers and may be analogous to an actual situation as a full-time teacher in a small or medium-sized school system.

It would be wise to visit several classes in a number of different schools in the quarter or semester before the practice teaching assignment. Arrangements can be made through the principal of the school, and advance notice can be given to the teachers involved. If the purpose of the visits is explained, it is quite likely that the prospective student teacher will be favorably received, particularly if it is a school in which student teachers have customarily been supervised.

The advantages of the visit can be manifold. The student will be able to refresh his memory of the atmosphere and activities of a high school classroom. He will be able to observe an experienced teacher in action. He will mentally attempt to project himself into an equivalent situation as a teacher in charge of a class—a desirable step in preparation for his actual practice teaching assignment. He may be able to talk briefly with the teacher at the close of class to gain further insight into the teaching situation. After several such visits to a variety of classes, including several outside the field of science, the prospective student teacher will be able to choose more intelligently the kind of teaching situation he wishes to select for his practice teaching experience.

Some suggestions of criteria to look for in the teaching situation are:

1. Is the teacher well prepared, and is he teaching in his major field?
2. Does the teacher have good control of the class?
3. Do the students appear to be alert and interested in the activities carried out?
4. Is there a genuine atmosphere of learning present?
5. Do the facilities and materials appear to be adequate for the kind of science being taught?
6. Does it appear that the teacher is a person from whom one can learn valuable teaching techniques?
7. Is there opportunity for a certain degree of flexibility in carrying out one's teaching plans?
8. Does the teacher have a moderate work load, thus affording time for constructive help for a student teacher?
9. Does the teacher appear to be interested in serving as a supervisor for a student teacher in his or her charge?

MEETING YOUR SUPERVISING TEACHER

Once the assignment is made for a particular school, class, and teacher, it is imperative that the student teacher arrange for a short interview before attendance at the first class. This can be brief but preferably should be a day or two in advance, and by appointment. This will avoid incurring the displeasure of the supervising teacher by intruding upon her last-minute preparation for class and will give an opportunity for an interchange of questions and answers by both parties.

At the interview, the student teacher should be punctual, interested, enthusiastic, and in tasteful attire. The purpose of the interview is to become acquainted and to exchange ideas and information. The supervising teacher is interested in knowing the background and preparation of the student teacher. In addition, he is interested in any special qualifications the student teacher may have, such as ability to handle audio-visual equipment, take charge of a science club, or talk on travel experiences. The student teacher is interested in learning what his role is to be in the classroom, what meetings he should attend, what text materials are in use, etc.

It is likely that the supervising teacher will suggest a period of class observation, perhaps a week or two, at the outset. There may be certain room duties to perform such as roll taking, reading announcements, and distributing materials. Each of these tasks will enable the student teacher to learn the names of pupils quickly—a necessary step in establishing good rapport with members of the class. The student teacher will probably be encouraged to prepare a seating chart immediately. Text materials may be discussed and the teacher's long-range objectives clarified. The student teacher will probably be asked to read certain assignments in order to be intimately acquainted with what the pupils are presently studying. He will find it imperative to do this regularly, so as to be of maximum assistance to pupils who call upon him for help.

Facilities and apparatus available for teaching the science class may be shown to the student teacher during the interview. Location of the library and special preparation rooms may be pointed out. The place in the classroom where the student teacher may observe the activities of the class may be designated. (In one school, it was customary for the student teacher to sit next to the demonstration desk, facing the class. In this way, it was possible to learn to recognize pupils more quickly; but, more importantly, this arrangement enabled the student teacher to see the expressions on the faces of the pupils as they responded to questions, or watched a demonstration, as they showed perplexity or registered insight into problems under discussion.)

YOUR FIRST DAYS IN THE CLASS

Observing pupils in the science class can be a profitable experience the first few days or weeks. The student teacher has an advantage in this situation because he is not preoccupied with teaching plans and conduct of the class as is the regular teacher. The alert student teacher can, in fact, be of assistance to the regular teacher in recognizing incipient discipline problems, lack of interest, or

Practice teacher assisting in the laboratory.

Photo courtesy of Ivo Lindauer, Laboratory School, Colorado State College.

special conditions which might lead to better teaching if recognized early. The student teacher may wish to engage in a systematic program of observation in order to gain familiarity with all members of the class. For this purpose, a checklist of individual differences is suggested:

Recognizing Individual Differences in a New Class
during the First Few Weeks

DOES THE PUPIL APPEAR TO (BE):	PUPILS
Health	1 2 3 4 [etc.]

Health
1. Pale
2. Tired and listless
3. Sleepy
4. Nervous
5. Often absent
6. Of normal health
7. Of robust health

Physical Defects—Differences
8. Left-handed
9. Wear glasses
10. Need to wear glasses
11. Wear a hearing aid
12. Need to wear a hearing aid
13. Possess a leg defect
14. Possess an arm/hand defect
15. Possess a weak speaking voice
16. Possess a nasal difficulty
17. Free from physical defects

Personality
18. Happy with a ready smile
19. Quiet
20. Shy
21. Easily embarrassed
22. Cynical
23. Passive
24. Effusive
25. Appreciative
26. Conscientious
27. Persistent in face of difficulties
28. Give up easily
29. Set high standards
30. Worry excessively
31. Indifferent
32. Average of any teenager

Basic Skills
33. Low in basic reading mechanics
34. Read slowly but carefully
35. Gain little understanding from reading
36. Outline or underline as an aid to reading understanding

DOES THE PUPIL APPEAR TO (BE):   PUPILS
                                                    1 2 3 4 [etc.]

37. Write in a fashion difficult to read _____
38. Write slowly _____
39. Encounter difficulty in expressing his thoughts orally _____
40. Encounter difficulty in expressing his thoughts on paper _____
41. Possess basic spelling difficulties _____
42. Low in basic math processes _____
43. Careless in spelling _____
44. Careless in working with numbers _____
45. Very neat (written work) _____
46. Disorganized in laboratory and other work involving procedure _____
47. Systematic in laboratory and other work involving procedure _____
48. Normal or above average [in] math skills _____
49. Normal or above average [in] writing skills _____
50. Normal or above average [in] spelling skills _____
51. Normal or above average [in] reading skills _____
52. Possess little recall of concepts previously studied _____
53. Have lower-than-normal ability to reason out solutions to problems involving numbers _____
54. Have poor mastery of problem-solving reasoning with ideas _____
55. Have excellent reasoning ability _____
56. Have average reasoning ability _____
57. Think slowly _____
58. Possess the ability to apply learning to everyday situations _____

Relationships with Fellow Pupils _____
59. A leader _____
60. Easily influenced by others in group _____
61. Anxious to be accepted by others _____
62. Attempt to impress others with knowledge _____
63. Have few friends _____
64. Oblivious of what others think of him _____

DOES THE PUPIL APPEAR TO (BE):	PUPILS
	1 2 3 4 [etc.]

    65. Liked and respected by others   _____

    66. Critical of others   _____

    67. Cooperative/helpful to others   _____

Relationship with Teacher   _____

    68. Resent suggestions   _____

    69. Disregard suggestions   _____

    70. Disregard specific requests   _____

    71. Show lack of respect of teacher   _____

    72. Deliberately "test" teacher's patience   _____

    73. Make it difficult for teacher through leadership of the group   _____

    74. Assist the teacher through leadership of the group   _____

    75. Respect teacher   _____

    76. Friendly with teacher   _____

    77. Rely too much on teacher for help   _____

Class Participation   _____

    78. Frequently show lack of preparation in class responses   _____

    79. Only volunteer answers when specifically called upon   _____

    80. Jump to conclusions without sufficient thought   _____

    81. Always anxious to volunteer   _____

    82. Often ask questions of a more complicated nature than the material at hand   _____

    83. Ask questions which would indicate not having paid attention in class   _____

    84. Ask questions when there is lack of understanding   _____

    85. Pay attention to the answers given by others   _____

    86. Indifferent to the contributions of others   _____

    87. Unable to grasp important ideas developed in a class discussion   _____

    88. Regulate participation so as to be a real asset to class   _____

    89. Afraid of making a mistake   _____

    90. Argue about accuracy of conclusions   _____

    91. Attempt to be humorous to gain attention   _____

DOES THE PUPIL APPEAR TO (BE):   PUPILS

1 2 3 4 [etc.]

Class Attitude and Cooperation

92. Listen attentively
93. Take notes
94. Have a short span of attention
95. Bored
96. Break into contributions of others
97. Work on other class assignments during discussion periods
98. Daydream
99. Not hear questions directed to him
100. Talk or argue with others while another "has the floor"
101. Make noises, etc. to interfere with the class
102. Show marked interest in the subject
103. Respond when corrected
104. Show indifference when majority are interested
105. Draw on paper or look out of window often
106. Seem disturbed when another student is interfering with class
107. Ask for special help when there is lack of understanding
108. Appear at general "help" sessions

Dependability

109. Submit written assignments on time
110. Give oral reports on time
111. Occasionally misinterpret assignments
112. Give alibis for assignments not done
113. "Give-up" easily
114. Complete assigned work in a sketchy manner
115. Volunteer for extra tasks
116. Appear for extra help sessions on time
117. Appear at class without the necessary materials for work
118. Leave laboratory desk in an unsatisfactory condition at the close of the period

DOES THE PUPIL APPEAR TO (BE):	PUPILS 1 2 3 4 [etc.]
119. Work with average dependability and thoroughness on assignments	_____
120. Quality of work on assignments excellent	_____
Probable Ability Combined with Effort	_____
121. Possess low ability and be discouraged	_____
122. Possess medium ability and be discouraged	_____
123. Possess low ability but make a conscientious effort	_____
124. Possess medium ability but encounter difficulty due to having no previous experience with science field	_____
125. Possess medium ability and make conscientious effort	_____
126. Possess medium ability but not to be motivated	_____
127. Possess high ability but not to be motivated	_____
128. Possess high ability but not to be challenged	_____
129. Possess high ability but not to be sufficiently thorough	_____
130. Memorize well but not to be able to apply it to new situations	_____
131. Possess high ability and perform in a very capable manner[2]	_____

The first days in the practice teaching class should afford opportunities to give individual help to pupils who need it. Do not answer questions directly but use inquiry methods—ask guiding questions. It is wise to confer with the supervising teacher about the extent of such help permitted. There may be some reason to withhold assistance on certain assignments. At the same time, contact with students on an individual basis is an excellent way to gain confidence in one's ability to explain, teach, or convey information. The student teacher should capitalize on every possible opportunity to develop this skill.

If the science class is one in which laboratory work plays a large part—i.e., chemistry, physics, or biology—there will be numerous opportunities to give individual help. The student teacher also can be of significant help to the regular teacher in the prepara-

---

[2] Checklist from Lawrence A. Conrey, Unpublished materials (Ann Arbor, Michigan, 1960).

tion of laboratory apparatus and supplies. It is in this situation that the student teacher may achieve the important realization that teaching a laboratory science requires extensive planning and attention to detail.

Because the initial period of observation may be rather brief —perhaps only a few days or a week—the student teacher will do well to begin thinking about the choice of a teaching area or unit. Such choice may have already been made in conference with the supervising teacher. It will most certainly be dependent on the subject-matter goals of the course during the semester or quarter of the assignment. In anticipation of the beginning of teaching, the student teacher will wish to gather appropriate materials and to prepare general plans. Some of the details of the preliminary planning are considered in the next section.

PREPARING TO TEACH A LESSON

Some of the problems involved in lesson planning were taken up in considerable detail in Chapter Five. However, from the standpoint of the student teacher planning to teach a unit for the first time, a brief review of the salient factors may be worthwhile.

A teacher facing a class for the first time may be inclined to expect far too much to be accomplished in a given amount of time. Although it is not necessarily wasteful to overplan a lesson, it is a mistake to attempt to teach everything on the lesson plan just because it is there, or when the learning pace of the pupils does not warrant it. One must constantly be in tune with his class, sensing the proper pace and modifying his presentation as the situation demands.

A second common fault of the beginning teacher is the tendency to teach at a level above the comprehension of the class members. This may be a result of his recent contact with college courses, in which the level is very high, or the inability to place abstract ideas into concrete terms for comprehension by secondary school students. The problem is important enough that it is worth extra consideration by the beginning teacher to make certain his presentation is at the appropriate level for the class involved. Perhaps a few "test trials" with individual students to acquire a realistic sense of the proper difficulty level might be carried out before teaching the entire class.

Construction of unit and daily lesson plans is an important task at this stage. (See Chapter Five for suggested formats.) The important thing is to have a clear idea of what one wishes to accomplish in the allotted time and what specific objectives are to be met. The student teacher should attempt to place himself in the position of a science pupil who is learning about the material for the first time. He should consider factors of interest, motivation, individual differences, time limitations, facilities, and equipment; he should try to anticipate the kinds of problems which may occur and prepare possible solutions to them. After he has done this, the more secure he will be and the less discipline problems he will have.

Of major concern to the beginning teacher is the problem of how to handle discipline when the need for it arises. More has been said about this in Chapter 15, but a few summarizing statements will suffice for review here:

1. The major responsibility for discipline-measures within the class lies with the supervising teacher; however, by previous agreement, the student teacher may have certain responsibilities in the matter when directly in charge of the class. From the standpoint of class respect for the student teacher and future harmony and cooperation, it is to his advantage to handle discipline matters himself, without requiring assistance from the supervising teacher.

2. An atmosphere of mutual respect between teacher and pupil should be cultivated if possible. This precludes the use of sarcasm or intimidation by the teacher in order to secure discipline. If pupils are treated as adults, they will in all likelihood respond favorably in an adult manner.

3. Avoid the tendency to begin the class by enumerating a list of "don'ts" in regard to possible infractions of classroom rules. It is better to maintain the attitude that the goals of the class are to teach science—that discipline problems are not to be tolerated and will be handled summarily if the need arises.

4. In most classes, the majority of pupils are seriously engaged in pursuit of an education, and it is a relatively small minority which is disruptive. Thus, it frequently is possible to allow peer pressure to exert its influence on individuals who create problems in the classroom. Open expressions of distaste by one's peers for unruly behavior frequently have beneficial effects.

5. Assignments of classwork or homework in science should never be used as "punishment" for discipline problems. At all times, the activities of the science class should be made to appear interesting and exciting. The surest way to destroy science interest is to assign extra work or give "tests" as punishment for misbehavior.

A further item of planning for the beginning teacher involves anticipation of questions from the class. First attempts at planning tend to neglect preparations for handling these questions and fail to provide sufficient time for dealing with them in the class period. Yet the frank interchange of ideas between teacher and pupils which is provoked by questions can be an effective teaching technique and should not be ignored. In planning, it is advantageous to try to anticipate the kinds of questions pupils may ask. If one remembers that the pupils may be encountering the subject matter for the first time, it is not too difficult to foretell what questions may come to their minds. These probable questions should be jotted down on the lesson plan with suitable answers or with suggested procedures for finding the answers if the questions come up. Time spent in this manner is not wasted, even if the specific anticipated questions do not arise. The beginning teacher will gain confidence in his own understandings of the subject matter and in his ability to provide suitable answers.

A final point for consideration is that of proper pacing and timing of the class period. The written lesson plans may have suggested time allotments for various activities, but the actual class is certain to deviate to some extent from these plans. The important thing is to be organized flexibly enough to accommodate minor variations within the class period. However, to avoid gross miscalculations of time requirements for certain activities, it is well to rehearse these in advance. A short lecture, for example, can be tried out on one's roommate, who will be able to give critical comments on clarity and organization, as well as timing. In the case of student activities or laboratory work, it is usually advisable to allot about 50 per cent more time than appears adequate for the teacher himself to perform the activity. This is also recommended in the giving of written tests.

At all stages of planning for the first day of teaching, it is imperative that the student teacher keep the supervising teacher informed of his plans, solicit advice and assistance, and in general plan in such a way as to make the transition from regular teacher to student teacher as smoothly as possible.

THE FIRST DAY OF TEACHING

If the student teacher has had frequent opportunities to work with individuals and small groups before his first day of actual teaching, he will find the new experience a natural extension of these tasks and a challenging opportunity for growth in the art of teaching.

A good introduction will get the class off to an interesting start. A brief explanation of the purpose of the lesson and the work at hand, followed immediately by plunging into the class activities, will convey to the students an appreciation of the tasks to be accomplished. A forthright and businesslike manner by the student teacher will elicit cooperation of the class and leave no doubt about who is in charge.

Attention should be given to proper speech and voice modulation. A good pace should be maintained; and, above all, genuine enthusiasm must be displayed. This enthusiasm will normally be infectious and will secure an enthusiastic response from the class. If possible, pupil participation should be employed. Questions from pupils should be encouraged, and a relaxed atmosphere maintained for free interchange of ideas.

It is usually advisable, especially with junior high school classes, to arrange to vary the activity once or twice during the class period. Perhaps a short lecture can be followed by a brief film and the period concluded with a summarizing discussion. Or a demonstration by the teacher might be followed by a period of individual experimentation. It is true that planning and execution of a varied class period requires more work on the part of the teacher; but it will pay dividends in the form of enthusiasm, alert attention, and better learning by the pupils.

The last five or ten minutes of a class period are frequently used for summarization of the major points of the lesson and for the making of appropriate assignments. It is important to recognize that pupils need to have a feeling of accomplishment and progress in order to keep their motivation high. A final clarification of what is expected of them in preparation for succeeding lessons is worth a few minutes at the close of a class period.

Completion of the first day of teaching by the student teacher should be followed as soon as possible by reflection on the successes and failures of the class period and an effort to diagnose any problems which may have arisen. This can usually be done profitably in conference with the supervising teacher and can be a useful follow-up to the day of teaching. Any required adjustments in future plans can be made at this time, necessary additional materials can be gathered, and the stage can be set for a new day of teaching to follow.

YOUR RESPONSIBILITIES AS A STUDENT TEACHER

The opportunity to practice teach in a given school system under a competent supervising teacher should be deemed a privilege by the student teacher. Contrary to an apprentice in a typical trade situation, the "apprentice teacher" is not working with inanimate materials such as wood and metal but with live human beings of infinite worth. One must never forget his responsibility to provide the best possible education for the pupils in the classroom and to avoid possible harmful measures.

It is, therefore, of extreme importance to make one's lesson plans with care, to consider individual differences in interest and ability, and to conduct the class in an atmosphere of friendly helpfulness. Each pupil should be considered a potential learning organism with capabilities for infinite growth. The teacher's responsibility is to develop this potential to the maximum extent.

The student teacher's responsibility to the supervising teacher rests in the area of recognition of authority and respect for experience. It is certain that disagreements about teaching methods or approach may exist, but the final authority in the matter is that of supervising teacher, who is officially responsible for the class. At the same time, an alert student teacher can be of infinite help by anticipating the needs of the class, suggesting materials, preparing materials, and in general earning the title of "assistant teacher" which is used in some school systems. The varied backgrounds of student teachers and willingness to share experiences and special talents which they may have can make the science classroom more interesting and educationally effective than it would be without these resources.

The responsibility of the student teacher toward himself and his potential as a teacher of science is important as well. It would be relatively easy to sit casually by, waiting for things to happen in the practice teaching assignment. The student teacher who gains the most, however, from the standpoint of personal growth, will be the one who enters into the experience with a dynamic approach, intent on learning everything he can in the time allotted. He will participate, when permitted, in meetings of the school faculty, in attendance and assistance at school athletic events, in dramatic and musical productions of the school, and other functions relating to school life. He will in this way see his pupils in a variety of roles outside of the science classroom and will gain insight into the total school program. He will be able to achieve a balanced perspective of his own role as a teacher of science among the other academic disciplines and curricular activities of the school. Such experience will enable him to become a mature teacher of science and complete the metamorphosis from the role of college science student.

TIPS FOR THE STUDENT TEACHER

In a recent report, the committee on student teaching of Colorado State College summarized the experiences considered essential for the student teacher. A partial list follows:

1. The student teacher should understand, and know how to plan for, developmental growth and learning extending over a period of time.
2. The student teacher should assist in organizing the school at the opening of the school year.
3. Student teachers should be provided with specific instruction in how to construct and administer tests, and to assign grades.
4. The student teacher needs directed experience in classroom speaking and in discussion techniques.
5. The student teacher should be prepared for teaching in such

a manner that he is capable of carrying out instruction in his field with limited equipment and materials.

6. The student teacher should be prepared for, and have experience in, the instruction of both the gifted and the slow learner.
7. The student teacher should have instruction in lesson planning.
8. The student teaching experience should provide an opportunity to plan, and to carry out, the ideas gained in college methods classes.
9. Much opportunity should be provided to observe master teachers in the classroom.
10. An opportunity should be provided to observe the work of other teachers during student teaching.
11. The prospective teacher should have experience in planning a program or a curriculum in his field.
12. The student teacher should take part in the program of the faculty in the school. This includes committee work, faculty meetings, etc.
13. The student teacher should take part in conferences with parents and have some direct relation with the home.
14. There should be no full-time teaching assignment the final quarter before graduation.
15. In some areas the student teaching experiences should be extended over more than one quarter.
16. The student teacher should be instructed in how to dress appropriately.
17. The student teacher should have some opportunity to have complete responsibility for the class.
18. The student teacher must have an opportunity to work under the supervision of a master teacher in his field.
19. He must have a supervisor who can give criticism followed by constructive ideas.
20. He should have an opportunity to consult jointly with the college supervisor and supervising teacher.
21. The student teacher should be assigned to teach where he is wanted.
22. He should have a supervisor who stays in the classroom most of the time.
23. His supervisor should not criticize him in the presence of the pupils.
24. He should have a student teaching handbook which guides him in the effective planning and carrying out of instruction.
25. The student teacher should have experiences leading to an understanding of the operation of the total school.
26. He should have experiences leading to an increased understanding of education as a profession.
27. He should work under the supervision of a teacher who is

well-qualified in his subject and has a broad perspective of the area.

28. The student teacher should be provided with means for self-evaluation.

29. He should have a "special problems" seminar either at the close of student teaching or between a split in the teaching assignment.

30. He should become aware that it takes time to develop the skills and understandings essential to effective teaching.[3]

In a survey of forty student teachers of secondary science at Colorado State College, a questionnaire listing nine areas of preparation was distributed, with the request that student teachers indicate those areas in which they felt the need of greater preparation. Four areas receiving the greatest number of responses were: evaluating students and grading, handling discipline problems, answering students' questions, and stronger preparation in subject matter, in that order. Other areas of consideration were: lesson planning, record keeping, extra-curricular activities, demonstrations, and handling laboratory work.

In the same survey, in response to the request to suggest improvements in the methods courses in physical and biological sciences, the following suggestions were made:

1. Put more emphasis on discipline problems and on answering students' questions.

2. Have more discussion on techniques for handling slow and fast learners.

3. Do more demonstrations and experiments.

4. Emphasize methods of evaluation.

5. Have opportunities to hear of the experiences of recent student teachers.

6. Evaluate the texts and materials of the new secondary curriculum projects.

7. Have more opportunities to speak in front of a group and do demonstration teaching.

8. Cover a greater variety of topics, including test construction, extra-credit work, developing interest, grouping students, policies regarding student failures, science fairs and exhibits, etc.

9. Have opportunities to observe a diversity of teachers in one's field.

10. More information on specific sourcebooks of activities, demonstrations, and experiments.[4]

---

[3] *Report of the Student Teaching Committee* (Colorado State College, Greeley), June 1, 1962.

[4] This survey was the work of Leslie Trowbridge.

SUMMARY

Practice teaching is the most important phase of the prospective teacher's training. Entered into with enthusiasm and a willingness to learn, the experience will be for the student teacher a valuable culmination to college preparation for teaching.

The selection of subject, school, and supervising teacher is enhanced by visits to schools before the semester or quarter of practice teaching. It is advisable to do one's practice teaching in the major field of preparation in order to capitalize on one's strength of subject-matter competency.

The usual pattern of preparation is to spend several days or a week observing the class one is going to teach. Such observation can be done on a systematic basis and may enable one to achieve real insight into the individual differences present in the class. The student teacher can be an "assistant teacher" in the truest sense if he is alert to developing problems, anticipates future activities of the class, and prepares himself accordingly.

Taking over the class to teach a lesson or a unit will be completely successful if the student teacher plans adequately in consultation with the supervising teacher and makes his preparations carefully. Advance rehearsal for the first day of teaching is an advisable procedure, particularly if the time budget is questionable or if class questions are anticipated. An immediate follow-up of a day of teaching with a brief conference with the supervising teacher is advisable. Necessary changes in lesson plans can be made at this time.

A desirable arrangement is to follow the practice teaching quarter with a final quarter on the college campus before graduation. At this time, seminars in special problems of teaching can be most profitable, and the student teacher can reflect upon the practice teaching experience to good advantage. The opportunity to give maximum attention to the very important choice of a first teaching position in the light of the recent experience in practice teaching is thus afforded.

Further Investigation and Study

1. In your observation of a science class use the checklist on pp. 260-264 to discover the individual differences present in the class. At the end of a week, discuss your observations with the teacher. How does the students' achievement appear to correlate with your observations of study habits and classroom behavior?
2. Make a list of the traits you would like to see in the supervising teacher with whom you wish to do your practice teaching. Using this list as a guide, objectively analyze your own traits and compare. Do you think similar or opposite traits are preferable, or that a judicious blend of both is preferable?

I often say that when you can measure what you are speaking about, and express it in numbers, you know something about it; but when you cannot express it in numbers, your knowledge is of a meagre and unsatisfactory kind; it may be the beginning of knowledge, but you scarcely, in your thoughts, have advanced to the stage of "Science," whatever the matter may be.[1]

Lord Kelvin

17

Inquiry through the Use of Mathematics

Mathematics has been an integral part of the advance of science through the years. No scientific discipline has become truly respectable until bolstered by data compiled and analyzed by mathematical methods. The evidence provided by natural phenomena, experimentally tested in the laboratory or in the field and subjected to intensive scrutiny by mathematics, forms the foundation upon which science rests. The data collected by Tycho Brahe did not contribute substantially to the understanding of astronomy until the mathematical genius of Kepler put it into order and formulated certain laws of planetary motion. The hypothesis, developed by Jonas Salk, of polio inoculation by weakened virus did not gain public acceptance until it was tested by statistical methods on a large scale.

The teacher of science in the junior and senior high school has an obligation to convey to his students an understanding of the role of mathematics in science. Every opportunity should be used to show the integral nature of mathematics and science. Because of the usual parallel pattern of science and mathematics courses in grades seven through twelve, little cross-over between these disciplines is afforded. The impression is gained by students that science and mathematics are unrelated entities.

---

[1] Quoted in Gerald Holton and Duane H. D. Roller, *Foundations of Modern Physical Science* (Reading, Mass.: Addison-Wesley Publishing Co., Inc., 1958), p. 229.

This attitude often is perpetuated by the teachers of both subjects, perhaps because of lack of familiarity with possible common objectives and applications.

In practice the difficulty of incorporating mathematics into science classes is compounded by extreme variations in mathematical ability among students. At any grade level, say the seventh grade, students in the science classes have mathematics competencies which range several grade levels above and below the average for the particular grade. Some students may have real difficulties with simple addition and subtraction operations. Others may have good understandings of ratio and proportion, percentage, and use of scientific notation.

It is important for the science teacher to realize this great variation and to plan his science activities accordingly. The mathematical requirements for any given activity or experiment are also extremely varied. By suitably individualizing the instruction, one can challenge students at their level and in the process help them to gain practice in the particular mathematical skill.

Junior high school students in the seventh grade learn that measurement is an integral part of science.

Photo courtesy of Bob Waters, Colorado State College.

> Mrs. Phelps planned to have her general science class do a half-life determination using the radioactivity demonstrator. The radioisotope for this experiment was obtained from the Atomic Energy Commission. It was iodine 131 which has a suitably short half-life for classroom purposes.
>
> Certain members of the class whose mathematical abilities were weak were assigned the task of recording the counts per minute registered by the scalar. Simple averaging of three successive readings taken thirty seconds apart was required for each scheduled observation time. Observations were taken every five minutes during each class period for a week. The task was rotated among several students throughout the week.

Data gathering is the beginning of mathematics usage in science.

Photo courtesy of Ivo Lindauer, Laboratory School, Colorado State College.

At the end of a week, the data were plotted on semilog paper. Several of the students needed help on this phase of the experiment. Others were able to handle it with ease.

For calculation of the half-life of the sample of iodine 131, a discussion period was scheduled. Questions of the following nature were discussed:

1. What happened to the counts-per-minute rate?
2. What caused this?
3. After what period of time will the count rate be half what the initial rate was?
4. What is the half-life?
5. Why were the data plotted on semilog paper?
6. What would the curve look like if plotted on regular coordinate paper?
7. What will the count rate be at the end of two half-life periods? Three half-lives? Ten?

In this experiment several opportunities were given for development of mathematical skills at varying levels. Counting, recording data, averaging, plotting a graph, analysis of a graph, predicting an outcome, etc. were used at various stages. The range of difficulty of these skills was broad. The teacher could fit the skill difficulties to individual differences within the class and also stimulate growth in previously unlearned skills.

The inquiry approach to science teaching requires increased use of mathematics skills. There are many opportunities for application of these skills in the solution of science problems. These problems are presented or arise normally in the pursuit of laboratory experiments. Junior high school students as well as those at the senior high level have increasing experiences in the laboratory. Solutions of laboratory problems require data. Collection and analysis of data implies mathematical operations.

Accurate observation is important in measurement.

Photo courtesy of Bob Waters, Colorado State College.

MATHEMATICS TAUGHT IN THE SECONDARY SCHOOL

Analysis of the mathematics courses in junior high school reveals the following types of skill operations presently being taught, or reviewed:

1. Addition and subtraction
2. Multiplication and division
3. Proper and improper fractions
4. Percentage
5. Ratio and proportion
6. Simple graphing (histograms, line graphs, and bar graphs)
7. Recognition and use of simple geometric figures
8. Area and volume problems
9. Use of units
10. Scientific notation

11. Metric system (mass, length, area, volume)
12. Basic algebra
13. Basic theory of sets
14. Number systems and bases
15. Other introductory topics

At the senior high level, a student is given further experience in all of those operations taught in the junior high school, by way of brief reviews and usage. In addition, the following topics are introduced:

1. Advanced algebra—series and power functions
2. Trigonometric functions
3. Logarithms
4. Coordinate systems in two and three dimensions
5. Use of the slide rule
6. Dimensional analysis
7. Advanced graphing techniques (Log and semilog, reciprocal, reciprocal powers, etc.)
8. Simple statistics (mean, median, standard deviation, quartiles, etc.)
9. Significant figures and standards of accuracy
10. Analysis of errors
11. Elements of basic calculus

For those students in their junior and senior years who are preparing for college, the following competencies are frequently added to the mathematics programs:

1. Solid geometry
2. Analytic geometry
3. Differential and integral calculus
4. Statistical techniques

Development of these skills in mathematics classes should be accompanied by application in science classes. Opportunities for use of these mathematics skills should be provided frequently. Such opportunities should arise in connection with the solution of laboratory problems and exercises, as well as in connection with word problems assigned from the textbooks.

RELATING SCIENCE TO CONCURRENT MATHEMATICS COURSES

Occasional joint planning between the mathematics teacher and the science teacher can bring about improved conditions, in both areas, for relating mathematics and science. If the mathematics teacher is aware of the uses of mathematics in the science classes at particular grade levels, he may point out the possible applications to his students. In assigning homework problems, he may use examples from science which have current significance. Textbooks in mathematics can be improved significantly on this point. The scientist is concerned with proper use of units and measurement. Attachment of appropriate units to the figures given in word problems in mathematics can develop skills of usage, recognition, and manipulation of units by the students. The problems will take on increased meaning and show the applications of mathematics to science.

Team-teaching arrangements between science and mathematics teachers can afford many opportunities for interrelating the two disciplines. Many teachers are trained equally well in both areas and have teaching responsibilities in both. In this case, maximum effectiveness should be achieved.

STIMULATING MATHEMATICS USAGE IN SCIENCE CLASSES

The laboratory provides the opportunity for many data-gathering problems. Practice can be gained in making measurements, keeping records, and graphing.

For an eighth-grade science project, Edith decided to study the germination of radish seeds under different temperatures.

She arranged her radish seeds in rows of ten each on wet cloth, rolled the cloth into a slender cylinder, and placed each in a large-mouth gallon jar with a small thermometer. Ten identical cloths were put in each jar. Four jars were used. Each was placed under a different temperature for the period of the experiment.

Her data sheet looked like this:

Per Cent Germination Each Day

	Days									
	1	2	3	4	5	6	7	8	9	10
Room Temp. 75°F (Control)	90	90	100	90	100	100	100	100	100	90
Freezer Temp. 5°F	0	0	0	0	0	100	100	100	100	100
Refrigerator Temp. 45°F	0	0	0	30	30	60	20	60	70	70
Hot Box Temp. 130°F	0	0	0	0	0	0	0	0	0	0

She made a graph of her results as follows.

Analysis of her graph gave an indication of the optimum conditions for germination of radish seeds. It also showed that a colder temperature delays the germination process. The hot-box temperature was evidently too high for germi-

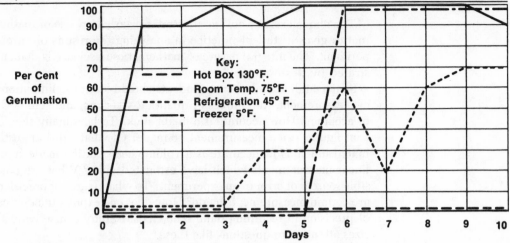

Per Cent of Germination

Key:
– – – – Hot Box 130°F.
———— Room Temp. 75°F.
- - - - - - Refrigeration 45° F.
–·——·– Freezer 5°F.

nation. Examination of these seeds showed deterioration and decay.

Analysis of experiments gives additional practice in using mathematics. The PSSC exercise entitled "Analysis of an Experiment" is an example of this. The data given in the exercise show a record of the periods of time required to empty a can of water through a hole punched in the bottom.

Times to Empty (sec)

d in cm.	h in cm.			
	30	10	4	1
1.5	73.0	43.5	26.7	13.5
2	41.2	23.7	15.0	7.2
3	18.4	10.5	6.8	3.7
5	6.8	3.9	2.2	1.5

Students are advised to plot graphs of the data to analyze the relationships between emptying times and two other variables, diameter of hole and height of water in the can. Types of graphs suggested are one showing times versus diameter for a constant height and one showing time versus square of diameter. Graphs for different heights are also suggested. Typical questions asked in this exercise are:

1. From your curve, how accurately can you predict the time it would take to empty the same container if the diameter of the opening was 4 cm.? 8 cm.?
2. Can you write down the algebraic relation between t and d for the particular height of water used?
3. Can you find the general expression for time of flow as a function of both h and d?[2]

---

[2] Physical Science Study Committee, *Laboratory Guide for Physics* (Boston: D. C. Heath & Company, 1960), p. 8.

The above exercise outline illustrates clearly how use of mathematics gives a student practice in analyzing the results of an experiment. The integral nature of mathematics in science is demonstrated by this example.

Senior high school science students should learn the limitations of measurement, the sources of quantitative errors, and standards of accuracy. How accurate is a meter stick? To how many significant figures can a measurement be made? Of what value are estimated units? How accurate is a volume computation made from linear measurements which have estimated units? What are possible sources of error in an experiment? To what degree of precision are certain measurements made? How does one express the degree of precision in recording data? The CHEM Study course emphasizes attention to questions like these.[3]

In the *Teacher's Guide*, the following comment is made on "Experiment 5, Heat Effects."

> Post-Lab Discussion. This experiment provides an excellent opportunity to discuss uncertainty both in measurements and in calculated quantities. Begin the discussion by calling for the student values for calculated heat of combustion and heat of solidification. Ask the students about the uncertainty involved in the calculated value. Why is the heat of combustion known only to about ±300 cal/g, and the heat of solidification only to about ±10 cal/g?[4]

Knowledge of significant figures is particularly important in chemistry and physics where physical measurements are made frequently in laboratory experiments.

SUMMARY

There is need for greater emphasis on relating mathematics and secondary school sciences. Students of science should see the role of mathematics as a tool of science. Students of mathematics should have opportunities to apply their mathematical skills to the solution of scientific problems; applications should be called to their attention.

The development of inquiry methods in science teaching provides numerous opportunities for use of mathematics. In this way, mathematics is seen as a tool of science for quantifying and testing hypotheses. Students receive practice, on a realistic and meaningful level, in the skills learned in their mathematics classes. In addi-

---

[3] Chemical Education Materials Study, *Teacher's Guide for Chemistry, an Experimental Science* (San Francisco: W. H. Freeman & Co., Publishers, 1963).
[4] *Ibid.*, p. 33.

tion to practice in the usual skills of addition, subtraction, scientific notation, logarithms, use of the slide rule, etc., students in modern science learn to evaluate measurements, express precision of data and results, work with significant figures, and apply statistical tests to their data. These skills are given practice at all levels of junior and senior high school science. Advanced students use calculus and other higher-level mathematics in some of their science classes.

The advent of new curriculums in science and mathematics is rapidly bringing about a revolution in the traditional patterns of teaching in these subjects. The interrelatedness of the two disciplines is being emphasized with beneficial results to both. Students involved in the modern programs are well-equipped to absorb the skills and concepts required of scientists, engineers, and mathematicians of this technological age.

Further Investigation and Study

1. Plan a laboratory assignment in which students are given maximum opportunity to practice mathematic skills with which they are currently familiar from their mathematics classes.
2. Obtain a mathematics textbook of the type usually used in eighth-grade mathematics. Select an appropriate chapter and rewrite all the problems at the end of a section or chapter in such a manner as to emphasize the interrelatedness of science and mathematics.
3. Interview a teacher of mathematics to discover the types of mathematics skills students are expected to learn by the time they have completed his course.
4. Write a two- or three-paragraph essay on how you would implement the teaching of needed mathematics skills in a science class for which you were the teacher.
5. Discuss the pros and cons of the use of slide rules in science classes at various levels. Give attention to time required to teach rudimentary skill in their use, accuracy, use in tests, etc.

18

Activities for Science Teaching

This chapter contains many suggestions for use in junior high school and high school. They are included to give prospective teachers ideas of the possible types of teaching procedures that can be used. Teachers should be encouraged to design similar activities using these suggestions as guides. All of these activities are designed to elicit inquiry. Described in the pages that follow are: student experiments, discovery demonstrations, invitations to inquiry, pictorial riddles, self-tests, and teacher aids.

Representative lessons are given for biology, physical science, earth science, and junior high school science. No attempt has been made to cover extensively all the science fields. Prospective or experienced teachers are encouraged to be creative in designing their own activities. It is the feeling of the authors that far too often student teachers and experienced teachers are given the impression that what is written in a book or a course of study is better than what they can produce. In many instances this may be true, but each teacher has a subject-matter strength and love which enables him to design truly creative experiences. Teachers who break out of the structure of a course of study or laboratory manuals are most likely to become dynamic and contribute to the growth of the teaching profession.

STUDENT EXPERIMENTS

These experiments are provided as examples of individual or small-group experiments which can be used to study natural phenomena. The materials are of simple design and can be constructed with minimum effort. The experiments can be modified in any way desired by the student or teacher. In each case, quantitative measurements can be made, records kept, and conclusions drawn. Inevitably, other problems for study will emerge from these experiments, and these may lead to further investigations.

Student Experiment I (Physical Sciences)

EXPERIMENT WITH SIMPLE MATERIALS TO FIND THE MAGNETIC FIELD OF THE EARTH

Materials:
1. Dry cell
2. Resistance box
3. Milliammeter (0–1 am. range)
4. Cardboard cylinder
5. Small sewing needle
6. Ten feet of No. 24 insulated copper wire
7. Protractor
8. Connecting wire
9. Knife switch
10. Terminal posts
11. Cellophane tape
12. Wood base

Construction as shown in Figure 27.

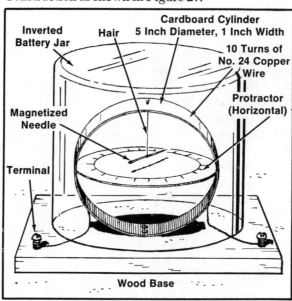

Figure 27–Magnetometer

Experiment (see Figure 28)

Align the magnetometer so that the needle which is pointing north-south will be parallel to the base line of the protractor. Make the connections as shown and throw the knife switch. If the needle makes a full ninety-degree turn, R must be increased so that the magnetic field H_c of the magnetometer is less strong. Adjust R so that the needle comes to rest somewhere between zero and ninety degrees. Read the milliammeter and the angular deflection of the needle (θ). Take several trials.

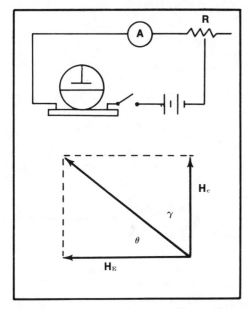

Figure 28

Calculations:

To find H_C, use $H_c = \dfrac{2\pi N I}{10\,R}$ where N = number of coils

I = current in amperes
r = radius of coil in cm.
H_c = magnetic field strength of coil in oersteds
H_e = magnetic field strength of earth in oersteds (to be found)

To find H_E, use $H_E = H_C \tan \gamma$ ☐ where $\gamma = 90° - \theta$

Your result should be in the neighborhood of 0.2 oersteds for H_E at 40 degrees latitude. The values of H_E in the United States range of 0.13 oersted at Gull Island in Lake Superior to 0.28 oersteds near Brownsville, Texas. The higher values are at lower latitudes because it is the *horizontal* component which is being measured.

Student Experiment II (Physical Sciences)

DIFFUSION CLOUD CHAMBER

Materials:
1. Cylindrical glass container, with top and bottom removed. (See Teacher Aid I for method of cutting top off a glass bottle.)
2. Two aluminum pie tins.
3. Flat sheet of sponge rubber.
4. Circular piece of black velvet.
5. Light source—e.g., slide-projector bulb.
6. Dry ice (small cakes several inches square).
7. Methyl alcohol.
8. Glue.
9. D.C. high-voltage source (90–200 volts) (desirable but not absolutely necessary).
10. Radioactive source (Scrapings from luminous clock face will do.)

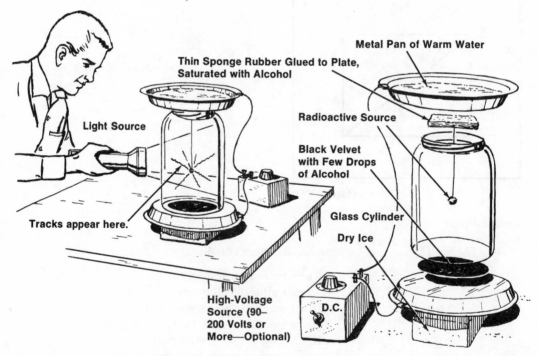

Figure 29

The diffusion cloud chamber can be used to give evidence of the existence of radioactive particles such as alpha particles, beta particles, gamma rays and cosmic particles.

A radioactive source can be obtained by taking a small fragment of a luminous dial or number of a watch or clock face which has been discarded. Also, it is possible to obtain a small pin coated with a radioactive salt from *Scientific American*, 415 Madison Avenue,

New York 17, New York. This may be obtained free of charge simply by writing for it.

Principle:

Radioactive particles traveling through a supersaturated area will cause small droplets to form by creating charged ions on which the droplets can condense.

Set-up:

Suspend the radioactive source as shown about three-quarters of an inch from the velvet at the bottom. Saturate the sponge rubber with methyl alcohol and place a few drops on the black velvet. Set the whole cylinder on a cake of dry ice, which may be in chunk form or crushed. Place a little warm water in the pan on top. Shine the light directly at the source near the bottom of the container. Wait about thirty seconds for supersaturation to occur. You should be able to tell that this has happened because of the appearance of a light "snow" falling slowly in the bottom inch or so of the container. It is in this region that the cloud tracks will appear. They will occur suddenly as a streak and will then disappear by evaporation in a moment or two. A bit of persistence will bring great satisfaction in the appearance of these very fascinating cloud tracks of radioactive particles.

Student Experiment III (Junior High School)

MAKING PERMANENT WAX PRINTS OF MAGNETIC LINES OF FORCE

Materials needed:

1. Alcohol lamp or hot plate
2. Several sheets of white or colored paper of extra heavy thickness
3. Two or three bar magnets or horseshoe magnets
4. Paraffin
5. Cake pan or bread tin, wide enough for 8½ x 11 inch sheet of paper to fit when dipped into the wax
6. Paper towels on which to lay the waxed papers for drying
7. Iron filings in a salt shaker
8. A 300-watt lamp and extension cord with socket

Prepare the wax sheets by melting the paraffin in the wide pan and dipping the sheets through the paraffin once and letting the excess drain off. Lay the sheets on paper towels for a minute or two until they are dry.

Lay the dried waxed sheets of paper over the top of a bar magnet or horseshoe magnet lying flat on the table. From a height of ten or twelve inches shake the iron filings onto the waxed paper until you can see definite lines-of-force patterns emerging. Without disturbing the patterns, hold the 300-watt lamp close to the surface of the waxed paper until you can see that the wax has just begun to melt or get shiny. Do this uniformly over the whole area covered by the iron filings. Remove the lamp and let dry a minute or so.

Principle:

The dark iron filings will absorb the heat from the lamp more rapidly than will the white waxed surface. The filings will melt the wax beneath them and settle into the waxed layer. When dry, they will remain permanently in place.

Suggestion:

By leaving the paper in place over the magnet and placing some half-inch wooden blocks on the surface, another waxed sheet can be supported above the first one. Then, repeating the process as before you can learn something about the three-dimensional shape of a magnetic field around a bar magnet. Several layers can be studied this way.

Student Experiment IV (Junior High School)
PRODUCING FIRE BY FRICTION

Materials needed:
1. Several newspapers
2. File or heavy scout knife
3. Piece of flint rock, quartzite, or quartz about 2 in. in diameter
4. Tinder (produced by fraying end of rope or wrapping cord)
5. Squares of cotton cloth about 10 in. square

Preparation of materials:

The squares of cotton cloth must be prepared by charring ahead of time because charred cloth is about the only satisfactory material for catching the spark from the flint and steel. Prepare them by igniting a corner, letting it flame for a few seconds, then smothering by thrusting between folded sheets of newspaper. Do this several times until you have a charred surface about six inches square.

Prepare the tinder by fraying several inches of soft hemp wrapping cord or small rope. Have a medium-sized handful for use when the spark is caught on the charred cloth.

Producing the fire:

Lay a freshly prepared piece of charred cloth on a protective board on top of the desk or table. Strike the piece of flint or quartzite several sharp glancing blows with the file or back of knife blade until a spark lands on the charred cloth. It will immediately start to glow and spread. Lay the tinder closely packed on top of the glowing area and blow intermittently until the tinder is ignited and bursts into flames. It will flash upward a few inches so do not place your face too close to the tinder as you blow.

Student Experiment V (Biology)
TEMPERATURE AND BACTERIAL GROWTH

Obtain the following materials:
1. Sterile swab

2. Sterile water
3. Three agar plates

Procedure:

Dip a sterile swab into sterile water (water boiled for ten minutes) and press the cotton against the wall of the container to drain off excess. "Mop" part of the floor with the swab. Inoculate three agar plates by rubbing gently across the plates in the manner shown below. Why do you think you inoculate the plate in this way?

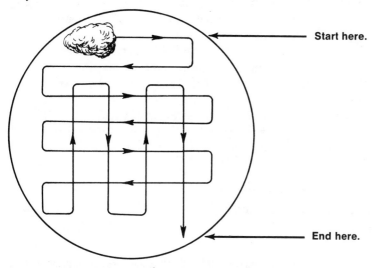

Figure 30

Mark these plates with a glass-marking pencil, or gummed labels, as follows: "cold," "slightly warm," and "very warm." Place the agar plates as follows:

1. The "cold" plate in a refrigerator for 24 hours.
2. The "warm" plate in a dark place at room temperature (closet or paper box).
3. The "very warm" plate next to the radiators, in an incubator at eighty to seventy-five degrees Fahrenheit, or in a sunny place. If the plate is placed in sunlight, cover with black paper or put the plate into a small paper box. Why do you think this is done?

Teacher's note: Concepts involved in the lesson:

Certain harmful bacteria enter our bodies at specific points; the most common portals of entry are the mouth and nasal passages, since these places usually provide the bacteria with proper temperature for their development.

Cold temperatures of about thirty degrees Fahrenheit inhibit or greatly reduce the rate of growth of bacteria.

Although most bacteria will grow at temperatures of sixty-eight to seventy degrees, bacterial growth is more abundant at temperatures approximating body temperature, or 98.6 degrees Fahrenheit.

Student Activity

1. From this experiment, what other requirements are needed for the growth of bacteria? Diagram what you found on your three plates.
2. Why do you often get bacterial infections in the mouth and nasal passages?
3. How could you control rapid growth of bacteria in your mouth?
4. From the experiment, what evidence do you have that the bacteria multiplied?
5. Describe several methods of heat sterilization. Summarize the main ideas you have learned from this experiment.
6. If you were going to repeat this experiment, how would you change it?
7. If you were going to design an experiment to determine the optimum temperature growth for your bacteria, what would you do?

Student Experiment VI (Biology)

EFFECT OF LIGHT ON PLANTS

Procedure:

Obtain several grain seeds. Wheat or oat seed will do.

Take six small milk cartons and cut them so they are about three inches high. Fill these with soil. Bury four seeds about one inch deep and one-half inch apart in the soil of each of the cartons. Water and let the seeds sprout.

When the sprouts are about an inch high, cut the tips about one-eighth inch from the top of the sprouts in two of the cartons and leave the sprouts in the other cartons untouched. The outer sheath of the oat seed is called the coleoptile. And that is what you have cut in this experiment. (See diagram.)

What do you hypothesize will happen to the plants whose epicotyl has been cut compared to those plants that were left uncut? Record your hypothesis on paper. (See the Student Activity page.)

Continue the experiment several days, watering and caring for both groups of plants under the same conditions. Record your observations about the growth of the plants each day.

Teacher's note:

Ask (before the students make their first observation): What should we do in order to keep accurate records about the growth of these plants? The instructor should endeavor to get the students to realize the importance of collecting data and the necessity of using some quantitative methods to determine the growth rate of the plants.

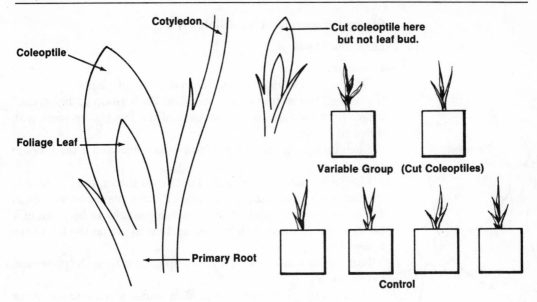

Figure 31

After several days, have the students evaluate their data and write their conclusions about the variations in growth in the two groups of plants.

Have the students complete the Student Activities.

In the section where the class is asked to theorize about why the plants grow the way they do, the instructor should inform the class that a theory tries to explain what occurs in fact. In this case something in the tip of the plant seems to control or direct the way the rest of the plant grows. This is a fact, but the theory must explain how this growth is controlled. The instructor might lead the class, by asking them questions, into a discussion about plant hormones and how they control growth.

Concepts involved in the lesson:

Light helps to direct the way plants will grow.

There is something produced in the tips of plants which helps to direct the growth of the plant.

Student Activity

1. What are your tentative hypotheses about the experiment?
2. Record your data about the experiment.
3. What are your conclusions about this experiment?
4. Why did we use two groups of plants in this experiment?
5. What is a "control" in an experiment? Which group of plants was the control, and which group was the variable?
6. What is your theory explaining why the plants whose tips were cut grew differently from those that were left uncut?
7. Can you think of any further experiments which we might do to help verify your theory about plant growth?

Student Experiment VII (Biology)

LEAF EPIDERMIS

Procedure:

Obtain several leaves from different types of plants.

Form groups of four or five students. Each group gather several leaves from the same plant, but each of the five groups work with different leaves.

Each group obtain several *plastic* cover slips and a small bottle of acetone.

Place a leaf on a microscopic slide. Cover the exposed surface of the leaf with a few drops of acetone. Place a plastic cover slip on top of the leaf and press it in place for one minute by holding it between your fingers. Don't allow acetone to get on the top of the cover slip.

Each group make several similar impressions from the upper and lower surfaces of the leaf.

Each group place their cover slips under a microscope. After having looked at several impressions of the upper and lower surface, diagram the leaf structure as accurately as possible on a Ditto master.

These Ditto masters will be collected by the teacher.

Concepts involved in the lesson:

There is variation of leaf structure. The upper part of the leaf varies from the lower surface.

The leaf has on its surface small openings called stomates through which it breathes.

Located around each of these openings are small guard cells.

Teacher's note:

Run the Ditto masters off and return them to the students the next day.

Have the students keep their plastic slips. Have individuals from different groups check the cover slips of another group with the Ditto diagram to determine its accuracy.

After the diagrams have been verified, ask the student to complete the Student Activity section.

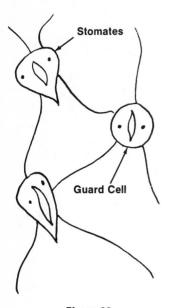

Stomates

Guard Cell

Figure 32

Student Activity

1. Draw as accurately as possible a diagram of your leaf surfaces (both upper and lower).
2. What conclusions do you note about the upper surface of a leaf compared to the lower surface?
3. Why do you think this variation exists?
4. Draw a general diagram of a leaf structure which would be typical of most leaves. Label it and describe the function of each of the parts.
5. Can you think of any other impressions you might make of bio-

logical specimens using the same technique as was used in this experiment?

6. Biologists say that structure is related to function. From your observation of leaves, what do you think they mean by this?

Dr. Schokley's Discussion Technique

Stressing Mental Tools for Scientific Thinking to Develop Comprehension of a Basic Scientific Principle or Law

Something Is Always True—No Matter What—Provided That

This approach as outlined by Dr. Schokley is to develop comprehension of the essential features of a basic scientific principle or law in elementary terms by stating it as something which is "always true," "no matter what" the particular circumstances may be, "provided that" the basic conditions for the law to be applicable are not violated. The qualifying phrases "no matter what" and "provided that" serve to convey the concept that a law has a certain range of validity; in a wide variety of cases it applies, but there are usually limits which must not be exceeded.[1]

This type of activity can be easily prepared by taking a scientific principle and modifying it by inserting the words *always true, no matter what, provided that* and then lead a discussion with the class. See the examples below:

Activity I (Physics)

1. Water always boils at 100° C—No matter what? Provided that?

Activity II (Physics)

1. "What goes up must come down" is always true—No matter what? Provided that?

2. The speed of diffusion of a gas varies inversely with the square root of their densities—No matter what? Provided that?

Activity III (Biology)

1. Bubonic plague will cause death—No matter what? Provided that?

Activity IV (Biology)

1. Population will increase—No matter what? Provided that?

Activity V (Biology)

1. After a forest is burned there always will be plant succession—No matter what? Provided that?

---

[1] From a press release describing a paper by Dr. William Schokley of the National Academy of Sciences, National Research Council, April 24, 1963, title: "Proposed Important Mental Tools for Scientific Thinking at the High School Level."

Activity VI (Chemistry)

1. If you increase the temperature 10° C the enzymatic activity will double—No matter what? Provided that?

Activity VII (Earth Science)

1. Atmospheric pressure decreases with an increase in altitude— No matter what? Provided that?
2. The rate of erosion is inversely proportional to the resistance of rocks—No matter what? Provided that?
3. Glacial abrasion occurs in proportion to the weight of the ice and the velocity of its movement—No matter what? Provided that?

DISCOVERY DEMONSTRATIONS

The following are examples of discovery demonstrations. This is an inquiry activity. The purpose of the demonstration is to have students discover the principles or concepts involved.

The discovery demonstrations are designed to pose problem situations to which answers are not immediately apparent. This will establish interest, enthusiasm, and curiosity in the classroom and promote better learning. By appropriate guiding questions the teacher can direct the thought processes of the students until a solution is found. It is recommended that answers not be given to the students except by guiding questions and inductive processes until the solution is "discovered" by the students themselves.

In writing a discovery demonstration, the instructor should use the following guide:

1. List concepts or principles you want to teach. Do this first.
2. Think of an activity or consult one of the sourcebooks in biology, physical science, or earth science for ideas. Get in the habit of looking at simple things, such as toys, for examples of ideas that can be used to teach principles. Often, many things in a science class can be used to show principles. For example: A faucet can be used to demonstrate simple machines, surface tension, or electrical force. Look at your room and you will see many more. How about the pencil sharpener, window shade, projection screen, or motion-picture camera? Look; you will get many ideas.
3. Outline a procedure, interspersed with questions which will help lead students towards discovery of the concepts you want to teach.
4. Write a student-activity sheet to evaluate how well students understood the lesson. This can also be used to suggest experiments, derived from the demonstration, that students could perform. Ask students to suggest how the demonstration

could be improved or modified. This gives students opportunities to be creative. (See Chapter 8 for more detailed ideas and select demonstrations.)

Discovery Demonstration I (Earth Science)

HOW CAN WE MAKE A CLOUD?

Materials:
1. Gallon jug
2. Matches
3. Ice
4. Two flasks

Procedure, Experiment I:
  If you were going to make a cloud in the classroom, how would you do it?
  Take a gallon jug, light a match, and drop it in the jug. Let it burn. As soon as it goes out, blow hard into the jug and then pull it away from your mouth quickly.

Ask:
  What did you notice about what happened in the jug?
  Where did the water come from that made the cloud in the jug?
  Try the experiment again, only this time don't use the match.

Ask:
  Why was the match important in the experiment?

Figure 33—Experiment I

Procedure, Experiment II:
  Take two flasks as shown on the right. Fill them about one-quarter full with water. Heat one of the flasks. After it is fairly warm, remove the burner and place an ice cube in the top of the flask. See the diagram.
  Record what happens below:
  1. When air rises, it cools. From what you have learned in this experiment, can you explain why there is more rain and snow in the mountains?
  2. What do we have to do to air so that we can see water in it?

In the jug experiment the match is necessary because it gives off tiny smoke particles which the water needs to have as a nucleus in order to condense easily. The sudden release of pressure in the moist air in the jug causes the temperature in the jug to drop, and the water then condenses. In the second experiment, the water in the flask is saturated with moisture. The ice cube cools the air and causes the water to condense. Emphasize to the class that the higher one goes in the lower atmosphere the more the temperature drops. This causes condensation and helps explain why there is greater rainfall and snow in mountain regions.

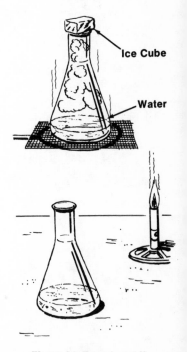

Figure 34—Experiment II

Discovery Demonstration II (Physical Sciences)

INVISIBILITY

Materials:
1. 500 ml Florence flask
2. Solution of 59% CCl_4 and 41% C_6H_6
3. Broken pieces of Pyrex glass
4. 500 ml beaker

Before beginning the study of refraction of light, completely fill a stoppered 500 ml flask with a mixture of 59 per cent carbon tetrachloride (CCl_4) and 41 per cent benzene (C_6H_6), in which have been placed several small chips of Pyrex glass. A broken Pyrex test tube will do. The glass will be invisible.

Ask each student to study the contents of the bottle. Ask a number of them what they see in the bottle.

Now instruct the students to shake the bottle and report what they hear. They should hear a rattling noise. Ask them to explain this noise.

Have a student carefully pour the mixture into a beaker and place the bits of glass in another beaker filled with water. The glass should now be visible.

Ask these questions:
1. Why is the glass visible in water but not in the other solution?
2. What is the other solution? Waft some fumes toward your nose.
3. Why is any object not giving off light of its own visible?
4. What is a "transparent" object?
5. Is any object perfectly transparent?
6. When light goes from air into a "transparent" object, what happens to some of the light? Why can you see a "transparent" object?
7. Would you be able to see the "transparent" object if no light reflected to your eyes?
8. If the light traveled the same speed in the "transparent" object as it did in air, would you be able to see it? (Note: the index of refraction would be the same in each material.)
9. An analogous situation is when you see "heat" waves over a hot radiator. The heated air becomes visible because it has a different index of refraction from the surrounding cooler air. Can you now answer why the pieces of glass are invisible in the solution but visible in water?

Teacher's note:

The mixture of carbon tetrachloride and benzene has the same index of refraction as Pyrex glass—about 1.55. Light entering the solution passes into the glass pieces without reflection from their surfaces—therefore sending back no visible light to the eye.

Discovery Demonstration III (Physical Sciences)

THE AMMONIA FOUNTAIN

Materials:
1. 500 ml flask
2. 1-hole stopper
3. Long glass tube, tapered at top end
4. Beaker on ring stand with a clear liquid in it (water and a few drops of phenolphthalein)

Have the apparatus shown in Figure 35 set up on the desk when the class enters. Without any explanation, ask the students to observe the demonstration. Have them watch carefully and try to decide what the reasons are for what is happening. Do not explain the procedure until the questioning period afterward.

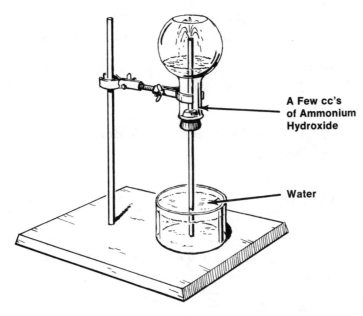

A Few cc's of Ammonium Hydroxide

Water

Figure 35

Procedure:
Heat the inverted flask gently with the Bunsen burner about one minute; remove Bunsen burner and lower end of tube into beaker of liquid.

Observe rise of liquid in the tube. Note fountain when liquid reaches the tapered part of tube.

Note color change to red in the liquid in the flask.

Note the final level of colored liquid in the flask and of the clear liquid in the beaker.

Ask these questions or similar ones:
1. What apparently is in the beaker?
    (Water with a few drops of phenolphthalein in it.)

2. What is in the flask to start with?
(A few cc's of ammonium hydroxide and air.)
3. What will heating do to it?
(Drive out the air and some ammonia gas.)
4. What is the purpose of heating?
(To drive out the air and thus leave a partial vacuum when the ammonia gas dissolves in the water.)
5. What condition will this leave in the flask?
(A partial vacuum caused by the ammonia gas dissolving in water.)
6. Why does the liquid rise in the tube?
(It is pushed up by atmospheric air when the vacuum is created in the flask.)
7. What could cause a color change in the liquid in the flask?
(An acid-base indicator.)
8. What must have been in the water?
(A base indicator which turns red in basic solutions—phenolphthalein.)
9. What principles does this illustrate?
(Solubility of ammonia gas in water. Air exerts pressure. Heat causes gases to expand.)

Discovery Demonstration IV (Physical Sciences)

THE RUBBER-BAND WHEEL

Materials:
1. Shoe box
2. Cardboard wheel made of corrugated cardboard, 6 in. in diameter
3. Knitting needle
4. Four fresh rubber bands, all of equal length and thickness
5. Strong light source, preferably a 150-watt spotlight
Set up the apparatus as shown. Without explanation, shine a bright light on the wheel.

Ask:
What do you observe? (Parts: cardboard wheel, rubber bands, knitting-needle axle, light source. Action: slow, counterclockwise turning. Setup: What part is in the light? What part is in the shadow?)

What are some possible explanations? (Convection currents. Expansion of contraction of rubber bands. Light pressure.)

Further experimentation:
What would happen if the light came from the opposite side? (Side nearest you.)
What would happen if the wheel were mounted in the open so light could strike all parts of it?
What would happen if the light were moved further away?

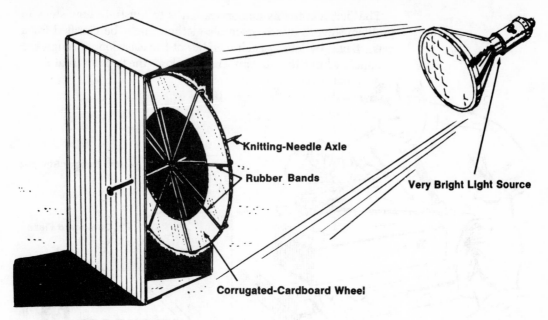

Knitting-Needle Axle

Rubber Bands

Very Bright Light Source

Corrugated-Cardboard Wheel

Figure 36

Suspend a weight on a single rubber band fastened to a support. Shine the light on the rubber band. What happens to the light?

Explanation:

Rubber bands in the light (heat) contract and pull the center of rotation toward the right. This makes the left side of the wheel heavier than the right side, and it turns counterclockwise.

Fact: Rubber bands under tension contract when heated, expand when cooled.

Principle: In general, solids expand when heated, contract when cooled; but rubber bands under tension are an exception.

Conclusion:

There are usually *exceptions* to most scientific generalizations.

Discovery Demonstration V (Physical Sciences)

BOTTLE IN THE BOX

Materials:
1. Two shoe boxes, cut diagonally on one end at 45° angle.
2. Piece of window glass, cut to fit the diagonal cut of the shoe boxes
3. Masking tape
4. Black rubber tape for light seal around trap doors
5. Bottle of red-colored liquid
6. Red rubber stopper of same color as the liquid
7. 25-watt light bulb mounted above trap door B

The purpose of this demonstration is to illustrate how steps in problem-solving by the scientific method might be clarified for a class. Begin by letting each member of the class look through the peephole while the teacher opens and closes the flaps alternately.

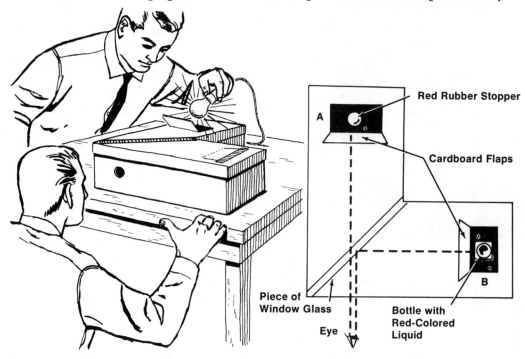

Red Rubber Stopper

Cardboard Flaps

Piece of Window Glass

Bottle with Red-Colored Liquid

Eye

Figure 37

What is the problem (or problems)? Is it a real problem to the students? What makes the device work? How is it built? What parts does it have?

What might be some explanations? It has mirrors. It is built like this (draw diagrams on the board). It has glass. (Try to select the most reasonable explanation after logical thinking.)

We need more information. (Let one student look the device over carefully and report the data to the class. We need accurate observations here.)

Draw conclusions about construction of the device. Draw conclusions about its operation.

Test the conclusion with something else (piece of mirror, piece of window glass, piece of one-way glass).

Explanation:
The eye responds to the light having the strongest intensity.

Other applications:
Why do you cup your hands around your eyes to look outside at night from a lighted room?

Some sunglasses are partially silvered mirrors. Why?

Discovery Demonstration VI (Physical Sciences)

HERON'S SIPHON

Materials:
1. Two Ditto-fluid cans or equivalent
2. Two double-hole rubber stoppers, #6
3. Glass tubing fashioned as shown in Figure 38.
4. Glass funnel, long-stem type
5. Support stands or boxes to hold cans at different heights
6. Vegetable coloring

Procedure:
   Without explanation, pour clear water into the funnel to start the operation.

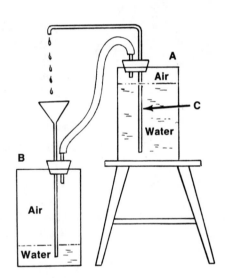

Figure 38

   Can A must be air-tight and filled with liquid at start.
   Can B must be air-tight and nearly empty at start.
   All connections must be air-tight.
   To start, pressure in can B must be increased by "priming"—i.e., by pouring water into the can until water flows out of the can A and falls into funnel.
   Effect may be heightened by coloring water in can A with vegetable coloring.

Possible uses in the classroom:
   To develop keenness of observation. What is the colored liquid? What is in the slanting pipe? When does it start to operate? When does it stop?
   To pose a problem-solving situation. What might be in can A? What might be in can B? How long is tube C? How long is the

funnel? What probably makes it work? How high must the liquid be in the funnel in order for the device to work? How long will it continue?

To develop functional knowledge of facts and principles. Water does not seek its own level but is pushed up by the weight of a connecting column of water of equal height (principle). Pressure applied to fluids is transmitted equally in all directions (principle). Air and water are both fluids (fact).

To see relationships to other commonly observed phenomena which operate with similar principles. How does this compare with a regular siphon? How does a regular siphon work? Can you think of any useful purpose this device might serve?

Explanation:

Siphons are pneumatic devices. They depend upon air pressure for their operation.

A regular siphon flows from higher level to lower level through a connecting tube filled with the fluid. The back pressure of the fluid in the shorter tube is less than the back pressure in the longer tube. The effective atmosphere pressure is therefore greater in the shorter tube, and the fluid flows toward the longer tube.

Discovery Demonstration VII (Physical Sciences)

WHY IS THE SKY BLUE? WHY IS THE SUNSET RED?

Materials required:
1. 12 in. or 14 in. rectangular aquarium (clear glass)
2. Flashlight
3. Concentrated sulfuric acid (H_2SO_4)
4. Sodium thiosulfate; may use sodium hyposulfite (photographic fix)
5. Water
6. White screen

Purpose:

To demonstrate the effect of the atmosphere on sun's rays. As white light passes through the atmosphere, various colors are removed by scattering and show up in the color of the sky. Violet is removed with smallest particles; blue, with next smallest; green, with next; and so on for yellow, orange, red, etc.

Procedure:

Mix thiosulfate, 10 grams per gallon of water (not critical) in the aquarium.

Project light through aquarium to screen.

Add few drops of concentrated sulfuric acid and stir with glass rod.

Questions:

At the beginning, what color is the water when the flashlight

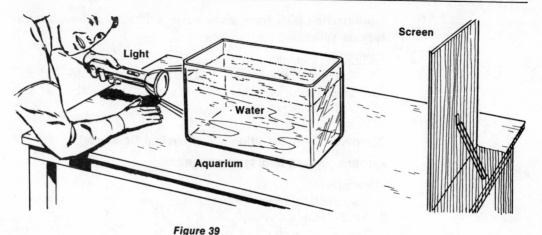

Figure 39

shines through it? What color is the light of the flashlight when looked at directly?

How does the color of the water change as time goes on? How does the color of the light from the flashlight change? To what is this analogous in nature?

What causes the water to change color?

What causes the light source to change color?

What is the final color of the water? Why?

What is the final color of the light source? Why?

To what natural sky condition is this analogous?

Explanation:

Reaction of the acid on the sodium thiosulfate releases very fine particles. Only very fine particles in the atmosphere cause the rays to scatter. This can be shown by the fact that smoke blown across a beam of light appears bluish, but chalk dust gives no coloration at all. This is because the chalk particles are too large.

The scattering effect first removes the violet and blue end of the spectrum, and later the red end as the particles grow larger. Observe the color of the "sky" water and also the color of the "sun" flashlight which remains. Color of the sun goes from white to yellow to orange to red to blackness, where it is not visible at all.

In nature the sunlight becomes redder near the horizon because the light passes through more atmosphere with larger particles when the sun is about to set.

Teaching concepts:

Light travels in waves.

White light contains all colors.

Short waves are scattered more than long waves.

Short waves are scattered by smaller particles than are long waves.

Scattering subtracts colors from a beam of white light.

Subtracting blue from white leaves yellow; therefore, the sun appears yellow.

Additional principle:

Use a Polaroid sheet and look at the beam from the side and turn your sheet through a ninety-degree angle. Observe the fact that scattered light is polarized.

Discovery Demonstration VIII (Physical Sciences)

KELVIN'S "WATER-DROPPER" GENERATOR

Materials:
1. Two small juice cans
2. No. 2½ can (reservoir)
3. Two 12 in. sections of rubber tubing
4. Coat-hanger wire shaped as shown in Figure 40.

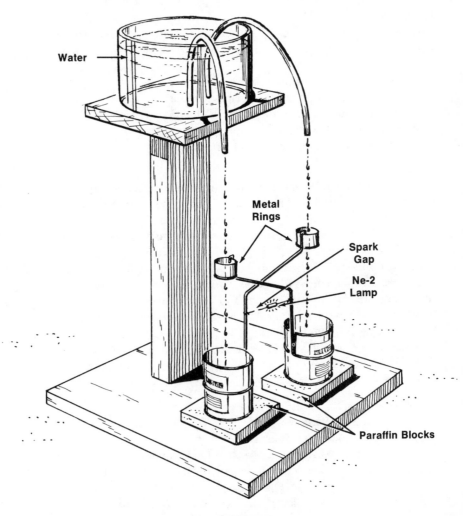

Figure 40

5. NE-2 neon lamp (0.25 watt)
6. Two blocks of paraffin
7. Blocks of wood for base and upright
8. Two small metal rings soldered to coat-hanger wire as shown

Procedure:

Fill the reservoir can with water. By siphon action, start water flowing through each outlet tube. Adjust lower cans and rings so water falls through the rings into the cans.

Adjust spark gap so it is about one millimeter width.

Watch the neon bulb for intermittent flashes. In a darkened room these flashes will be visible to a whole class.

Questions:
1. What did you observe as the apparatus was put into operation?
2. How long did it take for the first flash?
3. How much time elapses between flashes?
4. What happens to the length of time if the gap distance is changed?
5. What happens when the gap is eliminated entirely?
6. What is causing the flash?
7. Where does the electricity come from?
8. What kind of charged particles are in water?
9. Suppose you were to construct an apparatus like this. Would each half of the apparatus (small can, coat-hanger wire, and metal ring) be likely to have exactly the same initial charge?
10. Suppose the side labeled A had a slightly negative charge as compared to B. What kinds of charges would be attracted to A?
11. But these charges fall into side marked B. What kind of charge do they give to B?
12. By similar action, what charge does A acquire?
13. For how long will these charge accumulations go on?
14. What is the likely charge distribution after the flash?
15. What is the complete explanation of the operation of this "water-dropper" generator?

Explanation:

One side of the apparatus will have a slightly greater initial negative charge. The other side will have a slightly higher initial positive charge. This is an assumption but an extremely good one.

Ions in the water will be attracted to the metal rings differentially, with positive ions going toward the negative ring and negative ions going toward the positive ring.

But these ions do not neutralize the rings. Instead they fall *through* the rings and contribute to buildup of like charge in the cans.

Potential difference between the two halves of the apparatus increases until a small spark occurs at the gap. At this instant, the neon bulb flashes.

The process repeats cyclically. Widening the gap delays the discharge. Closing the gap completely prevents any build-up of potential difference. Consequently, there is no flashing.

Discovery Demonstration IX (Physical Sciences)

FALLING BODIES

Materials:
1. 3-foot piece of board (1 x 2 in.)
2. 2 small plastic cups (1-in. diam.)
3. Bearing ball (1-in. diam.)

Bearing Ball
Plastic Cups

Figure 41

Procedure:
Put the ball in the cup at the end of the stick. Raise the stick to an angle of about thirty degrees. Drop the stick. The ball transfers to the other cup.

Questions:
Why does the ball transfer to the other cup?

Is there a problem here? Is there anything out of the ordinary? Does it have an easy answer?

How did the ball get out of the first cup? Don't the ball and cup fall at the same rate of acceleration?

Something must be accelerating faster than gravity here. What is it? How can this happen?

Suppose you tossed a tumbling board over a cliff. Would all parts of it be accelerating downward at the same rate? What part of it accelerates at thirty-two feet per second per second?

What part of the stick in this demonstration accelerates at thirty-two feet per second per second? Where is this point?

Explanation:

The cup at the end accelerates faster than thirty-two feet/sec/sec. The ball accelerates only at thirty-two ft/sec/sec. The point on the stick which accelerates at thirty-two ft/sec/sec is the "center of percussion" which is two-thirds of the way from the pivot end to the end with the cup.

Discovery Demonstration X (Earth Science)

Junior High School
HOW IS SEDIMENTARY ROCK FORMED?

Concepts:

Sedimentary rocks are made from accumulation and cementing of sediments.

Sediments may include both organic and inorganic material.

Fossils may be found in the sedimentary material.

Procedure I:

Collect two quart jars, some rice and wheat kernels, sand, and dirt.

Fill both quart jars half full of water.

Ask:

What do you think I am going to show with these materials?

What do you think will happen to the soil if I place it in a jar and shake it? What will the water look like? Have you ever seen water that color? Where? What made it that color?

What will happen to the water and soil if I let it sit for a while?

What will happen to the suspended soil in the water?

What is the material suspended in water called?

When the sediment settles, what will it look like in the jar?

Class assignment:

Write on a piece of paper your hypothesis about the appearance of the sediment. Next time you come to class observe what happens and record as many things as you can about what you observe.

Procedure II, Sedimentary layers and fossils:

To the other jar half filled with water, add a little soil. Ask: What happened to the soil I added? Why?

Add some rice. Ask: What happens to the rice?

Add some sand and then some wheat kernels.

Add more soil.

Hold up the jar so the class can observe it.

Ask:

What do you notice about the appearance of the sediment?

Are all the layers you observe the same thickness?

If you see layers similar to these in a rock, how do you think it was formed?

What might the kernels of rice and wheat represent in a rock?

What would have to be done to the material in the jar to change it into a rock?

Teacher's note:

The purpose of this lesson is to emphasize observation and to show the student how sedimentary rock is formed; the lesson also shows how living things may be incorporated in a rock. A discussion of cementation and compaction should be carried on at the end of the lesson to explain the formation of sedimentary rock. The instructor should state that although most sedimentary rocks have a layered appearance, there are some which are not layered. He should also discuss what causes the appearance of layering.

Discovery Demonstration XI (Biology)

FOOD WEB

Materials:

1. Ball of string
2. Scissors

Procedure:

Take a string and cut it. Give one end of it to a student and tell him he is to represent a plant. Have another student hold the other end of the string and represent an insect. Ask the class what eats insects; connect a string from the insect to an animal that eats it. Each time you cut a piece of string have the class name an animal that feeds on the animal just named. Each time a new animal is named a student is to represent the animal and a string should connect him with other animals in the web. In this demonstration you might include:

1. Hawks
2. Prairie chickens
3. Meadow larks
4. Antelopes
5. Rabbits
6. Mice
7. Coyotes

After this process has involved all of the students in the class and the interconnections of strings is fairly complex, ask: What will happen if I cut the string of one of the animals in this web?

Pick an animal that has several strings going to and from him. Have him hold the strings up high and then cut them. Ask:

1. What does this show about the food web?

2. An insect is doing harm to a farmer's crop. Why might it not be desirable to spray to kill the insect?

Teacher's note:

The concepts involved in the lesson are an understanding of a food web and the interrelationships of plants and animals. You might carry the discussion further by asking: What would happen if various other parts of the web were destroyed?

INVITATIONS TO INQUIRY

Invitations to inquiry invite students to participate in solving problems as scientists solve them. Although there are forty-four prepared "invitations" published for biology teachers in the *Biology Teacher's Handbook* (New York: John Wiley & Sons, Inc., 1963), teachers are encouraged to make their own invitations, especially in fields other than biology.

The ones included in the *Handbook* and those that follow may be used as a guide. The main purpose of an invitation is to give students some understanding of what a scientist goes through in solving problems. An easy way to construct an invitation is as follows:

1. Take a problem from some scientific journal.
2. Ask the class how they would solve it.
3. Later, the teacher may outline the procedure of the experiment, give some of the data, and ask for interpretation of the data.

Invitations to inquiry are fun to write once the purpose and format are understood. A teacher in the process of writing then becomes more sophisticated in his understanding of science as a process and gains a better realization of the types of thought processes he wants to teach in science.

Invitation to Inquiry:

Discovery of Plant Growth Substances

(This may be used with Laboratory Exercise 18.3 of BSCS Biology Green Version)

To the student:

Some high school students were interested in determining whether light had an effect on plant growth, other than in photosynthesis. The following experiment was done to test some of their ideas.

They obtained four nearly identical plants grown in small pots. The plants had the same number of leaves; the stems were nearly identical in length; and all were straight. They placed their four pots as shown below. The plants were placed near a window so that they received direct sunlight from one side during the day.

Figure 42

1. What do you think happened to the plants?
2. Do you think they all changed, or did some remain unchanged?
3. After three days, students noticed that all four of the plants began to bend.
4. Now, make a diagram of how they moved.

To the teacher:
After students have drawn their diagrams, have several of them place their drawings on the board. Discuss why the students drew their drawings as they did.

Ask: Why do you suppose the students placed their plants in a number of different ways? Why didn't they just use one pot?

To the student:
The class found that all stems were bending toward the direct light source. What does this show about the interaction of light and the plant? They then wanted to know whether the entire plant controlled this reaction or whether some portion of the stem did this. What kind of experiment would you do to find the answer to these questions?

The students decided to pinch off three millimeters of the tips of the plants to see whether this had any effect. They noticed that after several days, growth was slowed and that bending ceased. What does this indicate about the shoots? If there is a growth-producing substance in the tips, what relation does the substance have to the bending of the plant? How did this substance cause the plant to bend toward the light? What do you suspect happens to the cells on one side of the plant, compared to those on the other, to cause bending?

Teacher's note:

At the present time plant physiologists generally believe that the growth substance is produced in the shoot tips and flows down the tips in the stem. It is thought that the plant hormone that stimulates cell elongation is destroyed by light. The cells therefore become more elongated on the shady side than on the sunny side, causing the plant to bend toward the light. Students can be led from this invitation to try an experiment to determine whether all wave lengths of light cause this reaction. Plants can be covered with different colors of cellophane, which will filter out different wave lengths, to see whether similar results will occur.

Invitation to Inquiry[2]

The Effect of Certain Soil Elements on Plant Growth

(*Introduction to Experimental Technique*)

Technique:

A plant physiologist designed an experiment to test the effects of certain elements, found in the soil, on plant growth. He used an experimental technique in which the plants were grown in distilled water instead of soil (hydroponics).

One hundred-twenty petunia seeds were selected for the experiment. Groups of ten were placed in individual solutions lacking one of the following elements: phosphorus, potassium, nitrogen, calcium, magnesium, sulphur, iron, boron, copper, manganese, zinc.

A group of ten more was placed in solutions containing all eleven of the above elements.

Hypothesis:

The following hypothesis was formulated: If the omission of a particular element results in stunted growth of tops, poorly developed root systems, failure of chlorophyll formation, or some other structural abnormality, it may be assumed that the element is essential for normal growth.

Data (hypothetical):

After periodic observations over a period of six weeks the following observations were recorded:

	Solution Void of:	Height Avg.	Weight Avg.	General Appearance
a	Phosphorus	4.51 cm.	647 g.	Stunted growth
b	Potassium	4.69 cm.	897 g.	Stunted growth, weak stems, shrivelled seeds, discolored leaves
c	Nitrogen	3.73 cm.	368 g.	Stunted growth, did not flower

[2] This invitation written by William Duffy, Meeker High School, Meeker, Colorado.

d	Calcium	1.43 cm.	258 g.	Stunted growth, poorly developed roots
e	Magnesium	6.01 cm.	1674 g.	Stunted growth, leaves pale and greenish yellow
f	Sulphur	13.28 cm.	4951 g.	Below-average growth, *retarded*
g	Iron	12.10 cm.	4765 g.	Below-average growth, *retarded*
h	Boron	2.25 cm.	400 g.	Stunted growth, abnormal, blackening of meristematic areas
i	Copper	10.57 cm.	4169 g.	Below-average growth, *retarded*
j	Manganese	11.58 cm.	4227 g.	Below-average growth, *retarded*
k	Zinc	9.32 cm.	4561 g.	Below-average growth, *retarded*
l	NONE	13.68 cm.	6046 g.	Healthy, normal

To the student:

What was the object of growing the plants in distilled water? (The chemical composition of the nutrient solution may be carefully controlled. No solids are present to hinder absorption. Replacement of the solution can prevent build-up of toxic substances. No tilling, no weeds.)

Can you foresee any difficulty in using distilled water as a medium? (Support of the plant stems, leaves, etc.)

Can you suggest any other medium that could be used? (Quartz sand or gravel from which all soluble materials have been removed, by chemical treatment and repeated washing.)

Why didn't the physiologist use only one or two seeds in each solution? (The greater the number of cases, the greater the validity of statistical data.)

Which was the control group in this experiment? (The seeds to which all eleven elements were added.)

What is a control? (The object of a control in an experiment is to run a portion of the samples under controlled conditions which can be exactly calculated in order that they may be compared with the experimental data.)

What is a hypothesis? (*Hypothesis* could be defined simply as the anticipation of the results of the experiment. A calculated guess.)

What factors in this experiment were used to determine growth? (Height and weight by volume)

What is growth? (This question can lead to an interesting discussion on how to measure growth. Can it be measured by weight? Is the measurement computed by a number of factors?)

Are the data complete for this problem? (Answers will vary, but students should be led to the conclusion that the data on measurements of plant size, weight, and appearance are not complete.)

From the data given, what would you conclude? (The students must realize the data are limited to visual observation, but they do indicate that the lack of these elements has a derogatory effect on petunias, possibly on all plants.)

What other data could have been obtained that would strengthen our experiment? (This is a good point to lead the students into a discussion of physiological processes.)

Does this experiment suggest any other experiments? (The students should come up with varied experiments that this experience has started them thinking about: Test the physiological effects of these elements; Test the percentage of these elements necessary for growth; etc.)

To the teacher:

This experiment and series of questions is prepared to lead the student through the experimental procedure step by step.

After the students have completed this exercise and a discussion, there will be a good opportunity to allow them to select a problem of their own and devise an experiment. If possible, this should be an actual experimental situation; if not, they may select hypothetical data to complete the exercise.

PICTORIAL RIDDLES

Pictorial Riddles are relatively easy to devise. They can be as simple or complex as a teacher desires. In devising a riddle, an instructor should go through the following steps:

1. Select some concept or principle he wishes to teach or elevate.
2. Draw a picture or show an illustration which demonstrates the concept.
3. An alternate procedure is to change something in a picture and ask students to find out what is wrong in the picture. An example might be a picture of a big man being held up on a seesaw by a small man. Ask, "How is this possible?" Or show a farming community in which all of the ecological principles are misapplied and ask what is wrong with what has been done in the community.
4. Devise a series of questions, related to the picture, which will help students gain insights into what principles are involved.

Pictorial Riddles (Earth Science)

An Old River.

1. What can you tell about the terrain in Figure 43?

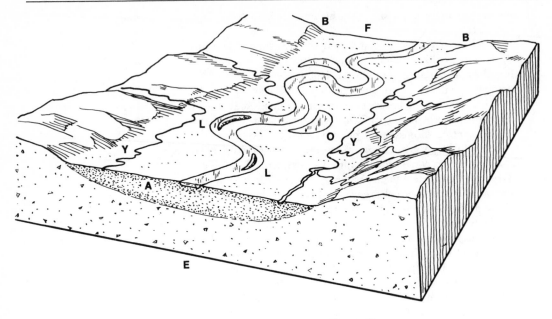

Figure 43

2. Why does the river appear the way it does?
3. How were the moon-shaped objects with water in them formed?
4. What did the valley look like?
5. What do you think will happen to the valley some time in the future?

How Was a Geological Feature Formed.

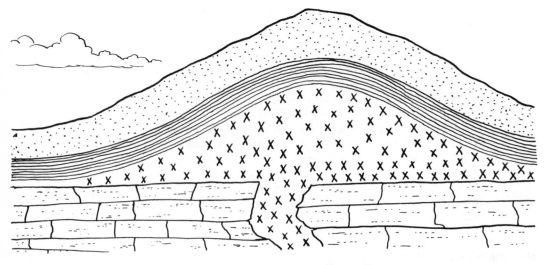

Figure 44

1. What caused this type of feature to develop?
2. What will happen to this mountain over millions of years?

3. What if the mountain is rising at the same rate as it is eroding—
   what will happen?

Pictorial Riddle (Physical Science)

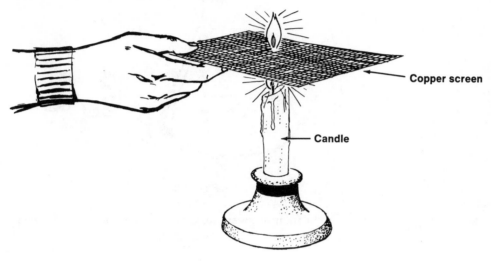

Copper screen

Candle

Figure 45

1. When would the above be possible?
2. When wouldn't it be possible?
3. Is there any evidence from what you observe that a candle
   gives off gas?
4. Would a different type of metallic screen make any difference?

Teacher's note:

Concepts involved in the riddle are:

1. Copper is an excellent conductor of heat.
2. Gas must reach kindling temperature in order to burn.

Placing a copper screen above the candle removes heat from
the flame immediately. Unburned gases come through the screen
but will not burn; however, if they are ignited above the screen,
they will burn.

Pictorial Riddle (Physical Science)

1. What will happen to the volume of water when the cubes of
   sugar are placed in it?
2. What would happen to the volume and the sugar if the water
   were warmer or colder?
3. Is there air in the cubes of sugar?
4. How will the air in the cubes affect the density of the sugar?
5. Will the sugar cube float because of the air in it?
6. Will the volume fluctuate as you add sugar to the beaker?

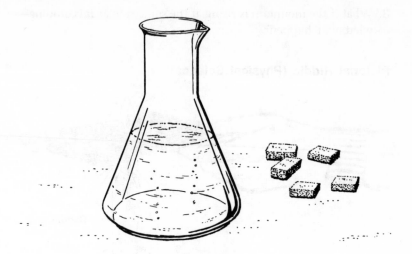

Figure 46

7. If different solutions were used would there be any differences in what happened to the sugar or the volume?

Teacher's note:

It is suggested that after the instructor has gone through the questions in the riddle he ask students how the answers could be determined. The class should then set up experiments to determine these answers. The instructor should ask the class how many times they should repeat their experiments in order to be sure of their answers.

Pictorial Riddle (Earth Science)

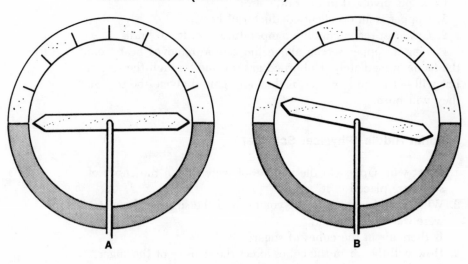

Figure 47–Dip Needle

1. The dip needle as shown in Figure 47-A changed during a walk to look like the one in Figure 47-B.
2. What would cause the dip needle on the right to change? In what way has it changed?
3. If the needle dipped even more at some other point, what would you suspect about the earth at that point?
4. If you were going to dig for iron ore, how would you go about selecting a site?
5. Using an airplane and a very sensitive compass-type instrument called a magnetometer, how would you go about mapping a region's magnetic variation?

Teacher's note:

Involved in this riddle are the concepts of magnetic field, variation in the earth's magnetic field, declination or dip of a magnetic needle, and that such a dip may indicate increased attraction due to deposits of magnetic types of ores such as iron in the crust. The lesson also develops understanding of the part instruments play in helping scientists study what they cannot sense directly.

Pictorial Riddle for BSCS Biology

(To be done several weeks after students have studied yeast population in the laboratory)

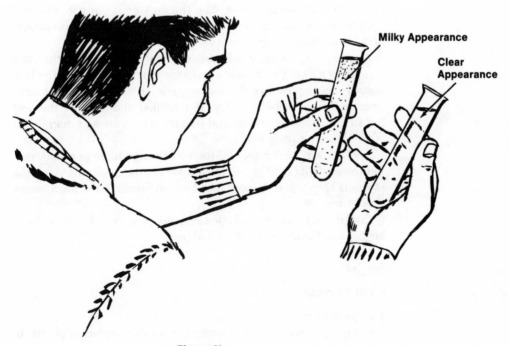

Milky Appearance

Clear Appearance

Figure 48

1. The tubes shown in Figure 48 have had one yeast cell each added to the solutions they contain. What can you conclude about the solutions?
2. What made one of them milky? Why aren't both of the tubes milky? Do you think that both of the tubes were kept under the same conditions?
3. In the milky tube, what type of food do you suspect is present?
4. Could you get the differences shown in Figure 48 by varying the temperature? pH? Amount of light present? Type of food?
5. If conditions were kept the same, what do you think would eventually happen to the milky tube? To the other tube?
6. If you took the clear tube, assuming it contained the same food material, and placed it in the environment where the milky tube was kept, what would happen?
7. If you wanted to clarify the milky tube, what would you do?
8. If you tested the milky tube's solution, what would you expect to find?

SELF-TESTS

Self-tests are tests students check and grade themselves. They are essentially learning devices, and they can be used in a number of ways. The answers to the tests can be given in class on the back of the test or on another paper. Then students score their own papers. In preparing the answers to the questions it is desirable to give information explaining why the answer is correct. The student reads the full answer in checking his score, and this contributes to his learning process.

Another way to use a self-test is to give the test after the class completes it. Ask the students to decide what they think is the best answer; use the test as a discussion guide. It is suggested that some questions from self-tests later be modified and used in the unit test so that students understand that these tests are an integral part of the learning program.

Another way to use the self-tests is to assign them as homework. Let the students read to find the answers to the questions. After the students have taken the test, the class can discuss what the answers should be.

Invitations to inquiry can be easily adapted as self-tests and can be given in the manner outlined above.

Self-Test

Plant Growth

To the student:
A biology class wanted to study growth movements in plants. In order to do this:

1. They placed a growing plant on its side for a few days and labeled its container A.
2. They placed a plant near a lamp that was on continuously and labeled its container B.
3. In a third container, C, equipped with a glass front for observing, a kernel of corn was planted with the radicle end upward, and another kernel was planted with the radicle end pointed downward.

All plants and seedlings were allowed to grow for a few days. The students noticed several responses the plants exhibited at the end of this time.

Directions:

Place an X before each statement that might serve to indicate the various growth movements of the plants the students observed.

_____ 1. In container A, the stem would grow continuously outward in a horizontal plane.

_____ 2. The plant in container A would eventually grow vertically, a response known as negative geotropism.

_____ 3. In container A, the roots would respond to gravity and grow downward.

_____ 4. The plant in container B would lean away from the light source.

_____ 5. In container B, the plant would bend toward the light source because the light is needed for photosynthesis.

_____ 6. Phototropism is exhibited in container B.

_____ 7. If the plant in container A were placed upside down, the roots would grow upward and the stem downward.

_____ 8. The seedling with the radicle end upward in container C would produce roots that would grow downward, as would the stem, in response to gravity.

_____ 9. In container C, the seedling with the radicle end down would produce roots growing downward and a stem growing upward.

_____10. Phototropism is the term used to refer to the roots' response to gravity in container C.

How would you change the design of the above experiments in order to be more certain of your results and gain better knowledge of plant growth?

Self-Test

What Does Oil Do To Fish?

To the student:

A zoologist was interested in whether oil had any effects on fish. The zoologist placed four fish in a good-sized fishbowl; he then poured a thick oily film over the entire surface of the water in the fishbowl. After about fifteen minutes he noticed that the fish began to swim in rapid motion. They appeared to swallow large amounts of water. From these reactions, the zoologist concluded that oil stimulated the fishes' actions.

Directions:

Indicate, by placing a "plus" sign before the appropriate remark, which of the following statements might serve to explain why the oil affected the fish. Explain in a few sentences the reason you chose each statement.

_____1. The fish were unfamiliar with the new substance placed in their bowl. This resulted in fear causing them to swim faster.

_____2. The fish had swallowed some oil and became sick.

_____3. The oily film on the surface of the water cut off the fishes' oxygen supply.

_____4. The fishes' skin became coated with the oil. This lessened their ability to breathe through their skin.

_____5. The fish became hungry, and since the oil was on the surface the fish wouldn't come to the surface to eat.

_____6. Because of the oil, the fish were afraid to come to the surface to gulp oxygen.

_____7. Fish normally act up from time to time. The fish's active movement was not unusual behavior.

Distribution of Vegetation in a Mountain Region
(Ecology)

To the student:

One summer three boys who had just graduated from high school decided to take a trip in a car to the Rocky Mountains. One of the boys was very interested in living things. He decided to keep a record of the various types of vegetation he saw on the trip. He noted the following information in ascending the mountains:

1. Flatland approaching the mountains—mainly grasses
2. Foothills before the mountains—some grass but a lot of brush and chaparral vegetation
3. In the first canyon—deciduous trees
4. Farther up the mountain—coniferous trees
5. High on the mountain—timberline—no trees above this point

The boy was fascinated with these differences in the way life was distributed in the region. He drew several conclusions from his notes.

Directions:

Place a plus before the statements below which tell what you think the boy might have concluded from what he saw. Briefly give your reasons for choosing these statements.

_____ 1. The vegetation varied because man planted different types of plants in the various locations.

_____ 2. The vegetation varied mainly because of temperature differences.

_____ 3. The coniferous trees would grow where the grass grew if they were planted there.

_____ 4. The main reason for variation in plant distribution was due to differences in the amount of moisture received in the various localities.

_____ 5. Although the boy didn't record the types of animals he saw, the animals found on the grasslands were different from those found at the timberline.

_____ 6. The main reason why there is no timber growing above timberline is that the soil is poor above that point.

_____ 7. When the boys went down the other side of the mountain they didn't find the same type of vegetation.

_____ 8. Chaparral vegetation requires more water to grow than coniferous trees.

_____ 9. There was no vegetation above timberline.

_____10. The higher you go in the altitude the taller will be the vegetation.

_____11. Wind was the main reason the vegetation was located where it was.

_____12. Although the boy didn't note it, mosses and ferns probably were also found among the grasses on the grasslands.

_____13. Mushrooms probably were seen most above timberline.

_____14. Vegetation probably was most dense near the streams.
Essay questions:

If you were going to take more accurate records of sampling the vegetation, what would you do?
To the teacher:

Possible types of things that may be included in the answer to this question are: Determine the altitude where samples were taken. Use a better method of sampling, such as a grid technique. Include all types of vegetation and animals. Measure properties of the soil and temperature, determine annual rainfall, measure variations in wind velocity, etc.

TEACHER AIDS

These aids are designed to assist the teacher of science in at least two ways. The devices described are constructed of simple and inexpensive materials and can be used to prepare items for the classroom. In addition, each device operates according to certain scientific principles, and students can be taught these principles when the apparatus is demonstrated. Also, some students can be encouraged to build these devices as projects or to modify them according to their needs. It is important to recognize the teaching value, as well as the utilitarian value, of the devices.

Teacher Aid I

Resistance Wire Glasscutter

Materials:
1. 600-watt heater coil
2. 2-3 ft. of nichrome wire, gauge #24
3. Knife switch

4. Button switch
5. 6 ft. of extension cord wire
6. Two wooden dowels (1 in. diam.)
7. Triangular file
8. Block of wood for base

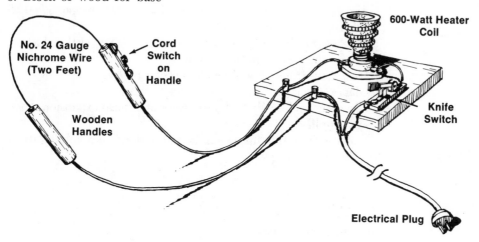

Figure 49–Wiring Diagram

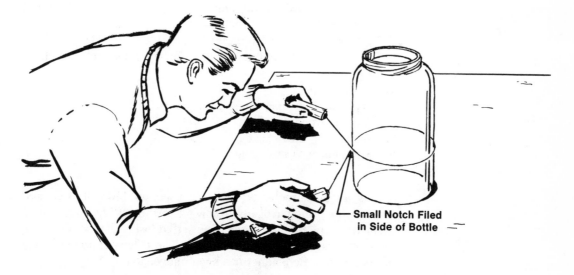

Figure 50–Cutting Diagram

Procedure:

First file a small groove on the glass jar where the nichrome wire will cross. Adjust the wire in a loop in the desired position for cutting. Keep the wires from touching where they cross in the groove. Plug into a regular household outlet. The wire will get red hot, and after a few seconds, the glass will usually crack in a clean cut where the wire has looped the jar. If this does not happen after fifteen to twenty seconds, quickly remove the nichrome-wire loop and hold the jar under a water faucet. This will cause the necessary contraction to break the jar on the desired line.

Concepts:

In order for current to flow, a closed circuit is needed.

Current flowing through a conducting wire produces heat.

The heat produced by an electrical current is proportional to the resistance of the conductor.

The heat produced by an electrical current is proportional to the square of the current in the conductor.

Heat flows from a hot object to a cooler object.

Glass is a relatively poor conductor of heat.

Glass has a relatively high coefficient of cubical expansion when heat is applied.

Materials will fracture when the molecular forces holding them together are exceeded.

Teacher Aid II

Magnet Rejuvenator

Materials:
1. Glass, cardboard, or aluminum cylinder, $1\frac{1}{4}$ in. in diameter, 6 in. in length
2. Light switch, closed type
3. Copper wire, insulated, gauge #22, approximately 30 ft. in length
4. Two alligator clips
5. Small glass jar and cover, 2 in. diam.
6. Block of wood for base
7. Connecting wire
8. Extension cord and plug

This magnet "recharger" can be used on 110-volt A.C. and employs the principle of fuse "blowout." After setting up as shown in the diagram, the bar magnet is inserted inside the cylinder, and the circuit is closed with the switch. The fuse wire immediately blows out and the magnet has been rejuvenated.

Principle:

As a current surges through the circuit, the fuse wire blows out at either point A or point B on the sine wave diagram in Figure 51. This leaves the polarity of the magnet oriented mainly in one direction. It is impossible to predict whether the polarity will be north or south on a given end; therefore, it is necessary to test the polarity with a compass after each trial. If polarity is wrong, try again until the polarity agrees with the labeled polarity on the bar magnet. (Note: A single strand of multistrand extension cord wire serves very well as a fuse wire.)

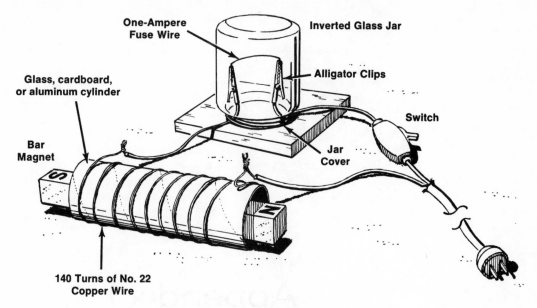

One-Ampere Fuse Wire

Inverted Glass Jar

Glass, cardboard, or aluminum cylinder

Alligator Clips

Switch

Bar Magnet

Jar Cover

140 Turns of No. 22 Copper Wire

Figure 51

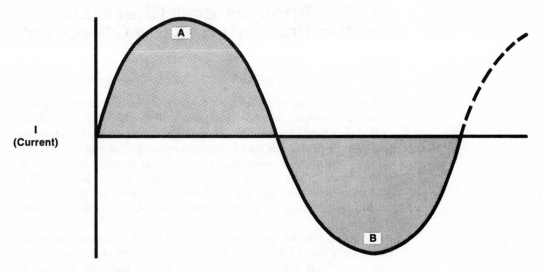

I (Current)

A

B

Figure 52

Question:

For an interesting student question, ask how to modify this apparatus so that a magnet will *always* be polarized to agree with its markings.

Answer:

Put two magnets inside the coil, side by side with opposite ends together. After fuse blow-out, one is certain to be correct!

Appendix I

An Analysis and Check List
on the Problem Solving Objective*

Achieving the Problem Solving Objective

Problem solving, or scientific thinking, is a widely accepted outcome of science teaching in schools over the country. In the past much attention has been given to this objective in science education literature and there appears to be an interesting increase in it at present.

Very little reliable evidence is available to indicate the extent to which the problem solving objective is provided for in day-to-day classroom activities. Still less evidence is available on the extent to which the objective is achieved with the young people who study science.

Among other difficulties in reaching the fullest attainment of the objective is the failure, on the part of many teachers, to recognize that problem solving behavior is a complex ability made up of elements which can be identified. Some of these elements are quite simple manipulative skills but many more are of a highly intellectual character.

Regardless of the category in which these skills fall, it is very important to recognize that they are developed by recurrent practice just as any skill related to problem solving, such as learning how to locate information in a library, the skill must first be taught thoroughly and then practiced until achieved. In a similar way, if the teacher wishes to develop the ability to analyze problems, or interpret evidence, the skills

---

* Prepared by Ellsworth S. Obourn, Specialist for Science, U.S. Office of Education (Science Teaching Service Circular).

must first be taught and then the teacher must provide classroom situations, day after day, when the pupil will have to use them. There is no easy way of teaching children to use the abilities of problem solving other than by setting classroom situations which call for their repetitive use.

Some authorities have characterized the steps in problem solving as a complete act of thought. This has led many teachers to believe that the act of problem solving thinking, beginning with the recognition of a problem and ending with a conclusion, must always be practiced in its complete cycle. This is not necessarily true. Scientists rarely ever use the method in its complete cycle. In fact, they are more likely to use it in other ways.

For example, it is quite possible, in fact even desirable, to use the science lesson of a given day for practicing whatever elements of the total problem solving pattern it may best be directed toward. In the development of a topic the teacher may plan to do a demonstration on a given day. This demonstration might provide material especially useful for practicing, among other things, the ability to interpret data. It should be used fully for this purpose and the teacher should see to it that all aspects of data interpretation afforded by the demonstration are carefully identified, clearly understood, and thoroughly practiced by the class.

On another day the teacher might find that a laboratory exercise could provide opportunities for testing an hypothesis or evaluating assumptions. This experience should be used to yield whatever practice for these purposes it might possess. The important thing to remember is that almost every classroom situation can in some way contribute opportunities for pupils to practice certain elements of problem solving. The teacher must be alert to recognize these opportunities and to make the fullest use of each one. This Service Bulletin provides an analysis of the attitudes of mind that accompany problem solving behavior and also an analysis of each of the major elements in problem solving. Such an analysis is essential first to suggest guides for teachers in planning classroom situations that will call for the practice of essential skills and second, to provide a basis for developing tests to evaluate the degree to which the skills have been attained.

Problem Solving Behaviors*

I. Attitudes which can be developed through science teaching.
   The science program should develop the attitude which will modify the individual's behavior so that he:
   A. Looks for the natural cause of things that happen
      1. Does not believe in superstitions such as charms or signs of good or bad luck.
      2. Believes that occurrences which seem strange and mysterious can always be explained finally by natural cause.
      3. Believes that there is necessarily no connection between two events just because they occur at the same time.

---

* This analysis was prepared by Dr. Darrell Barnard, Professor of Education and Head of the Department of Science Education, New York University, and Dr. Ellsworth Obourn, U.S. Office of Education.

B. Is openminded toward work, opinions of others, and information related to his problem
   1. Believes that truth never changes, but that his ideas of what is true may change as he gains better understanding of the truth.
   2. Bases his ideas upon the best evidence and not upon tradition alone.
   3. Revises his opinions and conclusions in light of additional reliable information.
   4. Listens to, observes, or reads evidence supporting ideas contrary to his personal opinions.
   5. Accepts no conclusion as final or ultimate.

C. Bases opinions and conclusions on adequate evidence
   1. Is slow to accept as facts any that are not supported by convincing proof.
   2. Bases his conclusions upon evidence obtained from a variety of dependable sources.
   3. Hunts for the most satisfactory explanation of observed phenomena that the evidence permits.
   4. Sticks to the facts and refrains from exaggeration.
   5. Does not permit his personal pride, bias, prejudice, or ambition to pervert the truth.
   6. Does not make snap judgments or jump to conclusions.

D. Evaluates techniques and procedures used, and information obtained
   1. Uses a planned procedure in solving his problems.
   2. Uses the various techniques and procedures which may be applied in obtaining information.
   3. Adapts the various techniques and procedures to the problem at hand.
   4. Personally considers the information obtained and decides whether it relates to the problem.
   5. Judges whether the information is sound, sensible, and complete enough to allow a conclusion to be made.
   6. Selects the most recent, authoritative, and accurate information related to the problem.

E. Is curious concerning the things he observes
   1. Wants to know the "whys," "whats," and "hows" of observed phenomena.
   2. Is not satisfied with vague answers to his questions.

II. Problem solving abilities which can be developed through science teaching.
   The science program should develop those abilities involved in problem solving which will modify the individual's behavior so that he:

A. Formulates significant problems
   1. Senses situations involving personal and social problems.
   2. Recognizes specific problems in these situations.
   3. Isolates the single major idea in the problem.
   4. States the problem in question form.
   5. States the problem in definite and concise language.

B. Analyzes problems
   1. Picks out the key words of a problem statement.
   2. Defines key words as a means of getting a better understanding of the problem.
C. Obtains information regarding a problem from a variety of sources
   1. Recalls past experiences which bear upon his problem.
   2. Isolates elements common in experience and problem.
   3. Locates source materials
      a. Uses the various parts of a book:
         (1) Uses key words in the problem statement for locating material in the index.
         (2) Chooses proper sub-topics in the index.
         (3) Uses alphabetical materials, cross references, the table of contents, the title page, the glossary, figures, pictures and diagrams, footnotes, topical headings, running headings, marginal headings, an appendix, a pronunciation list, and "see also" references.
      b. Uses materials other than textbooks such as: encyclopedias, popularly written books, handbooks, dictionaries, magazines, newspapers, pamphlets, catalogues, bulletins, films, apparatus, guide letters, numbers, signs, marks in locating information, bibliographies.
      c. Uses library facilities such as: the card index, the Readers' Guide, and the services of the librarian.
   4. Uses sources materials
      a. Uses aids in comprehending material read.
         (1) Finds main ideas in a paragraph.
         (2) Uses reading signals.
         (3) Formulates statements from reading.
         (4) Phrases topics from sentences.
         (5) Skims for main ideas.
         (6) Learns meanings of words and phrases from context.
         (7) Selects the printed material related to the problem.
         (8) Cross-checks a book concerning the same topic.
         (9) Recognizes both objective and opinionated evidence.
         (10) Determines the main topic over several paragraphs.
         (11) Takes notes.
         (12) Arranges ideas in an organized manner.
         (13) Makes outlines.
      b. Interprets graphic material
         (1) Obtains information from different kinds of graphic material.
         (2) Reads titles, column headings, legends and data recorded.
         (3) Formulates the main ideas presented.
         (4) Evaluates conclusions based upon the data recorded.
   5. Uses experimental procedures appropriate to the problem
      a. Devises experiments suitable to the solution of the problem.
         (1) Selects the main factor in the experiment.
         (2) Allows only one variable.

       (3) Sets up a control for the experimental factor.
   b. Carries out the details of the experiment.
       (1) Identifies effects and determines causes.
       (2) Tests the effects of the experimental factor under varying conditions.
       (3) Performs the experiment for a sufficient length of time.
       (4) Accurately determines and records quantitative and qualitative data.
       (5) Develops a logical organization of recorded data.
       (6) Generalizes upon the basis of organized data.
   c. Manipulates the laboratory equipment needed in solving the problem.
       (1) Selects kinds of equipment or materials that will aid in solving the problem.
       (2) Manipulates equipment or materials that will aid in an understanding of its function to the outcome of the experiment.
       (3) Recognizes that equipment is only a means to the end results.
       (4) Determines the relationship between observed actions or occurrences and the problem.
       (5) Appraises scales and divisions of scales on measuring devices.
       (6) Obtains correct values from measuring devices.
       (7) Recognizes capacities or limitations of equipment.
       (8) Returns equipment clean and in good condition.
       (9) Avoids hazards and consequent personal accidents.
     (10) Practices neatness and orderliness.
     (11) Avoids waste in the use of materials.
     (12) Exercises reasonable care of fragile or perishable equipment.

6. Solves mathematical problems necessary in obtaining pertinent data.
   a. Picks out the elements in a mathematical problem that can be used in its solution.
   b. Sees relationships between these elements.
   c. Uses essential formulae.
   d. Performs fundamental operations as addition, subtraction, multiplication and division.
   e. Uses the metric and English system of measurement.
   f. Understands the mathematical terms used in these problems; i.e., square, proportion, area, volume, etc.

7. Makes observations suitable for solving the problem
   a. Observes demonstrations.
       (1) Devises suitable demonstrations.
       (2) Selects materials and equipment needed in the demonstration.
       (3) Identifies the important ideas demonstrated.
   b. Picks out the important ideas presented by pictures, slides, and motion pictures.

      c. Picks out the important ideas presented by models and exhibits.

      d. Uses the resources of the community for purposes of obtaining information pertinent to the problem.

        (1) Locates conditions or situations in the community to observe.

        (2) Picks out the essential ideas from such observation.

  8. Uses talks and interviews as sources of information

      a. Selects individuals who can contribute to the solution of the problem.

      b. Makes suitable plans for the talk or interview.

      c. Appropriately contacts the person who is to talk.

      d. Selects the main ideas from the activity.

      e. Properly acknowledges the courtesy of the individual interviewed.

D. Organizes the data obtained

  1. Uses appropriate means for organizing data.

      a. Constructs tables.

      b. Constructs graphs.

      c. Prepares summaries.

      d. Makes outlines.

      e. Constructs diagrams.

      f. Uses photographs.

      g. Uses suitable statistical procedures.

E. Interprets organized data

  1. Selects the important ideas related to the problem.

  2. Identifies the different relationships which may exist between the important ideas.

  3. States these relationships as generalizations which may serve as hypotheses.

F. Tests the hypotheses

  1. Checks proposed conclusion with authority.

  2. Devises experimental procedures suitable for testing the hypotheses.

  3. Rechecks data for errors in interpretation.

  4. Applies hypothesis to the problem to determine its adequacy.

G. Formulates a conclusion.

  1. Accepts the most tenable of the tested hypotheses.

  2. Uses this hypothesis as a basis for generalizing in terms of similar problem situations.

An inventory of problem solving practices can be used by a teacher in making an appraisal of the extent to which he provides for the suggested items under the various elements in problem solving. By making a self analysis of practices in regard to this objective, a teacher should be able to locate his strengths and weaknesses. This would provide a reliable basis for improving classroom practice.

Inventory of Problem Solving Practices

Directions: Check your response to each of the following items in the proper space at the right.

	Often	Occasion-ally	Seldom	Never

A. *Sensing and Defining Problems*:

To what extent do you:

1. help pupils sense situations involving personal and social problems?

2. help pupils recognize specific problems in these situations?

3. help pupils in isolating the single major idea of a problem?

4. help pupils state problems as definite and concise questions?

5. help pupils pick out and define the key words as a means of getting a better understanding of the problem?

6. help pupils evaluate problems in terms of personal and social needs?

7. help pupils to be aware of the exact meaning of word-groups and shades of meaning of words in problems involving the expression of ideas?

8. present overview lessons to raise significant problems?

9. permit pupils to discuss possible problems for study?

10. encourage personal interviews about problems of individual interest?

B. *Collecting Evidence on Problems*:

To what extent do you:

1. provide a wide variety of sources of information?

2. help pupils develop skill in using reference sources?

3. help pupils develop skill in note taking?

4. help pupils develop skill in using aids in books?

	Often	Occasion-ally	Seldom	Never

5. help pupils evaluate information pertinent to the problem?

6. provide laboratory demonstrations for collecting evidence on a problem?

7. provide controlled experiments for collecting evidence on a problem?

8. help pupils to develop skill in interviewing to secure evidence on a problem?

9. provide for using the resources of the community in securing evidence on a problem?

10. provide for using visual aids in securing evidence on a problem?

11. evaluate the pupils' ability for collecting evidence on a problem as carefully as you evaluate their knowledge of facts?

C. *Organizing Evidence on Problems*:

To what extent do you:

1. help pupils develop skill in arranging data?

2. help pupils develop skill in making graphs of data?

3. help pupils make use of deductive reasoning in areas best suited?

4. provide opportunities for pupils to make summaries of data?

5. help pupils distinguish relevant from irrelevant data?

6. provide opportunity for pupils to make outlines of data?

7. evaluate the pupils' ability to organize evidence on a problem as carefully as you evaluate their knowledge of facts?

D. *Interpreting Evidence on Problems*:

	Often	Occasion-ally	Seldom	Never

To what extent do you:

1. help pupils select the important ideas related to the problem?

2. help pupils identify the different relationships which may exist between the important ideas?

3. help pupils see the consistencies and weaknesses in data?

4. help pupils state relationships as generalizations which may serve as hypotheses?

5. evaluate the pupils' ability for interpreting evidence as carefully as you evaluate their knowledge of facts?

E. *Selecting and Testing Hypotheses*:

To what extent do you:

1. help pupils judge the significance or pertinency of data?

2. help pupils check hypotheses with recognized authorities?

3. help pupils make inferences from facts and observations?

4. help pupils devise controlled experiments suitable for testing hypotheses?

5. help pupils recognize and formulate assumptions basic to a given hypothesis?

6. help pupils recheck data for possible errors in interpretation?

7. evaluate the pupils' ability for selecting and testing hypotheses as carefully as you evaluate their knowledge of facts?

	Often	Occasion- ally	Seldom	Never

F. Formulating Conclusions:

To what extent do you:

1. help pupils formulate conclusions on the basis of tested evidence?

2. help pupils evaluate their conclusions in the light of the assumptions they set up for the problem?

3. help pupils apply their conclusions to new situations?

4. evaluate the pupils' ability to formulate conclusions as carefully as you evaluate their knowledge of facts?

Appendix II

Commercially Prepared Transparencies

(Or Producers of Masters from Which to Make Transparencies)

Audio-Visual Library of Science
 Transparencies
General Aniline and Film Corp.
Binghamton, New York 13900

Encyclopaedia Britannica Films,
 Inc.
1150 Wilmette Ave.
Wilmette, Illinois 60091

Harcourt, Brace & World, Inc.
757 Third Ave.
New York, N. Y. 10017

State University of Iowa
Bureau of Audio-Visual
 Instruction
Extension Division
Iowa City, Iowa 52240

McGraw-Hill Book Company
330 W. Forty-second St.
New York, N. Y. 10036

RCA Educational Service
Camden, New Jersey 08108

Tweedy Transparencies
321 Central Ave.
Newark, New Jersey 07103

United Transparencies, Inc.
57 Glenwood Ave.
Binghamton, New York 13905

Ward's Natural Science
 Establishment, Inc.
P. O. Box 1712
Rochester, New York 14603

Sources of Laboratory Furniture

Browne-Morse Co.
110 Broadway
Muskegon, Michigan 49444

Equipment and Furniture Co.,
Inc.
116 E. Thirty-second St.
New York, N. Y. 10016

Hamilton Manufacturing
Company
1935 Evans St.
Two Rivers, Wisconsin 54241

Hampden Engineering Corp.
Shaker Road
East Longmeadow,
Massachusetts 01028

Kewaunee Manufacturing
Company
5019 S. Center St.
Adrian, Michigan 49221
(also at Statesville, N. C.)

Maurice A. Knight
Akron, Ohio

Laboratory Furniture Co., Inc.
3720 Northern Blvd.
Long Island City,
New York 11101

Metalab Equipment Corp.
210 Duffy Ave.
Hicksville, New York 11801

Leonard Peterson and Co., Inc.
Fullerton and Racine Avenues
Chicago, Illinois

E. H. Sheldon and Co.
149 Thomas St.
Muskegon, Michigan 49444

John E. Sjostrom Co., Inc.
1717 North Tenth St.
Philadelphia,
Pennsylvania 19122

W. M. Welch Manufacturing Co.
1515 Sedgwick St.
Chicago, Illinois 60610

Textbook Publishers

Allyn and Bacon, Inc.
150 Tremont St.
Boston, Massachusetts 02111

American Book Company
55 Fifth Ave.
New York, N. Y. 10003

D. C. Heath & Company
285 Columbus Ave.
Boston, Massachusetts 02116

Ginn & Company
Statler Building
Boston, Massachusetts 02117

Harcourt, Brace & World, Inc.
757 Third Ave.
New York, N. Y. 10017

(publisher of sourcebooks in
biology, physical science and
elementary science)

Holt, Rinehart & Winston, Inc.
383 Madison Ave.
New York, N. Y. 10017

Iroquois Publishing Co., Inc.
Iroquois Blvd.
Syracuse, New York 13215

Charles E. Merrill Books, Inc.
1300 Alum Creek Drive
Columbus, Ohio 43216

Scott, Foresman, & Company
433 E. Erie St.
Chicago, Illinois 60611

Silver Burdett Company
Park Ave. and Columbia Rd.
Morristown, New Jersey 07960

The L. W. Singer Company, Inc.
249 W. Erie Blvd.
Syracuse, New York 13202

D. Van Nostrand Co., Inc.
120 Alexander St.
Princeton, New Jersey 08540

John Wiley & Sons, Inc.
605 Third Ave.
New York, N. Y. 10016

How To Do It Series

of the
National Science Teachers' Association
1201 Sixteenth Street N.W.
Washington 6, D. C.

How to Utilize the Services of a Science Consultant	No. 471-14286	$.35 ea.
How to Care for Living Things in the Classroom	471-14288	.35
How to Teach Science through Field Studies	471-14290	.35
How to Record and Use Data	471-14292	.35

Curriculum Newsletter

BSCS Newsletter
Biological Sciences Curriculum
 Study
University of Colorado
Boulder, Colorado 80302

CBA Newsletter
McGraw-Hill Book Company
330 W. Forty-second St.
New York, N. Y. 10036

CHEM Study Newsletter
Twelfth St. at Columbia Ave.
Claremont, California 91711

ESI Newsletter
Educational Service,
 Incorporated
Watertown,
 Massachusetts 02172

ESCP Newsletter
P. O. Box 1559
Boulder, Colorado 80301

*Harvard Physics Project
 Newsletter*
Harvard Physics Project
Harvard University
Cambridge,
 Massachusetts 02138

Professional Science Teaching Journals

*American Biology
 Teacher*
Indiana University
Editor: Paul Klinge
Bloomington, Indiana 47401

*Journal of Research in Science
 Teaching*
John Wiley & Sons, Inc.
605 Third Ave.
New York, N. Y. 10016

Mathematics Teacher
National Council of Teachers of
    Mathematics
1021 Sixteenth St. N.W.
Washington, D. C. 20006

Review of Educational Research
American Educational Research
    Association
1201 Sixteenth St., N.W.
Washington, D. C. 20006

School Science and Mathematics
P. O. Box 108
Bluffton, Ohio
Business Manager: Luther Setler

Science Education
49 Sheridan Ave.
Albany, New York 12210

Science Teacher
National Science Teachers'
    Association
1201 Sixteenth St. N.W.
Washington, D. C. 20006

Subject-Matter Journals

American Journal of Physics
American Institute of Physics
335 E. Forty-fifth St.
New York, N. Y. 10017

Chemical and Engineering News
American Chemical Society
1155 Sixteenth St. N.W.
Washington, D. C. 20006

Journal of Chemical Education
Twentieth and Northampton
    Streets
Easton, Pennsylvania 18042

Natural History
American Museum of Natural
    History
Central Park West at
    Seventy-ninth St.
New York, N. Y. 10024

Scientific American
415 Madison Ave.
New York, N. Y. 10017

Science
1515 Massachusetts Ave. N.W.
Washington, D. C. 20005

Science News Letter
Science Service
1719 N Street N.W.
Washington, D. C. 20006

Sky and Telescope
Harvard Observatory
Cambridge,
    Massachusetts 02138

Turtox News
General Biological Supply House
8200 South Hoyne Ave.
Chicago, Illinois 60620

Ward's Bulletin
Ward's Natural Science
    Establishment, Inc.
P. O. Box 1712
Rochester, New York 14603
            or
Ward's of California
P. O. Box 1749
Monterey, California 93943

Weatherwise
American Meteorological Society
3 Joy Street
Boston, Massachusetts 02108

*Welch Physics and Chemistry
    Digest* and *Welch General
    Science and Biology*
Welch Scientific Company
7300 N. Linder Ave.
Skokie, Illinois 60076

A SOURCE LIST FOR
Programmed Instructional Materials

Accelerated Instruction Methods
  Corp.
179 North Michigan Ave.
Chicago, Illinois 60601

Addison-Wesley Publishing Co.
Reading, Massachusetts 01867

Appleton-Century &
  Appleton-Century-Crofts
60 E. Forty-second St.
New York, N. Y. 10017

Applied Educational Systems
110 Edison Place
Newark, New Jersey 07102

Astra Corporation
31 Church Street
New London,
  Connecticut 06320

Billerett Company
1559 Embasy St.
Anaheim, California 92802

Center for Programmed
  Instruction
365 West End Ave.
New York, N. Y. 10024

Coronet Instructional Films
Chicago, Illinois 60600

The Devereux Foundation
Box 717
Devon, Pennsylvania 19333

Doubleday & Company, Inc.
277 Park Ave.
New York, N. Y. 10017

Dyna-Slide Company
600 S. Michigan Ave.
Chicago, Illinois 60605

Educational Aids Publishing
  Corp.
Carle Place So.
Long Island, New York

Educational Development
  Association
2302 J Street
Eureka, California 95501

Educational Development
  Laboratories
75 Prospect St.
Huntington, New York 11743

Educational Engineering, Inc.
3810 Pacific Coast Highway
Torrance, California 90505

Encyclopaedia Britannica Films
1150 Wilmette Ave.
Wilmette, Illinois 60091

General Atronics Corporation
1 Bala Ave.
Bala Cynwyd,
  Pennsylvania 19004

General Education, Inc.
96 Mt. Auburn St.
Cambridge,
  Massachusetts 02138

General Programmed Teaching
  Corp.
1719 Girard N.E.
Albuquerque,
  New Mexico 87106

Harcourt, Brace & World, Inc.
750 Third Ave.
New York, New York 10017

Hamilton Research Association
Four Genesee Street
New Hartford, New York 13413

Holt, Rinehart & Winston, Inc.
383 Madison Ave.
New York, New York 10017

HRB Singer, Inc.
P. O. Box 60
Science Park
State College, Pennsylvania
State College,
  Pennsylvania 16081

Inrad
P. O. Box 4456
Lubbock, Texas 79409

Institute for Instructional
  Improvement, Inc.
110 E. Thirtieth St.
New York, N. Y. 10016

Keystone View Company
Meadville, Pennsylvania 16335

Koncept-O-Graph Corp.
Box 533
Rochester, New York 10003

Learning Incorporated
1317 W. Eighth St.
Tempe, Arizona 85281

The Macmillan Company
60 Fifth Ave.
New York, N. Y. 10011

McGraw-Hill Book Company
330 W. Forty-second St.
New York, N. Y. 10036

New York Institute of
  Technology
500 Pacific Ave.
Brooklyn, New York 10017

Programed Teaching Aids, Inc.
3810 South Four Mile Run Drive
Arlington, Virginia 22206

Publishers' Company
1106 Connecticut Ave., N.W.
Washington, D. C. 20006

R.C.A. Educational Services
Camden, New Jersey 08108

Rheem Califone Corp.
5922 Bowcroft St.
Los Angeles, California 90016

Roto-Vue
211 North Seventh St.
1212 Holland Bldg.
St. Louis, Missouri 63101

Science Research Associates, Inc.
259 East Erie St.
Chicago, Illinois 60611

Smith-Harrison Incorporated
Box 717
Devon, Pennsylvania 19333

Teaching Materials Corporation
575 Lexington Ave.
New York, N. Y. 10022

TMI-Grolier
575 Lexington Ave.
New York, N. Y. 10022

Universal Electronics Labs Corp.
510 Hudson St.
Hackensack, New Jersey 07601

Univox Institute, Inc.
510 Hudson St.
Hackensack, New Jersey 07601

USI Educational Science
  Division
U. S. Industries Inc.
New York, N. Y.

Varian Associates
611 Hansen Way
Palo Alto, California 94304

John Wiley & Sons, Inc.
605 Third Ave.
New York, N. Y. 10016

Jay A. Young
Kings College
Wilkes-Barre,
  Pennsylvania 18702

Addresses of Supply Houses

Aero Service Corporation
210 East Courtland Street
Philadelphia,
  Pennsylvania 19120
(Aero True-Raised Relief maps
  and globes and Farquhar
  globes)

Ainsworth & Sons
2151 Lawrence St.
Denver, Colorado

Allied Chemical & Dye Corp.
40 Rector St.
New York, N. Y. 10006

Aloe Scientific
1831 Olive St.
St. Louis, Missouri 63103

American Optical Co.
Box A
Buffalo, New York 14215

American Type Culture
   Collection
2112 M Street, N.W.
Washington, D. C. 20007

Applied Sciences, Inc.
12435 Euclid Ave.
Cleveland, Ohio 44106
(portable lab with built in overhead projector)

Atomic Accessories, Inc.
811 West Merrick Road
Valley Stream, New York 11582
(Nuclear training aids, instruments, and accessories for
   teaching nuclear science)

Bausch & Lomb Incorporated
635 St. Paul St.
Rochester, New York 14602
(microprojectors, microscopes,
   and other optical scientific
   instruments)

The Bendix Corporation
3625 Hauck Road
Cincinnati, Ohio 45241
(science teaching kits and
   instructional scientific
   instruments)

Charles Beseler Company
219 South Eighteenth St.
East Orange, New Jersey 08818
(projection equipment for
   science teachers)

Biddle & Company
1316 Arch St.
Philadelphia,
   Pennsylvania 19107

Biological Research Products Co.
243 W. Root St.
Chicago, Illinois 60648

Bioscope Manufacturing
   Company
P. O. Box 1492
Tulsa, Oklahoma 74101
(display and demonstration of
   microscopes and microprojectors)

Black Light Planetarium
   Company
329 North Elmwood
Oak Park, Illinois 60302
(miniature planetariums)

Buck Engineering Company,
   Inc.
Lab-Volt Division
37-41 March St.
Freehold, New Jersey 07728
(Unit power supplies and multi-
   range protected meters)

California Biological Service
1612 W. Glenoaks Blvd.
Glendale, California 91201

California Botanical Materials
   Co.
861 E. Columbia Ave.
Pomona, California 91767

Cambosco Scientific Company,
   Inc.
342 Western Ave.
Boston, Massachusetts 02135
(science apparatus for schools)

Carolina Biological Supply
   Company
Burlington, North Carolina
            and
Gladstone, Oregon
(biological models, microscopes,
   plast-o-mounts, and laboratory
   equipment)

Central Scientific Company
1700 Irving Park
Chicago, Illinois 60613
(classrooms and laboratory
   science equipment)

Certified Blood Donor Service
146-16 Hillside Avenue
Jamaica, New York 11435

Chemical Rubber Company
2310 Superior Ave.
Cleveland, Ohio 44114

Chem-Products, Inc.
1619 East First St.
Austin, Texas 78700

Chicago Apparatus Co.
1735 N. Ashland Ave.
Chicago, Illinois 60622

Cole-Parmer Instrument and
    Equipment Co.
7330 North Clark St.
Chicago, Illinois 60626

College Biological Supply, Inc.
9230 Woodlawn Ave.
Seattle, Washington 98125

Conso-Lab Supply Co.
7 Endo Blvd.
Garden City, New York 11533

Corning Glass Works
Corning, New York 14830
(Pyrex laboratory ware)

The George F. Cram Company,
    Inc.
730 East Washington St.
Indianapolis, Indiana 46204
(Thin Man, charts, models,
    globes, and maps)

Criterion Manufacturing
    Company
331 Church St.
Hartford, Connecticut 06109
(astronomical telescopes and
    science projectors)

W. H. Curtin and Co.
P. O. Box 1546
Houston, Texas 77001

Denoyer-Geppert Company
5235 Ravenswood Ave.
Chicago, Illinois 60640
(models, charts, skeletons,
    specimens, and museum
    preparations)

Difco Laboratories, Inc.
Detroit, Michigan 48201

Dow Chemical Co.
Midland, Michigan 48640

The Ealing Corporation
2225 Massachusetts Ave.
Cambridge,
    Massachusetts 02140
(science teaching equipment)

Eastman Kodak Co.
343 State St.
Rochester, New York 14604

Eckert Mineral Research, Inc.
110 East Main St.
Florence, Colorado 81226
(mineral collections for all
    grades)

Edmund Scientific Company
Barrington, New Jersey 08007

Edex Corporation
3940 Fabian Way
Palo Alto, California 94303
(automated teaching system)

Eimer and Amend
Greenwich and Morton Streets
New York, N. Y. 09014

Elgeet Optical Co., Inc.
838 Smith St.
Rochester, New York 14606

Encyclopaedia Britannica Films,
    Inc.
1150 Wilmette Ave.
Wilmette, Illinois 60091
(projection equipment for display
    of films, film strips, pegboard
    backdrop, and promotion-
    literature display)

Erb & Gray Co.
854 S. Giguerca St.
Los Angeles, California 90014

Essex International
308 Springfield Ave.
Berkeley Heights,
New Jersey 07922
(elementary and high school
science labs)

Farquhar Transparent Globes
5007 Warrington Ave.
Philadelphia,
Pennsylvania 19143
(transparent globes of the sky
and earth)

Faust Scientific Supply, Ltd.
5108 Gordon Ave.
Madison, Wisconsin 53716
(microscopes, optical instruments, plastic teaching
models, wall charts, projection
slides, and other quality science teaching aids)

Fisher Scientific Co.
717 Forbes Ave.
Pittsburgh, Pennsylvania 15200

General Biochemicals, Inc.
677 Laboratory Park
Chagrin Falls, Ohio 44022

General Biological Supply House
8200 South Hoyne Ave.
Chicago, Illinois 60620

Gradwohl Laboratories
3514 Lucas Ave.
St. Louis, Missouri 63103

The Graf-Apsco Company
5868 Broadway
Chicago, Illinois 60626
(microscopes, dissecting and
surgical instruments)

Henry J. Green Instruments, Inc.
2500 Shames Drive
Westbury, New York 11590
(meteorological instruments)

Hamden Engineering
Corporation
99 Shaker Road
East Longmeadow,
Massachusetts 01028
(electrical power and test equipment for science laboratories)

Harshaw Scientific Division
Harshaw Chemical Co.
1945 E. 9th St.
Cleveland, Ohio 44114

Heath Company
Benton Harbor, Michigan 99022
(educational electronic
equipment)

T. N. Hubbard Scientific
Company
P. O. Box 105
109 Pfingsten Road
Northbrook, Illinois 60062
(earth science teaching aids)

Jewel Aquarium Company, Inc.
5005 West Armitage Ave.
Chicago, Illinois 60639
(aquariums, terrariums, germinating beds, and modular
units)

Kelly-Koett Manufacturing Co.
24 E. Sixth Street
Covington, Kentucky 41011

Ken-A-Vision Manufacturing
Company, Inc.
5615 Raytown Road
Raytown, Missouri 64133
(micro-projectors, microscopes,
and planetarium)

Kimble Glass
P. O. Box 1035
Toledo, Ohio 43601

Klinger Scientific Apparatus
Corp.
83-45 Parsons Blvd.
Jamaica, New York 11432
(scientific equipment for
teaching)

Knickerbocker Blood Donor
Service
300 W. Forty-third Street
New York, N. Y. 10036

Lab-Aids, Inc.
Cold Spring Harbor
Long Island, New York 11100
(student work aids including
blood-typing aids, colony
counters, short-wave ultra-
violet light sources, and new
vortex generator)

Lab-Line Instruments, Inc.
Fifteenth and Bloomington
Avenues
Melrose Park, Illinois 60160

LaPine Scientific Company
6001 South Knox Ave.
Chicago, Illinois 60629
(live demonstrations and experiments in classical, modern,
and atomic physics performed
with Leybold physics
equipment)

Leahy Manufacturing Co.
Higginsville, Missouri 64037

Lederle Laboratories
Div. American Cyanamid Co.
Midtown Rd.
Pearl River, New York 10965

E. Leitz, Inc.
468 Park Ave. South
New York, N. Y. 10016
(microscopes and micro-
projectors)

The Lemberger Co.
1222 W. So. Park Ave.
P. O. Box 482
Oshkosh, Wisconsin 54901

Los Angeles Biological
Laboratories
2977 W. Fourteenth St.
Los Angeles, California 90006

The Lumiscope Company
836 Broadway
New York, N. Y. 10003
(microscopes, optical equipment and accessories)

Macalaster Scientific Corp.
60 Arsenal St.
Watertown, Massachusetts
02172

(laboratory materials for the
PSSC physics and the BSCS
biology programs)

Malge Co., Inc.
Rochester, New York 14602
(plastic ware)

Marine Biological Laboratories
Woods Hole,
Massachusetts 02543

Merck & Co.
Rahway, New Jersey 07065

Misco Biological Corporation
6780 Jackson Road
Ann Arbor, Michigan 48103
(biological materials)

Monsanto Chemical Co.
1700 S. Second St.
St. Louis, Missouri 63104

National Biological Laboratories,
Inc.
P. O. Box 511
Vienna, Virginia 22180

National Biological Supply
Company, Inc.
2325 South Michigan
Chicago, Illinois 60616
(supplies for biology, chemistry,
and physics)

National Teaching Aids, Inc.
386 Park Ave. South
New York, N. Y. 10016
(micro-slide-viewers, slides and
texts for elementary and secondary school life science)

New York Scientific Supply Co.
28 W. Thirtieth St.
New York, N. Y. 10001

Northern Biological Supply
Box 222
New Richmond, Wisconsin
54017

Northwest Biological
Laboratories
3581 Shelbourne Street
Victoria, British Columbia
Canada

Nuclear-Chicago Corporation
333 East Howard Ave.
Des Plaines, Illinois 60016
(instruments for demonstration
    of and experimentation in
    radioactivity, plus working
    classroom set-up)

Nutritional Biochemicals Corp.
21010 Miles Ave.
Cleveland, Ohio 44128

A. J. Nystrom & Company
3333 Elston Ave.
Chicago, Illinois 60618
(charts and models)

Ohaus Scale Corporation
1050 Commerce Ave.
Union, New Jersey 07083
(laboratory balances and
    weights)

Oregon Biological Supply Co.
1806 S.E. Holgate Blvd.
Portland, Oregon 97202

Pacific Laboratory Apparatus
    Co.
3555 Whittier Blvd.
Los Angeles, California 90023

Charles Pfizer & Co.
11 Bartlett St.
Brooklyn, New York 10006

Phipps and Bird, Inc.
6th at Byrd Streets
P. O. Box 2V
Richmond, Virginia 23205

Physicians and Hospitals
    Supply Co.
1400 Harmon Place
Minneapolis, Minnesota 55403

Pickett & Eckel, Inc.
542 South Dearborn St.
Chicago, Illinois 60605
(all-metal slide rules, approved
    plastic slide rules, templates,
    lettering guides, science-
    discoveries lab kits, and
    triangles)

Polaroid Corp.
Cambridge,
    Massachusetts 02139

Preiser Scientific, Inc.
900 MacCorkle Ave. S.W.
Charleston, West Virginia 25322

Product Design Co.
2796 Middlefield Rd.
Redwood City, California 44063
(conservation kits)

Research Specialties Co.
2005 Hopkins St.
Berkeley, California 94707

Schaar Scientific Company
7300 W. Montrose Ave.
Chicago, Illinois 60634

Schlueter Scientific Supplies,
    Inc.
8609 Lincoln Ave.
Morton Grove, Illinois 60053

Science Electronics Inc.
195 Massachusetts Ave.
Cambridge,
    Massachusetts 02139
(PSSC and conventional physics
    apparatus, general science
    electricity and electronics
    learning units)

Science Kit, Inc.
2299 Military Road
Tonawanda, New York 14140
(science supplies and equipment,
    science-kit sets, portable lab
    tables, microscopes, audio-
    visuals and teaching aids)

Science Materials Center
59 Fourth Ave.
New York, N. Y. 10003

Science Teaching Aids
Box 386
Pell Lake, Wisconsin 53157
(fiberglass biological models)

Scientific Products
1210 Leon Place
Evanston, Illinois 60201
(apparatus and supplies with
    special emphasis on dis-
    posable products)

Sherer-Gillett Company
604 South Kalamazoo Ave.
Marshall, Michigan 49068
(mobile greenhouse)

Sherwin Scientific Co.
North 1112 Ruby St.
Spokane, Washington 99202

Southern Precision Instrument
    Co.
710 Augusta St.
San Antonio, Texas 78215

Sprague-Dawley, Inc.
P. O. Box 2071
Madison, Wisconsin 53705
(laboratory rats)

Standard Scientific Corp.
34 W. Fourth St.
New York, N. Y. 10018

Standard Scientific Supply Corp.
808 Broadway
New York, N. Y. 10003

Stansi Scientific Company
1231 North Honore St.
Chicago, Illinois 60622
(scientific apparatus)

E. G. Steinhilber and Co., Inc.
P. O. Box 888
Oshkosh, Wisconsin 54902

Swift Instruments, Inc.
1190 North Fourth Street
San Jose, California 95112
(microscopes and accessories)

Taylor Instrument Companies
95 Ames St.
Rochester, New York 14611
(meteorological instruments for
    science teaching programs)

Teaching Materials Corp.
575 Lexington Ave.
New York, N. Y. 09022

Testa Manufacturing Company
10126 East Rush St.
El Monte, California 91733
(elementary and secondary
    student microscopes)

The Torsion Balance Company
35 Monhegan St.
Clifton, New Jersey 07013
(balances, weights, and science
    teaching aids)

Trippensee Planetarium
    Company, Inc.
2200 South Hamilton St.
Saginaw, Michigan 48602
(planetariums, solar systems,
    astronomy and physical
    geography teaching aids)

United Scientific Co.
204 Milk St.
Boston, Massachusetts 02108

Unitron Instrument Company
66 Needham St.
Newton Highlands,
    Massachusetts 02161
(microscopes and accessories for
    student labs, including new
    budget-priced Phase Contrast
    microscopes for examination
    of unstained, living
    specimens)

Universal Scientific Company,
    Inc.
120 Alexander St.
Princeton, New Jersey 08540
(textbooks and reference books)

Van Waters and Rogers, Inc.
P. O. 5287
Denver, Colorado 80206

Ward's Natural Science
    Establishment, Inc.
3000 Ridge Road East
P. O. Box 1712
Rochester, New York 14603
(teaching aids for biology and
    earth science)

The Welch Scientific Company
7300 N. Linder Ave.
Skokie, Illinois 60076
(scientific laboratory apparatus)

Western Laboratories
826 Q St.
Lincoln, Nebraska 68508

Western Seed Testing Service
439 Pierce St.
Twin Falls, Idaho 83301

Wilkens-Anderson Company
4525 West Division St.
Chicago, Illinois 60651
(semi-micro chemistry equip-
    ment, laboratory apparatus
    and supplies)

Will Corporation
P. O. Box 1050
Rochester, New York 14603

INDEX

INDEX